Attainment's
Aligning
Life Skills
to Academics
Worksheet Directory

Math
Social Studies
Science/Health
Language Arts

650 transition worksheets

Ellen McPeek Glisan, Ph.D

Aligning Life Skills to Academics is a collection of 650 worksheets that support life skill activities and align with math, science/health, social studies, and language arts curriculum areas. Depending on an individual student's needs, these materials can be used to supplement regular class activities or can provide the core material for an academic class focused primarily on life skill transition objectives.

Author: Dr. Ellen McPeek Glisan, Ph.D

Cover and book design: Jo Reynolds

Production coordinator: David Nelson

Aligning Life Skills to Academics

ISBN 1-57861-668-9

©2008-2015 Attainment Company, Inc.

All rights reserved.

Attainment Company, Inc.

P.O. Box 930160
Verona, Wisconsin 53593-0160 USA
1-800-327-4269
www.AttainmentCompany.com

Table of Contents

Math

Social Studies

Science/Health

Language Arts: Expressive Literacy

Language Arts: Receptive Literacy

Incorporating life skills into academic classes helps students understand the connection between school and their daily lives. Having such an understanding often helps students find school more meaningful and helps them see a bigger picture in which many daily-living functions take on a logical order. Students who are comfortable with this bigger picture are more likely to successfully manage their personal lives.

The 650 functional life skills addressed by the *Aligning Life Skills to Academics Program* smoothly integrates life skill activities into a subject-based academic curriculum through the concept of "functional academics." Each life skill is supported by both the worksheets catalogued in this book and by the interactive lesson plans in the companion *Life Skill Lessons* book. Both collections are aligned with math, social studies, science/health, and language arts curriculum areas. Curriculum alignment means that these worksheets and lessons are optimized for integration with departmentalized academic programs. Depending on an individual student's needs, these materials can be a quick daily addition to a regular academic class or can provide the core material for a life skills-based core functional academic class.

To maintain student interest and to meet the objective of the widely varied 650 skills, the *Life Skill Worksheets* include many types of activities, including matching, cut-and-paste, multiple choice, checklists, fill-in-the-blank, drawing, short answer, listing, chart completion, banking forms, and calendar notations. The *Life Skill Lessons* are guided activity plans that support the same life skill topics. Both the worksheets and the guided activities focus on giving students an understanding of a specific skill as well as providing opportunities to practice the skills.

Students with minimal disabilities in mainstream classrooms

For students with minimal disabilities who are part of a mainstream classroom environment, successful transition planning depends on a balanced relationship to curriculum. The *Life Skill Worksheets* can be used in regular-level academic classrooms as well as special needs classrooms. From the top gifted child down to the student with the most struggles, all students in a regular-curriculum classroom can benefit from life skill awareness activities. For example, a regular math class might start out each day with a quick life skill activity.

Alternate assessment students

Students who qualify for alternate achievement standards, usually involving cognitive disabilities, especially need instructional material that aligns with general education – the worksheets and lessons provide a method of integrating life skills without disrupting a school's academic requirements or daily structure. The *Life Skill Worksheets* can be used as the basis for a classroom experience focused on transition planning while also coordinating with academic subjects.

If working with worksheets is too difficult for students, the *Life Skill Lessons* provide learning materials that support the same life skill topics with teacher-guided activities. Both the worksheets and the teacher-guided activities can be adapted and modified to suit each student and teacher.

The IEP team

The Individuals with Disabilities Act (IDEA) requires that a student's Individual Educational Plan (IEP) include a coordinated set of transition activities. Life skill training is a key component in assuring that each student has a reasonable chance of a smooth movement from school to post-school activities.

The instructional domains mandated by the IDEA initiative represent a broad set of student needs. The *Life Skill Worksheets* and *Life Skill Lessons* were created to help teachers and IEP teams address those needs with outcome-oriented, process-specific objectives.

Use the printed directory to find and preview worksheets, then use the document software to save worksheet PDF documents to your computer. The worksheets may be used as either color or black and white pages. An answer key version of each worksheet is also available.

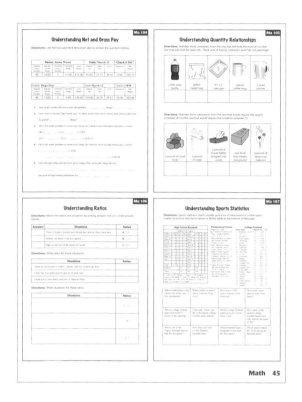

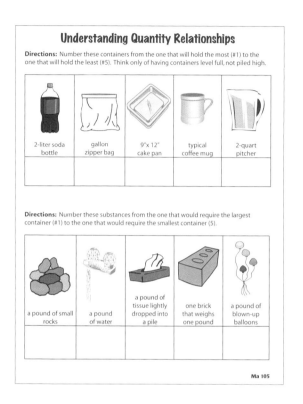

Each worksheet has a companion activity lesson plan (see page 14) that addresses the same life skill theme. These guided activities are available as PDF documents or as MS Word files that can be edited.

The 650 *Aligning Life Skills to Academics* worksheets are available as PDF documents for printing. Adobe Acrobat Reader software is required to display and print the worksheets (Acrobat Reader is available from the installation disk).

The document software makes it easy to locate and save worksheet and activity files.

The *Aligning Life Skills to Academics* worksheets are available as PDF files to be printed out for student use. Find and save files to your computer by using the provided document management software tool.

System Requirements
- Windows 2000 or higher
- Mac OS 10.2 or higher
- 32 MB RAM
- Adobe Acrobat Reader
- Java

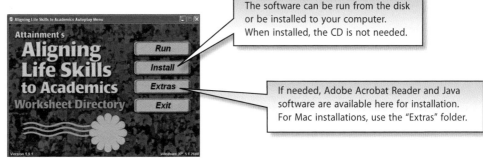

The software can be run from the disk or be installed to your computer. When installed, the CD is not needed.

If needed, Adobe Acrobat Reader and Java software are available here for installation. For Mac installations, use the "Extras" folder.

Windows auto-play installer screen

STEP ONE: Find the worksheets that you want to use.

The document software provides three ways to find worksheets:

Use the directory identifier codes

Each worksheet has a directory ID code. One or more of these IDs can be entered to pull up those worksheet titles to the file selection list.

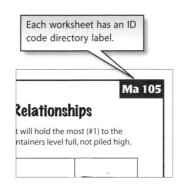

Each worksheet has an ID code directory label.

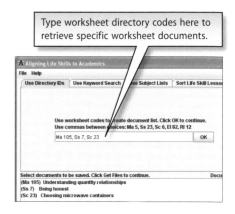

Type worksheet directory codes here to retrieve specific worksheet documents.

Use title keywords

One or more keywords can be entered to find worksheet titles that contain those keywords.

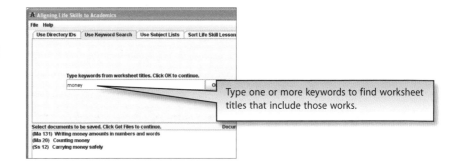

Type one or more keywords to find worksheet titles that include those works.

Choose from complete subject lists

Browse through a complete subject group of worksheet titles.

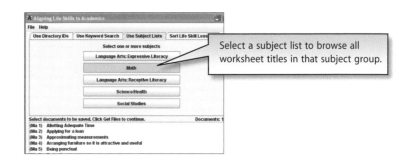

Select a subject list to browse all worksheet titles in that subject group.

STEP TWO: From the listing of worksheet titles, select the ones to be saved and then click the "Get Files" button.

Select the worksheet files to be saved from the list of found titles.

Click the "Get Files" button after choosing the worksheets to be saved.

STEP THREE: Choose which document formats are to be saved. Files will be saved to your desktop unless you select a different folder location.

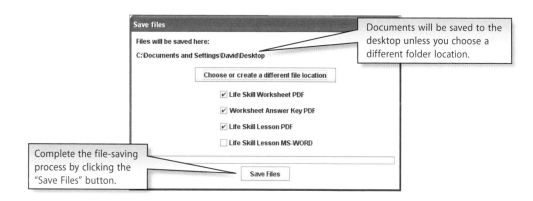

Documents will be saved to the desktop unless you choose a different folder location.

Complete the file-saving process by clicking the "Save Files" button.

STEP FOUR: Click the "Save Files" button. The documents are now ready to print or send as an email attachment.

NEED HELP?
Detailed user instructions are available from the software.

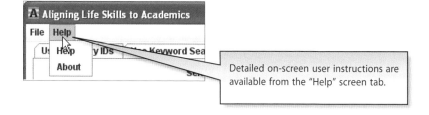

Detailed on-screen user instructions are available from the "Help" screen tab.

Each of the worksheet life skills is supported by an activity plan from *Life Skill Lessons*. The 650 activities in this book each take only a few minutes to complete, and cover different tasks, ideas, and skills that adults use in their daily lives.

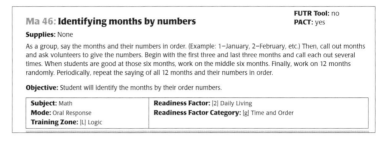

Related to the same life skill themes as the worksheets, the activity lessons are further categorized by learning styles, training zones, and readiness factors. The software uses these classifications to allow you to find activities most appropriate for your students. The lesson documents are available as PDF files and also MS-Word files that can be edited for individual needs.

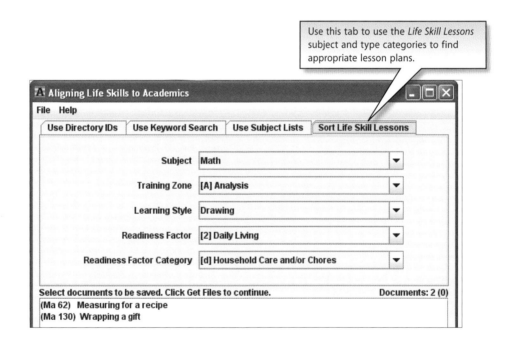

Dr. Ellen McPeek Glisan received her Ph.D. in Education from the University of Nebraska, her Master's degree from Northern Illinois University, and her Bachelor's degree from Illinois State University. With more than 25 years of experience in the education field, her teaching methods have helped thousands of students and teachers. Her early success with life skill training methods in junior high and high school special education classrooms led also to innovative training methods for the corporate environment. From her Master's thesis work, the life skill writing program *Footsteps* became her first education product, and since then she has developed over 200 educational programs and spoken at many educational conferences.

Her interest and involvement in making education meaningful for her students led her to develop a comprehensive program for teaching life skills and assessing life skill competency. Her *Forecasting and Understanding Transition Readiness* (FUTR) program is a tool that provides training goal information about individual students' life skill abilities. In addition to *Aligning Life Skills to Academics* and other Attainment Company publications (*PACT Life Skill Review, Life Skill Academics Series, Job Ads and Career Paths,* and *Geography Reader*), she is the author of *Real Life Math, Basic Work Skills,* and *Day-to-Day Life Skills Series*. Dr. Glisan can be contacted for training or workshops at eglisan@swbell.net.

Math

Alotting Adequate Time

Directions: Write an answer for each question.

1. It is 4:00, and Dani just got home from school. She has swim practice at 6:30. She needs 20 minutes to get to the pool and get ready. She wants to watch a 30 minute TV show before practice. What is the lastest time she can start watching the TV show?

Practice	Get ready	TV	Latest Time
6:30	20 min.	30 min.	

2. It is 1:00 and Paris has an interview at 6:00. The drive is 45 minutes and he needs five minutes to walk from the car, stop at the restroom, and go to the office. What time should he leave to be five minutes early? Fill in the missing subheading and answer.

Interview		Car to office	Early	Leaving Time
6:00	45 min.	5 min.	5 min.	

3. It is 2:30 and class starts at 2:36. Matt needs to go to the office (30 seconds), to his locker (30 seconds), and then to the classroom (20 seconds). For how long can he talk to Anna before he goes to the office? Fill in the missing pieces and the answer.

2:30

Class Starts	Office	Locker		Time for Talking to Anna
2:36	30 sec.		20 sec.	

4. It is 11:45 and Misha's friends are coming at 3:30. Before 3:30, she wants to work out for 30 minutes, do an hour of homework, and take a nap. What time should she start working out so she can sleep for an hour? Fill in the missing pieces and the answer.

11:45

Friends	Homework		Time to Start Working Out
3:30	30 min.	1 hour	

Applying for a Loan

Directions: Match the vocabulary words to the meanings.

Answers	Meanings	Vocabulary Words
	1. Ongoing fees that people pay to use others' money	A. bank
	2. A group that provides money-related services to its members	B. credit union
	3. A one-time fee that people pay at the beginning of an agreement	C. loan
	4. A business that provides money-related services to the general public	D. down payment
	5. An agreement where a person gets money to use in exchange for paying fees and eventually paying the money back	E. interest

Answers	Meanings	Vocabulary Words
	6. To use something of someone else's for a while	F. lend
	7. A page or pages with blanks for collecting information	G. borrow
	8. To ask for a loan by providing the requested information	H. loan form
	9. To let someone use something of yours for a while	I. qualify for a loan
	10. To meet the requirements to get money to use from a bank or credit union	J. apply

Approximating Measurements

Directions: Draw or describe each answer. Do not actually measure.

Draw or describe something in the room that......	Draw or describe two things in the room that......
Weighs about 20 pounds	Are about 3 yards apart
Is about 16 inches long	Are shorter than your arm
Weighs about an ounce	Are longer than 2 feet

Arranging Furniture So It Is Attractive and Useful

Directions: Use an 8 ½ in. x 11 in. piece of paper as the layout of a furniture store. Draw the front entrance of the store. Cut out and arrange the furniture below in attractive groupings so customers can try the pieces out.

Arranging Furniture So It Is Attractive and Useful

Directions: Use an 8 ½ in. x 11 in. piece of paper as the layout of a furniture store. Draw the front entrance of the store. Cut out and arrange the furniture below in attractive groupings so customers can try the pieces out.

Being Punctual

Directions: Choose the BEST time for each question.

1. You are bowling with friends at 2:00. At the bowling alley, you have to pay, change your shoes, and find a ball. What time should you get there?
   a. 1:30
   b. 1:55
   c. 2:00
   d. 2:30

2. At 1:15, the bell rings to start class. What time should you be in your seat?
   a. 1:00
   b. 1:12
   c. 1:15
   d. 1:20

3. Your father tells you that dinner will be at 6:30. What time should you go to the kitchen?
   a. 6:00
   b. 6:15
   c. 6:27
   d. 6:35

4. You did your homework in a computer and need to print it. You finished at 8:30 p.m. and need to have it in your backpack when you leave for school at 8:00 a.m. tomorrow. When should you print your homework and put it in your backpack?
   a. 8:30 p.m.
   b. 11:00 p.m.
   c. 7:30 a.m.
   d. 8:00 a.m.

5. You have friends coming over at 7:00. You want to take a shower before they come. What time should you be sure to be ready?
   a. 6:15
   b. 6:45
   c. 6:59
   d. 7:00

6. You have a doctor appointment at 3:30. What time should you sign in at the receptionist's desk?
   a. 3:00
   b. 3:15
   c. 3:25
   d. 3:30

7. You have an 11:15 appointment to talk to the school counselor. What time should you report to the counselor's office?
   a. 11:00
   b. 11:05
   c. 11:14
   d. 11:20

8. You are to meet at your friend's house so you can leave for a ball game at 5:45. What time should you arrive at your friend's house?
   a. 5:00
   b. 5:40
   c. 5:45
   d. 5:50

Budgeting

Directions: To the first column, add five things you could buy. Fill in the middle columns for all 10 items. Use the last column to rank all ten things in order of importance.

Item	Want or Need?	Where would you get it?	What would it cost?	Rank
cell phone				
brand name tennis shoes				
backpack				
stapler				
pro football jersey				

Buying the Best Deal

Directions: Look at the sizes and prices of the lotion bottles. Then, answer each question.

32 oz.	16 oz.	20 oz.	3 quart	8 oz.
$4.58	2 for $4.50	$4.00	$5.00	$3.00

1. If you need only a small amount of lotion, which size is the best buy? Explain. _____

2. Which is a better buy: two 16 oz. bottles of lotion or one 32 oz. bottle? Explain. _____

3. Rank the five sizes of lotion from most expensive to least expensive per unit.
   _____
   _____
   _____
   _____
   _____

4. If you use about 12 oz. of lotion each month, which size bottle would it make sense for you to buy? Explain. _____

Calculating Quantities

Directions: Circle the amount needed for each situation.

Situation	Circle Amount Needed
Bottled water for 4 people who are going on an all-day hiking trip	*(rows of water bottles)*
Milk for your family for two weeks	*(six 2% MILK jugs)*
Packages of poster hangers to put one hanger on each corner of five posters	*(six packages labeled "6 Poster Corners")*
Paper cups for a party of 25 people	*(eight packages of "18 paper cups")*
Index cards for 30 students to each use 25 cards for vocabulary flash cards	*(ten boxes of "100 index cards")*

Checking to See What Will Fit In a New Home

Directions: Use your feet to decide which suggested moves will work.

TIP: For the first suggested move activity, place your feet end-to-end to measure the length and width of the space filled by three desks — count your "feet" and write the number in the first column.
Use the same procedure to measure one waste basket.
Multiply the waste basket measurement by 10 for the second column.
Decide whether or not the move will work, and complete the last two columns.

Suggested move	Measurement of area in your feet	Measurement of furniture or room item in your feet	Will the suggested move work? (Circle)	If the move will not work, why not?
Place ten of the classroom wastebaskets in the space currently filled with three student desks.	____ "feet" wide ____ "feet" long	____ "feet" wide ____ "feet" long	yes no	
Place three teacher desks in the space currently filled with seven student desks.	____ "feet" wide ____ "feet" long	____ "feet" wide ____ "feet" long	yes no	
Place three classroom doors in the space that is (or could be) filled with three classroom windows.	____ "feet" wide ____ "feet" long	____ "feet" wide ____ "feet" long	yes no	
How many student chairs can be placed side-by-side across the width of the classroom?	____ "feet" wide ____ "feet" long	____ "feet" wide ____ "feet" long	yes no	
Choose a furniture item in classroom: How many can be placed side-by-side down the length of the room?	____ "feet" wide ____ "feet" long	____ "feet" wide ____ "feet" long	yes no	

Choosing a Lid That Will Fit Based on Shape

Directions: Match the lids to the containers.

Matches	Containers	Lids
	1.	A.
	2.	B.
	3.	C.
	4.	D.
	5.	E.
	6.	F.
	7.	G.
	8.	H.
	9.	I.
	10.	J.

Choosing Appropriate Box Sizes

Directions: As a group, place ten boxes of different sizes in the front of the room. Number the boxes from 1 to 10. Name something in the room that would come close to filling each box and would fit in without sticking out. Check to see if your guesses are correct.

Box #	Item in room that you think would fit	Did it fit?
1		Yes No
2		Yes No
3		Yes No
4		Yes No
5		Yes No
6		Yes No
7		Yes No
8		Yes No
9		Yes No
10		Yes No

Choosing Clothes That Look Good Together

Directions: Cut out these clothes and tape them together into attractive outfits.

Choosing Clothes That Look Nice On You

Directions: Find pieces of paper or clothing in each of the colors below. Look in a mirror and decide which of the colors you think are good colors for you. Rate each color 3, 2, or 1. Then, ask four others to give their opinions about the colors that are good for you.

Color	Your Opinion	Other Opinion #1	Other Opinion #2	Other Opinion #3	Other Opinion #4
Yellow	3 (good color) 2 (OK color) 1 (not good color)	3 (good color) 2 (OK color) 1 (not good color)	3 (good color) 2 (OK color) 1 (not good color)	3 (good color) 2 (OK color) 1 (not good color)	3 (good color) 2 (OK color) 1 (not good color)
Pale Green	3 (good color) 2 (OK color) 1 (not good color)	3 (good color) 2 (OK color) 1 (not good color)	3 (good color) 2 (OK color) 1 (not good color)	3 (good color) 2 (OK color) 1 (not good color)	3 (good color) 2 (OK color) 1 (not good color)
Dark Green	3 (good color) 2 (OK color) 1 (not good color)	3 (good color) 2 (OK color) 1 (not good color)	3 (good color) 2 (OK color) 1 (not good color)	3 (good color) 2 (OK color) 1 (not good color)	3 (good color) 2 (OK color) 1 (not good color)
Red	3 (good color) 2 (OK color) 1 (not good color)	3 (good color) 2 (OK color) 1 (not good color)	3 (good color) 2 (OK color) 1 (not good color)	3 (good color) 2 (OK color) 1 (not good color)	3 (good color) 2 (OK color) 1 (not good color)
Light Blue	3 (good color) 2 (OK color) 1 (not good color)	3 (good color) 2 (OK color) 1 (not good color)	3 (good color) 2 (OK color) 1 (not good color)	3 (good color) 2 (OK color) 1 (not good color)	3 (good color) 2 (OK color) 1 (not good color)
Dark Blue	3 (good color) 2 (OK color) 1 (not good color)	3 (good color) 2 (OK color) 1 (not good color)	3 (good color) 2 (OK color) 1 (not good color)	3 (good color) 2 (OK color) 1 (not good color)	3 (good color) 2 (OK color) 1 (not good color)
Orange	3 (good color) 2 (OK color) 1 (not good color)	3 (good color) 2 (OK color) 1 (not good color)	3 (good color) 2 (OK color) 1 (not good color)	3 (good color) 2 (OK color) 1 (not good color)	3 (good color) 2 (OK color) 1 (not good color)
Purple	3 (good color) 2 (OK color) 1 (not good color)	3 (good color) 2 (OK color) 1 (not good color)	3 (good color) 2 (OK color) 1 (not good color)	3 (good color) 2 (OK color) 1 (not good color)	3 (good color) 2 (OK color) 1 (not good color)
Black	3 (good color) 2 (OK color) 1 (not good color)	3 (good color) 2 (OK color) 1 (not good color)	3 (good color) 2 (OK color) 1 (not good color)	3 (good color) 2 (OK color) 1 (not good color)	3 (good color) 2 (OK color) 1 (not good color)
White	3 (good color) 2 (OK color) 1 (not good color)	3 (good color) 2 (OK color) 1 (not good color)	3 (good color) 2 (OK color) 1 (not good color)	3 (good color) 2 (OK color) 1 (not good color)	3 (good color) 2 (OK color) 1 (not good color)

Choosing Measurement Instruments

Directions: For each situation below, draw or describe the measurement tool that you would use.

Situation	Measurement Tool	Situation	Measurement Tool
Your Height		Amount of postage needed on an extra-stuffed envelope	
Amount of water in a bucket		Whether or not DVDs will fit on a shelf you would like to buy	
Amount of flour for baking a cake		The length of a driveway in front of a garage	
Amount of sugar for a cup of coffee		The weight of a loaded semi truck	
Your Weight		Amount of water to make a package of lemonade	

Choosing the Right Kind of Screwdriver

Directions: Cut out the screws at the bottom of the page and tape them in the correct boxes.

Phillips Screwdriver	Slot Screwdriver	Allen Wrench

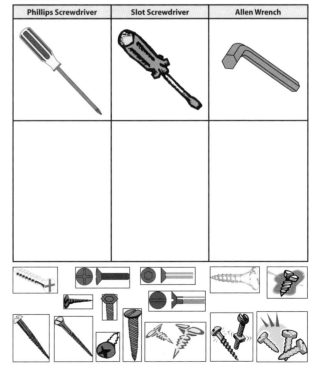

Collecting Tax Information and Filing Taxes

Directions: Use the words in the word box to write four tax-related things you should gather for each category below.

Word Box

W-2 form	total amount of tips	Girl Scout cookie receipt	hotel receipt for businesss trip
textbook receipt	dental cleaning bill	doctor appointment bill	savings account interest report
prescription bill	stock income report	Good Will donation receipt	health insurance payment amounts
business miles	college tuition bill	school fundraiser receipt	school silent auction receipt

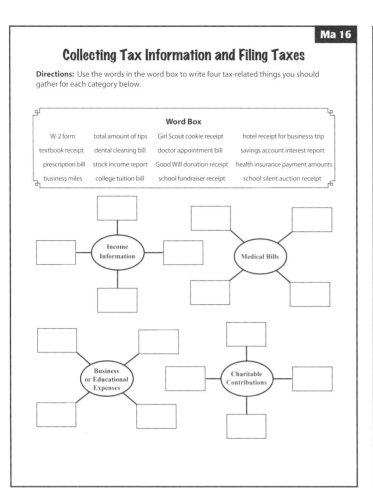

Controlling Credit Card Levels

Directions: Complete each sentence.

1. One reason not to charge more on a credit card than you can pay off each month is because
   _____
   _____

2. Another reason not to charge more on a credit card than you can pay off each month is because
   _____
   _____

3. A good use for a credit card is _____
   _____ because _____
   _____

4. A poor use for a credit card is _____
   _____ because _____
   _____

5. If you make $1000 per month, you should not charge clothes that cost $500 because
   _____
   _____

6. If you make $2000 per month, you could probably afford to charge
   _____
   _____

Correlating Room Numbers and Floors

Directions: Assume you work in a hotel that has three buildings. The Eisenhower building is three stories high, the Kennedy building is five stories high, and the Johnson building is eight stories high. Guests often get confused about which part of the building they are staying in. In the picture, the dark windows are offices. Answer these guests' questions for them.

1. In which building is room 321? _____

2. In which building is room 100? _____

3. In which building is room 842 _____

4. In which building is room 501?

   _____

5. In which building is room 300?

   _____

6. In which building is room 205?

   _____

7. In which building is room 736? _____

8. In which building is room 800 _____

9. In which building is room 700? _____

10. In which building is room 601? _____

11. In which building is room 222? _____

12. In which building is room 412? _____

Counting from 1-30

Directions: Count the number of items in each section. Write the numbers in the boxes.

Items to count	Number
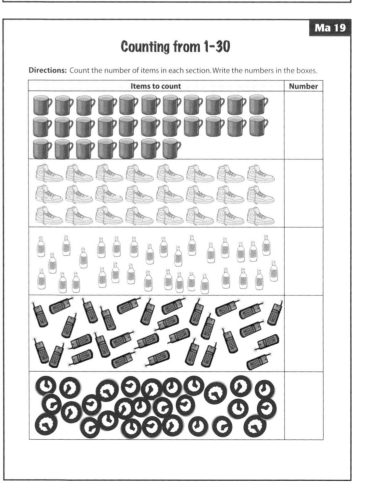	

Math 23

Counting Money

Directions: Count the amount of money in each section. Write the amounts in the boxes.

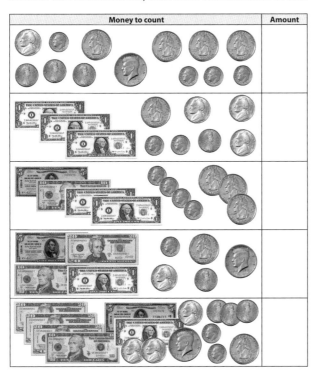

Money to count	Amount

Counting Ply

Directions: Ply is another word for strand. If you unravel string, rope, or yarn, you can see the ply or strands. Count the ply in each piece of rope, string, or yarn. Write the numbers in the boxes.

Rope, String, or Yarn	Ply	Rope, String, or Yarn	Ply

Counting Using the Skip Method

Directions: Circle the correct numbers.

1. Circle the numbers you would use to count by 2s.

1 2 3 4 5 6 7 8 9 10 11 12 13 14 15 16 17 18
19 20 21 22 23 24 25 26 27 28 29 30

2. Circle the numbers you would use to count by 3s.

1 2 3 4 5 6 7 8 9 10 11 12 13 14 15 16 17 18
19 20 21 22 23 24 25 26 27 28 29 30

3. Circle the numbers you would use to count by 5s.

1 2 3 4 5 6 7 8 9 10 11 12 13 14 15 16 17 18
19 20 21 22 23 24 25 26 27 28 29 30

4. Circle the numbers you would use to count by 10s.

1 2 3 4 5 6 7 8 9 10 11 12 13 14 15 16 17 18
19 20 21 22 23 24 25 26 27 28 29 30

5. Circle the numbers you would use to count by 12s.

1 2 3 4 5 6 7 8 9 10 11 12 13 14 15 16 17 18
19 20 21 22 23 24 25 26 27 28 29 30 31 32 33
34 35 36

Creating a Comparison Shopping Chart

Directions: Choose an item you might like to buy. Write the name of the item at the top of the chart. Down the side, write the names of five places where you could buy the item. At the top of the columns, write five types of information you could find out about the item, such as brand, color, size, functions, and price. Use your completed chart to compare the item at the five different places.

ITEM: _____

Information→ Places to Buy↓					

Deciding If a Temperature is Too High

Directions: Look at each person's tempeature below. Circle the temperatures that show that a person is probably sick.

97.3°F	99.5°F	103.7°F
98.9°F	96.9°F	100°F
104.1°F	102.6°F	98.6°F
99.1°F	103.5°F	99.9°F

Deciding on Level of Tip

Directions: Read each situation below and circle a level of tip that seems right.

#	Name of Restaurant	Type of Restaurant	Description of Service	Level of Tip
1	Josie's	Fancy sit-down place	A very pleasant waitress gave excellent service.	None 15% / 5% 20% / 10% 25%
2	Blissful Buffet	All-you-can-eat buffet where you serve yourself and a waiter takes your drink orders	The waiter took your drink orders as soon as you sat down and brought your drinks quickly.	None 15% / 5% 20% / 10% 25%
3	Hamburgers and Fixin's	Fast-food hamburger place	Your food came quickly and with a smile.	None 15% / 5% 20% / 10% 25%
4	Momma's Cafe	Casual sit-down place	The food was quite good, but the waitress spilled your drink and only brought silverware after you asked for it twice.	None 15% / 5% 20% / 10% 25%
5	Pizza Palace	Carry out pizza place	You ordered your pizza, waited 15 minutes, and left with it.	None 15% / 5% 20% / 10% 25%
6	Rockin' Rita's	Drive-up place with waitresses and waiters on roller skates	Your waiter was cheerful but he wrote your order wrong so you didn't get the sandwich you ordered.	None 15% / 5% 20% / 10% 25%
7	Lincoln Street Deli	Deli where you order at a counter and a waiter brings your food and drinks to your table	Your food and drinks came in a timely manner.	None 15% / 5% 20% / 10% 25%
8	Cowboy Campfire	An all-you-can-eat barbecue place where a waitress brings you all the food you want	The food was good, but you had to wait 15 and 20 minutes for refills.	None 15% / 5% 20% / 10% 25%

Determining Miles from a Mileage Chart

Directions: Use the mileage chart to find the distance between each pair of cities below.

	Boise, ID	Boston, MA	Charleston, SC	Chicago, IL	Cleveland, OH	Denver, CO	Des Moines, IA	Detroit, MI	Houston, TX	Indianapolis, IN	Minneapolis, MN	Philadelphia, PA
Boise, ID	x	2697	2359	1705	2037	814	1369	1968	1837	1850	1467	2454
Boston, MA	2697	x	968	1015	648	2003	1326	834	1858	941	1425	314
Charleston, SC	2359	968	x	913	717	1719	1205	871	1110	726	1323	665
Chicago, IL	1705	1015	913	x	355	1011	334	286	1085	185	409	772
Cleveland, OH	2037	648	717	355	x	1343	666	174	1304	319	765	437
Denver, CO	814	2003	1719	1011	1343	x	675	1271	1020	1101	920	1757
Des Moines, IA	1369	1326	1205	334	666	675	x	597	931	479	243	1083
Detroit, MI	1968	834	871	286	174	1274	597	x	1324	298	696	591
Houston, TX	1837	1858	1110	1085	1304	1028	931	1324	x	1021	1176	1558
Indianapolis, IN	1850	941	726	185	319	1101	479	298	1021	x	595	656
Minneapolis, MN	1467	1425	1323	409	765	920	243	696	1176	595	x	1182
Philadelphia, PA	2454	314	665	772	437	1757	1083	591	1558	656	1182	x

#	First City	Second City	Distance Between	#	First City	Second City	Distance Between
1	Cleveland, OH	Philadelphia, PA		9	Minneapolis, MN	Boston, MA	
2	Denver, CO	Boise, ID		10	Boise, ID	Houston, TX	
3	Detroit, MI	Cleveland, OH		11	Des Moines, IA	Charleston, SC	
4	Boston, MA	Philadelphia, PA		12	Denver, CO	Minneapolis, MN	
5	Cleveland, OH	Detroit, MI		13	Chicago, IL	Denver, CO	
6	Indianapolis, IN	Des Moines, IA		14	Philadelphia, PA	Chicago, IL	
7	Charleston, SC	Indianapolis, IN		15	Houston, TX	Chicago, IL	
8	Detroit, MI	Chicago, IL		16	Philadelphia, PA	Houston, TX	

Differentiating Between Relative Traits

Directions: Fill in the blanks with things that relate to each other as described.

#	Name something that is.......	Name something that is.......
1	Bright	Brighter
2	Sour	More sour
3	Short	Shorter
4	Silly	Sillier
5	Delicious	Delicious if eaten for breakfast
6	Fun to do	Fun to do if you have a pet
7	Tall	Tall, and makes the tall thing you named look short
8	Heavy	Heavy, but light compared to the heavy thing you named
9	Exciting	Exciting, but not as exciting as the exciting thing you named
10	Unusual	Unusual to some people, but not to you

Dividing Into Equal Sections

Directions: Fold or use a ruler to divide the two rectangles below into equal sections as marked.

Fold to divide this rectangle
into
four equal sections.

Use a ruler to divide this rectangle into
12 equal sections

Doing Your Banking

Directions: Enter the transactions in the check register. Use the current year.

#	Date	Explanation	Amount	#	Date	Explanation	Amount
1	May 8	You use your debit card at Ed's Groceries.	$39.56	5	May 13	You get money at the ATM machine.	$20.00
2	May 9	You put money in your checking account.	$125.67	6	May 15	You write Check #129 to Sally's Shoes for a new pair of shoes.	$32.87
3	May 12	Your electric bill is paid by automatic withdrawal.	$63.45	7	May 15	You use your debit card at TicketSource for basketball tickets.	$22.00
4	May 12	You buy a pie from the Wilson Elem. School fundraiser with Check #128	$10.00				

Number	Date	Description of Transaction	Payment/Debit (-)	Code	Fee	Deposit/Credit (+)	Balance $253.87

Estimating to Check Expectations

Directions: Choose the BEST answer for each question.

1. There were 43 girls at the dance and about 80 people altogether. About how many boys were there?
   a. 20 boys
   b. 30 boys
   c. 40 boys
   d. 50 boys

2. Chris is reading a book that has 150 pages. He has read about 60 pages. Which of these numbers of pages does he most likely have left to read?
   a. 39 pages
   b. 65 pages
   c. 82 pages
   d. 94 pages

3. Beth and Ivan are playing a card game called War. They started with 104 cards and, between them, they have all the cards in their hands. Beth has about 42 cards now. About how many cards does Ivan have?
   a. 40
   b. 50
   c. 60
   d. 70

4. Denise needs $38.00 to buy a gift. She has about $25.00 now. About how much more does she need?
   a. $1.00
   b. $5.00
   c. $15.00
   d. $25.00

5. Oberto has about 50 math problems to do for homework. He has finished 16 of the. About how many does he have left to do?
   a. 10
   b. 20
   c. 30
   d. 50

6. Shawn gets 212 TV channels. He has watched about 40 of them. About how many has he not checked out yet?
   a. 40
   b. 80
   c. 120
   d. 160

7. Nan won 90 days of free food at Miss Allie's. She has eaten there about 22 days so far. About how many days does she have left to eat there?
   a. 28
   b. 40
   c. 53
   d. 70

8. Dana had about 80 pennies in her purse. She spilled her purse and could only find 48 of the pennies. About how many pennies did she lose?
   a. 5
   b. 10
   c. 30
   d. 50

Estimating Travel Time

Directions: Write an approximate time in each empty box.

Fill in the blanks in these two boxes with locations in your local area.

You are going to drive from

_____

to

_____

About how long would it take at each of these times?

7:00 a.m. on a Friday	
Noon on Saturday	
5:00 p.m. on Wednesday	

You are going to drive from

_____

to

_____

About how long would it take at each of these times?

7:00 a.m. on a Friday	
Noon on Saturday	
5:00 p.m. on Wednesday	

For these two boxes, figure about 60 miles every hour.

You are going to drive the 243 miles from

Des Moines, IA

to

Minneapolis, MN.

About how long do you think the trip will take?

About _____ hours

You are going to drive the 437 miles from

Cleveland, OH

to

Philadelphia, PA.

About how long do you think the trip will take?

About _____ hours

Evaluating Purchasing Power

Directions: Imagine that you are buying each of the items on the list below.
For each, choose the price that would make the most sense for you.

ITEM	PRICE 1	PRICE 2	PRICE 3
Bicycle	$50: Used, but looks and works well	$180: Department store; an OK bike	$750: Bike shop; a great bike
TV	$250: A good 32"TV, but not the latest technology	$500: A 20"TV with the latest technology	$1800: A 40"TV with the latest technology
Computer monitor	$50: Used; 20"; in good shape	$50: New; 14"	$700: New; 30"
Cell phone	$50: Basic options; no camera	$100: Basic options; with camera	$250: All current options
Skateboard	$45: Offbrand; not very attractive	$70: 3rd best brand; very striking	$250: Top brand; best decorations
Blue jeans	$25: Budget store brand	$50: Popular brand; last season's style	$100: Popular brand; this season's style
Backpack	Free: Hand-me-down; in good shape	$15: Generic department store version; in a color that is OK	$45: Top brand; in your favorite color
Portable music player	$30: Holds 100 songs	$50: Holds 1000 songs	$100: Holds 10,000 songs

Exploring Banking Options

Directions: Match the banking options to the descriptions.

Answers	Descriptions	Banking Options
	1. an investment service banks offer	A. checking account
	2. a set-up that allows you to keep your money in a bank and use the money to write checks, withdraw for cash, or spend with a bank card	B. debit card
	3. using a computer and the Internet to pay bills, transfer money, and check your account balance	C. credit card
	4. bank card that you can use to charge purchases that you will pay for later	D. online banking
	5. bank card that you can use to withdraw money or to pay for purchases	E. CD (Certificate of Deposit)

Answers	Descriptions	Banking Options
	6. a service banks offer where the bank uses your money to pay your bills	F. savings account
	7. a computer terminal that people can use to deposit to and withdraw from their bank accounts without going to a bank or talking to a teller	G. automatic deposits
	8. a set-up that allows you to keep money in a bank and let it grow as interest is added	H. ATM (Automated Teller Machine)
	9. the process by which you access your bank account online and pay your bills from there instead of writing checks or using bank cards	I. automatic bill payment
	10. a service banks offer where your employer puts money directly into your bank account.	J. online bill payment

Figuring Ages

Directions: Find each person's age.

#	Name	Current Year	Year Born	Calculation	Age
Sample:	Carrie	2007	1995	2007 - 1995 = 12	12 yrs old
1.	Adam		1992		
2.	Beth		2003		
3.	Nettie		1955		
4.	Ching Yu		1967		
5.	Craig		1982		
6.	Marcos		1975		
7.	LaFrancine		1998		
8.	Sam		2005		
9.	Del		1961		
10.	LeBron		1980		

Figuring Elapsed Time

Directions: Answer each question.

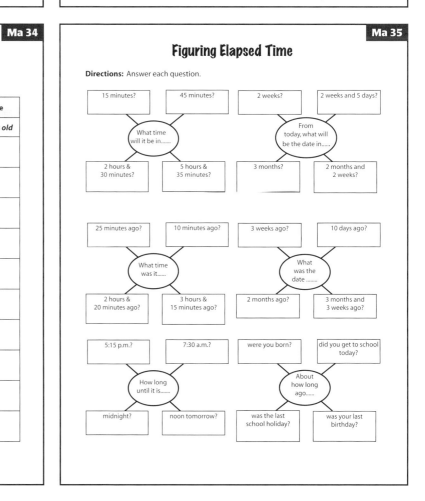

Figuring Tips

Directions: Figure each tip.

#	Name of Restaurant	Type of Restaurant and Service Received	Level of Tip	Calculation (use a calculator)
1.	Josie's	Fancy sit-down place A very pleasant waitress gave excellent service.	20%	Bill: $78.55 Tip: _____
2.	Blissful Buffet	All-you-can-eat buffet where you serve yourself and a waiter takes your drink orders The waiter took your drink orders as soon as you sat down and brought your drinks quickly.	5%	Bill: $24.58 Tip: _____
3.	Momma's Cafe	Casual sit-down place The food was quite good, but the waitress spilled your drink and only brought silverware after you asked for it twice.	15%	Bill: $21.73 Tip: _____
4.	Rockin' Rita's	Drive-up place with waitresses and waiters on roller skates Your waiter was cheerful and did a good job with your order.	20%	Bill: $7.35 Tip: _____
5.	Lincoln Street Deli	Deli where you order at a counter and a waiter brings your food and drinks to your table Your food and drinks came in a timely manner.	10%	Bill: $43.16 Tip: _____
6.	Cowboy Campfire	An all-you-can-eat barbecue place where a waitress brings you all the food you want The food was good, and your waitress was very attentive.	20%	Bill: $35.91 Tip: _____

Finding an Address

Directions: Use the map and the numbered circles to answer each question.

1. Which of these street names is MOST LIKELY the missing street name?
   a. Washington
   b. Canary
   c. Oak
   d. Westwood

2. Look at 374 Plum Street. About how far away is 1542 Plum Street?
   a. 1 block
   b. 5 blocks
   c. 8 blocks
   d. 12 blocks

3. The four house numbers in the circle belong to houses on the left side of Cherry Street. Which of these houses is most likely on the right side of Cherry Street?
   a. 215
   b. 231
   c. 242
   d. 253

4. Which of these street names is MOST LIKELY the missing street name?
   a. Main
   b. Peach
   c. San Pedro
   d. Henrietta

5. Which of these house numbers might be found in this block?
   a. 288
   b. 465
   c. 550
   d. 607

6. Which of these street names is MOST LIKELY the missing street name?
   a. Bush
   b. Maple
   c. Fifth
   d. Tenth

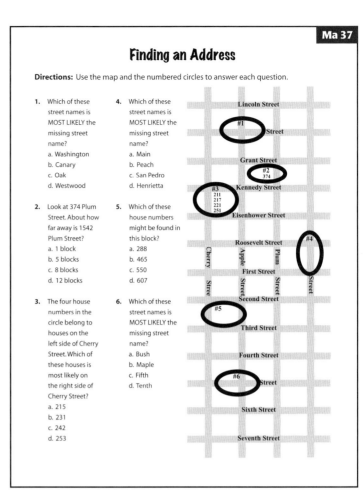

Finding Fun Activities That Are Inexpensive or Free

Directions: Fill in the boxes with fun activities.

Fun, free things to do by yourself

Fun, free things to do with friends

Fun, free things to do with your family

Fun, inexpensive things to do by yourself

Fun, inexpensive things to do with friends

Fun, inexpensive things to do with family

Finding the Desired Newspaper Page

Directions: Use the newspaper directory to name the pages where you would MOST LIKELY find each item in the chart.

Directory	
Business	1D
Classifieds	5F
Comics	4E
Life/Entertainment	1E
Deaths	3A
Local	1C
Movies	3E
Puzzles	4E
Real Estate	1F
Sports	1B
State	2A
Stocks	4D
TV Listings	5E

#	Item	Page	#	Item	Page
1.	Ads selling used computers		9.	Overview of someone who has died	
2.	A story about a local football team		10.	Listings of prices on the stock market	
3.	Shows and times for the local movie theater		11.	An article about your mayor's plan for a city event	
4.	Names of shows on TV tonight		12.	Your favorite cartoons	
5.	Pictures and information about homes that are for sale		13.	A human interest story about a teenager who published a book	
6.	An article about the governor of your state		14.	Summaries of soap operas	

Finding Your Car in a Parking Lot

Directions: Answer the questions.

1. Explain why, before you leave your car in a parking lot, it is important to take special note of where your car is located. _____

2. Where would you look to find a mark in a parking lot that is intended to help you find your car? _____

3. Give three examples of landmarks that were not necessarily intended to help you find your car but that you could use for that purpose. _____

4. Give three examples of things you might see in a parking lot that would not make good landmarks to help you find your car. _____

5. Explain how you might be able to use your car keys to help you find your car. _____

6. What would you do if you return to a very large parking lot and cannot find your car? _____

Folding Laundry

Directions: Choose the BEST answer for each question.

1. When is the best time to fold laundry?
   a. Before putting the clothes into the dryer
   b. As soon as the dryer stops
   c. After the dryer stops and the clothes have cooled down
   d. Whenever it is convenient

2. What happens to laundry that is not folded at the right time?
   a. The clothes do not fit well.
   b. The clothes become stained.
   c. The clothes get wrinkled.
   d. The clothes shrink.

3. When should you fold a dress shirt instead of putting it on a hanger?
   a. As soon as it comes out of the dryer
   b. When the shirt is made of cotton
   c. Only when you have to put it into a suitcase
   d. When the shirt is a larger size

4. When should you fold jeans with the sideseams together?
   a. Never
   b. Always
   c. When you want a crease down the front
   d. When you are folding children's jeans

5. For which of the following types of clothes is folding least important?
   a. t-shirts
   b. underwear
   c. shorts and pants
   d. dresses and skirts

6. If you have clothes that you do not want to dry all the way in the dryer, when should you fold them?
   a. As soon as they come out of the dryer
   b. Right before you wear them
   c. After they have air dried
   d. Whenever it is convenient

7. If you do not have time to fold your laundry when it should be done, what can you do to help keep the clothes looking nice?
   a. Leave them in the washing machine for a day or two.
   b. Put them in a laundry basket.
   c. Put them in plastic bags.
   d. Spread them out on flat surfaces until you can get to them.

8. About how long does it usually take to fold a basket of laundry?
   a. 5 to 10 minutes
   b. about 30 minutes
   c. over an hour
   d. a couple of hours

Having Good Attendance

Directions: Using the letter A to mark absences, follow the directions to mark each calendar. Scatter the absenses throughout the month however you would like.

April Directions: Mark the least number of absences that a student could have and still have bad school attendance.

June Directions: Mark the least number of absences that an employee could have and still have bad work attendance.

March Directions: Mark the most number of absences that would allow a student to have good school attendance.

May Directions: Mark the most number of absences that would allow an employee to have good work attendance.

April, June, March, May calendars.

Identifying Basic Object Charateristics, Such as Size, Color, and Shape

Directions: Choose ten items around the room. List the names of the items in the "Object" column. Then, fill in the rest of the table.

#	Object	Size	Color	Shape
1				
2				
3				
4				
5				
6				
7				
8				
9				
10				

Identifying Coins and Bills

Directions: Match the coins and bills to their names and values.

Answers	Coins and Bills		Names	Values
	1.		A. dime	J. 1¢
	2.		B. one dollar bill	K. 10¢
	3.		C. quarter	L. $20
	4.		D. twenty dollar bill	M. $1
	5.		E. penny	N. 5¢
	6.		F. ten dollar bill	O. 50¢
	7.		G. half dollar	P. $5
	8.		H. five dollar bill	Q. $10
	9.		I. nickel	R. 25¢

Identifying Interest and Principal

Directions: Say these statements are all yours. Answer the questions.

House Payment

Payment Due Date:	04/01/07
Statement Date:	03/02/07
Principal	550.19
Interest	479.34
Account Information as of 03/02/07	
Current Principal Balance	104,582.75
Year to Date Interest	1,453.58
Interest Rate	5.500%
03/01/07 Payment: $547.59 prin, $481.94 int	1,029.53
Additoinal Principal Payment	20.47

Overdue Dentist Bill

30-day Balance	$0
60-day Balance	$0
90-day Balance	$85
Overdue Fees	$10
Total	$95

Savings Account Statement

Balance as of Dec 12, 2007	$256.93
Credits:Deposits	$139.00
Interest	$7.73
Debits:	$0.00
Balance as of Jan 10, 2008	403.66

1. Which of the three statements shows interest that is money you have gained? _____

2. House payment: How much principal do you owe? _____

3. House payment: How much principal did you pay the previous month? _____

4. House payment: How much interest have you paid so far for the year? _____

5. Dentist bill: How much interest are you being charged? _____

6. Dentist bill: How much was your bill for the dental work? _____

7. Savings account: How much interest did you earn for the month? _____

Identifying Months By Number

Directions: Write the month for each date.

#	Date	Name of Month
1.	6-27-55	
2.	1-28-98	
3.	11-7-82	
4.	2-26-07	
5	10-31-63	
6.	4/15/72	
7.	3/17/95	
8.	7/19/34	
9.	10/24/2004	
10.	12/19/1950	
11.	05/02/1937	
12.	09-13-81	
13.	07-04-1776	
14.	9/11	
15.	1/1	

Judging Comparitive Sizes

Directions: For each number, read the six words and then use them in a sentence that compares sizes.

#	Six Words	Sentence That Compares Sizs
1.	small, smaller, smallest, cup, bowl, basket	
2.	tall, taller, tallest, Jeremy, Cindy, Heinz	
3.	funny, funnier, funniest, Claire, Jose, Mick	
4.	frightened, more frightened, most frightened, cricket, puppy, duck	
5.	easy, easier, easiest, math, reading, gym	
6.	sure, more sure, most sure, 10:00, 12:00, 2:00	
7.	sour, more sour, most sour, lemon, lime, vinegar	

Judging Mailing Time

Directions: Fill in the chart.

	Think of Someone who lives......	Name of person (If you do not know anyone personally, use a famous person.)	Where does the person live?	You want a letter to arrive two weeks from today. Write that day and date.	When will you mail it? Write the day and date.	Explain your mailing date choice.
1.	within your local area.					
2.	in a nearby city within your state.					
3.	in a large city in a state next to you.					
4.	in a very small town or rural area in a state next to you.					
5.	in a large city that is at least 1000 miles away.					
6.	in a very small town or rural area that is at least 1000 miles away.					

Knowing Months in Order and Number of Days in Month

Directions: In the first column, write the months in order. Use the verse below to help you fill in the second column.

> 30 days hath September,
> April, June, and November.
> All the rest have 31,
> Except for February,
> Which alone has 28,
> And every four years has 29.

#	Months in Order	Number of Days in Month
1.		
2.		
3.		
4.		
5.		
6.		
7.		
8.		
9.		
10.		
11.		
12.		

Knowing the Days of the Week in Order

Directions: Beginning with the first day in each row, write the next four days.

Sunday				
Friday				
Wednesday				
Saturday				
Thursday				
Monday				
Tuesday				

Directions: Beginning with the first day in each row, write the four days before it. (Go backwards in order.)

Sunday				
Friday				
Wednesday				
Saturday				
Thursday				
Monday				
Tuesday				

Knowing Where to Find Other Area Codes

Directions: List five cities that are in your phone book. Use the phone book to find area codes for these cities and towns.

City	Area Code	City	Area Code

Directions: List five cities or towns from five different states. Use the Internet to find area codes for these cities and towns.

City	Area Code	City	Area Code

Directions: Without using one you've already used, list a city from a different state. Call directory assistance to find the area code for this city.

City	Area Code	City	Area Code

Knowing Where to Find Other Zip Codes

Directions: List five cities that are in your phone book. Use the phone book to find zip codes for these cities and towns.

City	Zip Code	City	Zip Code

Directions: List five cities or towns from five different states. Use the Internet to find zip codes for these cities and towns.

City	Zip Code	City	Zip Code

Directions: Without using one you've already used, list a city from a different state. Call directory assistance to find the zip code for this city.

City	Zip Code	City	Zip Code

Knowing Your Area Code and Phone Number

Directions: Fill in these forms.

Name	Phone

Name: (last) _____ (first) _____

Address (Street address) _____

(City) _____ (State) _____ (Zip) _____

Phone
( ) _____ - _____

Phone
_____ _____ – _____ ext _____
Area Code

Phone ( ) _____

Phone: _____ – _____ – _____

Phone ☐☐☐ - ☐☐☐ - ☐☐☐☐

Phone with area code _____

Knowing Your Clothing and Shoe Sizes

Directions: Choose your best size for each of the following items.

t-shirt	S	M	L	XL	XXL	XXXL

Jeans	Guys/ All (choose L & W)	Length	26	28	30	32	34	36	38	40	42	44	46
		Waist	26	28	30	32	34	36	38	40	42	44	46
	Girls		0	2	4	6	8	10	12	14	16	18	20	22	24	26

Tennis shoes	Guys	Ch 12	Ch 13	A 1	A 2	A 3	A 4	A 5	A 6	A 7	A 8	A 9	A 10	A 11	A 12
	Girls	Ch 11	Ch 12	Ch 13	A 1	A 2	A 3	A 4	A 5	A 6	A 7	A 8	A 9	A 10	A 11

Guys Socks	Shoe size	Ch 12	Ch 13	A 1	A 2	A 3	A 4	A 5	A 6	A 7	A 8	A 9	A 10	A 11	A 12
	Sock size	6	7		8		9		10		11		12	13

Girls Socks	Shoe size	Ch 11	Ch 12	Ch 13	A 1	A 2	A 3	A 4	A 5	A 6	A 7	A 8	A 9	A 10	A 11
	Sock size	6–7			7–9			9–10			10–12		

Underwear	Guys	S	M	L	26	28	30	32	34	36	38	40	42	44
	Girls	4/ 5	6/ 7	8/ 9	10/ 11	Ch S	Ch M	Ch L	Ch XL	A S	A M	A L	A XL	A XXL

Belt	20	22	24	26	28	30	32	34	36	38	40	42	44

Bra	Around	28	30	32	34	36	38	40	42	44
	Cup	A	B	C	D	DD	DDD	E	EE	EEE

Knowing Your Height and Weight

Directions: Answer the questions.

1. Which of these weights is MOST likely for a 4th grader?
   40 pounds   80 pounds   120 pounds

2. Which of these weights is MOST likely for a high school girl?
   40 pounds   80 pounds   120 pounds

3. Which of these weights is MOST likely for a high school boy?
   40 pounds   80 pounds   150 pounds

Directions: Put an X where you fall on this chart.

Follow Height Down and Weight Across																								
	57	58	59	60	61	62	63	64	65	66	67	68	69	70	71	72	73	74	75	76	77	78	79	80
80																								
90																								
100																								
110																								
120																								
130																								
140																								
150																								
160																								
170																								
180																								
190																								
200																								
210																								
220																								
230																								
240																								
250																								
260																								

Making a Bed

Directions: Cut out the pictures. "Make the bed." As you add each piece, write on it a description of how you use it to make a bed.

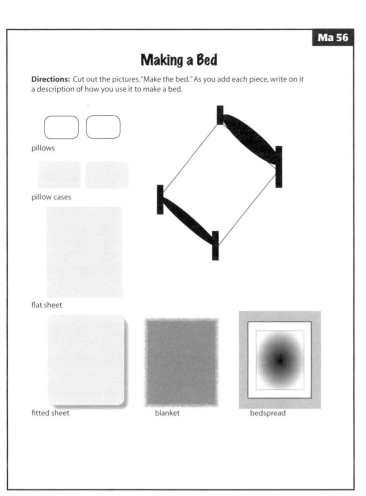

pillows

pillow cases

flat sheet

fitted sheet

blanket

bedspread

Making a Savings Plan

Directions: Use this budget sheet to divide up a person's $3,500 monthly take-home pay. Make sure to plan to save some money, even if it is a small amount.

Budget for One Month		
Income	$3,500	
Rent/Mortgage		
Utility Bills		
Phone/Internet/TV		
Groceries/Food		
Car/Transportation		
Insurance		
Toiletries		
Clothing/Shoes		
Household Maintenance		
Household Goods		
Entertainment		
Savings		
Total Expenses (Should equal $3,500)		

Making Accurate Reservations

Directions: Fill in the blanks in these reservations.

Examples: I'd like to make a reservation for four people at 7:00 on Saturday, April 8th.

I'd like to reserve a room for one person for two nights, Tuesday, August 11th and Wednesday, August 12th. I'd like a king-sized bed.

1.   **a dinner with five friends on your birthday:** This is _____ .

I'd like to make a _____ for _____ people at _____

on _____ , _____ .

2.   **a hotel room for next Thursday for you and one parent:** I'd like to reserve a room for

_____ people on Thursday, _____ .

My name is _____ . I'd like two double _____ .

3.   **a banquet confirmation for you and Kyle Smith. You are eating fish, and he is eating chicken:**

My name is _____ .

I'd like to make _____ reservations for the banquet. I would like _____ ,

and _____ _____ would like chicken.

4.   **lunch at noon today for you and three relatives:** This is _____

I'd like to make _____ for _____ people at

_____ today.

5.   **a hotel room for three nights beginning in two days for three people with two double beds**

and a rollaway: _____

_____

_____

6.   **a dinner with two friends tonight at 6:00:** _____

_____

_____

Making Change

Directions: Find the correct amount of change for each purchase.

Item Bought	Cost of Item	Money Paid	Change
	$3.25		
	$34.26		
	$4.98		
	$14.92		
	$12.24		
	$19.12		

Making Payment Choices

Directions: Use the information in the table to answer the questions.

	Payment Choices		
Car Loan Amount: $12,000	$293 per month will pay the loan off in four years and cost a total of $2062 in interest	$376 per month will pay off in three years and cost a total of $1535 in interest	
House Loan Amount: $125,000	$917 per month will pay the loan off in 30 years and cost a total of $205,189 in interest	$1046 per month will pay the loan off in 20 years and cost a total of $125,932 in interest	$1,195 per month will pay the loan off in 15 years and cost a total of $90,02 in interest.

1. Ben has to be very careful with his money so he can afford all his bills.

   Which car payment choice is probably best for him? _____

2. Karen can afford to save $300 per month. Which car payment choice is probably best for her?

   _____

3. At the ends of some months Tia has extra money and other months she doesn't. Explain why she should choose the $293 per month plan, but pay the $376 per month plan as often as possible.

   _____

4. Explain why anyone would want to make house payments for 30 years instead of 20 years.

   _____

5. Nell does a good job of saving money.

   Explain why the $1,195 per month choice might be a good one for her.

   _____

6. Hank thinks he can afford $1195 per month, but he chose the $1046 per month house payment choice. Explain why he would have chosen the lower payment if he could afford the higher one.

   _____

Making Sure You Wake Up On Time

Directions: Fill in the boxes with your opinions.

Your Situation	Wake-Up Plan	Why this choice is or is not a good one for you	If not a good choice for you, suggest a better choice
You need to get up at 6:45 to get ready for school. You are the only one home.	Your mother will call from work to wake you up.		
You are taking a nap after school. You need to wake up after one hour so you can get to work on time. You and your sibling are home alone.	You told your sibling to wake you up.		
You are going to sleep until 8:00 and then get up to do your homework.	You have set the alarm on your cell phone.		
It is Saturday, and your friend is coming over for the day.	You asked your friend to wake you when he or she gets there.		
You have to leave for the airport at 4:00 A.M. You are a sound sleeper and have a hard time hearing alarms at that time of day.	You asked a friend to call and wake you up.		

Measuring for a Recipe

Directions: Circle the correct measurements.

1/2 cup		1 teaspoon	
1/3 cup		1 tablespoon	
2/3 cup		1/4 cup	
3/4 cup		2 cups	
1 cup		1 1/4 cup	

Measuring for Curtains, Frames, Etc.

Directions: Make trim marks on this picture so it will fit in a 3" x 5" frame.

Directions: A curtain should be about twice as wide as the widow and just a little bit longer than the widow. Draw an arrow to the correct curtain sizes for these windows.

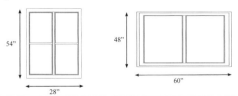

54" 28"   48" 60"

Curtain Sizes (W x L)						
45 x 63	60 x 48	60 x 63	80 x 48	80 x 63	120 x 48	120 x 63
45 x 84	60 x 54	60 x 84	80 x 54	80 x 84	120 x 54	120 x 84

Mending Clothes

Directions: Describe a good way to fix each clothing problem.

Clothing Item with Problem	Good Way to Fix the Clothing Problem

Mixing Proper Amounts

Directions: Find the needed amount of cleaning product for each situation.

Directions from bottle of cleaning product	Amount of water you are using	Amount of cleaning product needed
Mix 4 ounces (1/2 cup) of solution to one gallon of water.	2 gallons	
Dilute 1 1/4 oz. (2 1/2 tbsps) per gallon of water.	2 quarts	
Mix 1/4 cup with 1 quart of water.	1 gallon	
Add 1 quart of solution for each 2 gallons of water.	3 gallons	
Combine with equal parts of water.	2 quarts	
Combine with water in a 1:3 ratio.	6 quarts	

Monitoring Miles Per Gallon

Directions: Fill in the blanks in the chart.

Beginning Odometer Reading	Ending Odometer Reading	Miles Driven	Gallons of Gas Used	Miles Per Gallon
63,521	63,846		15	
137,327	137,500		18	
25,985	26,388		17	
2,000	2,301		13	
98,672	99,000		10	
45,639	45,906		26	
165,984	166,385		47	
32,264	32,608		14	
77,777	77,999		8	

Ordering at a Restaurant On a Budget

Directions: Use a menu from a local sit-down restaurant to complete this table. Use your local tax percentage.

Amount of money you have to spend	What you would order	Cost of food	Amount of tax (% =)	Amount you would leave for a tip
$5.00				
$6.72				
$7.87				

Ordering at a Restaurant
When Someone Else is Paying

Directions: Use a menu from a local sit-down restaurant to complete this table.

If the person who is paying orders this........	Cost	I would order this.......	Cost
(enter the third entree on the menu)			
(enter the sixth entree on the menu)			
(enter the last entree on the menu along with two other side items)			

Packing for a Trip

Directions: Say you are going on a one-week trip to a beach vacation resort. Use the table below to make a list of everything you will pack. Use details such as fabric colors and design to describe specific items you own.

Shirts	Shoes & Socks	Beach Wear/Supplies

Pants/Skirts	Underwear	Things to Take to Do

Shorts/Skirts	Toiletries/Supplies	Other

Planning Around Daylight Saving Time

Directions: Fill in this table. TIP: *Spring ahead, Fall back.*

This is the current time....	It is in the spring and time to change the clocks for daylight saving time. To what time will you change your clock?	It is in the fall and time to change the clocks for daylight saving time. To what time will you change your clock?

Planning Around Time Zones

Directions: Fill in the table based on where you live and these guidelines:
- You are calling four friends who live in the four time zones in the table.
- You do not want to call your friends
  – before 8:00 A.M. their time
  – during their lunch hours (12:00–1:00 their time)
  – after 9:00 P.M. their time

Time Where You Live (Your time zone)	Is this a good time to call the Eastern Time Zone?	Is this a good time to call the Central Time Zone?	Is this a good time to call the Mountain Time Zone?	Is this a good time to call the Pacific Time Zone?
Example: 2:00 P.M. Eastern	Yes, it is 2:00	Yes, it is 1:00	No, it is lunch time	Yes, it is 11:00
8:00 A.M.				
9:00 A.M.				
11:00 A.M.				
Noon				
1:00 P.M.				
7:00 P.M.				
10:00 P.M.				
Midnight				

Planning to Remember Birthdays of Friends and Relatives

Directions: Read through the different ideas for remembering birthdays. For each pair, circle the one that would work best for you and explain why it would work best.

#	First idea in a pair	Second idea in a pair	Why would the idea you circled work better for you?
1.	At the beginning of each month, write the birthdays for the month on the calendar.	Place the birthdays on a computer calendar that sends you an e-mail reminder the week before each calendar entry.	
2.	At the beginning of each month, address all the birthday cards you will send that month. Write the "to mail" date where the stamp goes and add stamps as the dates roll around.	Join an online birthday club and have all your friends and relatives also join. The club will then send e-mail reminders to all people in your group for all birthdays in your group.	
3.	Gather all the cards for a year and place them in a file with sticky notes to identify who each card is for. Check the file each week.	At the beginning of the year, take a calendar and place reminder stickers on the calendar one week before all key birthdays.	
4.	Put reminder notes with the bills you have to pay.	Make a list of all the birthdays and check your list every week so you can prepare the cards for that week.	

Projecting Needed Time for an Activity

Directions: Write the number of minutes you think each activity will take. Then compare your list with a classmate. Discuss any differences. Change any times that you think should be changed.

Activities	How long do you think the activities will take?	How much time did your partner say?	Time changes, if any, that you want to make.
Make your bed			
Put the clean dishes away			
Make a peanut butter and jelly sandwich			
Wash the car			
Take out the garbage			
Clean your room			
Eat breakfast			
Brush your teeth			
Read the newspaper			
Research online to find facts for a school paper			
Go to the store for milk and bread			
Walk three miles			

Providing Quality Work

Directions: Match the examples of quality work to the jobs.

Answers	Examples of Quality Work	Jobs
	1. Proofread all letters very carefully.	**A.** Nurse
	2. Glance in the mirror from time to time to make sure everything is OK.	**B.** Mechanic
	3. Smile to try and make others feel better.	**C.** Waiter
	4. Listen carefully so you can bring everything you are asked to bring.	**D.** Secretary
	5. Keep tools organized.	**E.** Bus driver

Answers	Examples of Quality Work	Jobs
	6. Make sure to pack breakables carefully.	**A.** Teacher
	7. Keep customers' seats and handles clean and fresh.	**B.** Doctor
	8. Keep track of customers' choices so you know them the next time.	**C.** Check-Out Person
	9. Pay careful attention so you know when someone is confused.	**D.** Cab Driver
	10. Listen carefully so you understand how the customer feels.	**E.** Beautician

Putting Names in a Cell Phone Address Book

Directions: Fill in the blanks in the steps for entering this name in a cell phone address book: **Jacob Entwistle**

Step 1: Push this button _____ time(s)
Step 2: Push this button _____ time(s)
Step 3: Push this button _____ time(s)
Step 4: Push this button _____ time(s)
Step 5: Push this button _____ time(s)
Step 6: Push this button _____ time(s)
Step 7: Push this button _____ time(s)
Step 8: Push this button _____ time(s)
Step 9: Push this button _____ time(s)
Step 10: Push this button _____ time(s)
Step 11: Push this button _____ time(s)
Step 12: Push this button _____ time(s)
Step 13: Push this button _____ time(s)
Step 14: Push this button _____ time(s)
Step 15: Push this button _____ time(s)

Math 37

Putting Things in Order

Directions: Put the items in each box in order by writing the numbers from 1 to 8.

My Friends' Birthdays
___ March 8: Katie
___ July 5: Karen
___ May 2: Ami
___ December 12: Cambria
___ July 17: Mitzi
___ February 12: Becca
___ October 1: Monica
___ January 5: Mel

Tuesday Schedule
___ 9:00 A.M. Horseback riding
___ 11:00 A.M. Relaxation
___ 8:00 P.M. Bonfire
___ 9:00 P.M. Dancing
___ 8:00 A.M. Breakfast
___ 11:45 A.M. Lunch
___ 1-30 P.M. Massages
___ 5-30 P.M. Dinner

Phone Book Listings
___ Abe Scibona 347-8930
___ Morgan Booth 347-2910
___ Cindy Sanchex 347-9348
___ Beth Townsend 347-8323
___ LaTisha Brown 347-8342
___ Dee Dee Torring 347-1001
___ Ana Mercer 347-4523
___ Mih Fron 347-2365

Shades of Red
___ pink
___ red
___ hint of pink
___ maroon
___ bright pink
___ deep maroon
___ bright red
___ pale pink

Reading and Writing Dates

Directions: Write today's date using each of the sample formats. Then use your own words to describe each date format.

Sample Formats	Today's Date	Description of Each Format
6/27/07		
6-27-07		
6.27.07		
June 27, 2007		
'07 Jun. 27		
27 July '07		

Reading and Writing Numbers

Directions: Work with a partner. Take turns completing this task: Circle 20 numbers. Choose at least one from each row. Do not show your partner. Call the numbers out so your partner can write them.

1	3	4	9	12	16	19	24	32	33	35	37	44	46	48
53	55	59	61	62	64	67	68	70	72	73	80	81	82	85
87	88	97	98	99	100	104	106	110	112	118	121	125	129	130
138	144	148	152	157	159	163	167	169	173	174	177	179	184	185
190	192	197	199	200	207	213	215	219	222	227	231	237	239	243
247	250	255	256	259	262	267	269	271	279	283	286	288	289	291
297	298	302	308	310	313	315	317	324	322	326	328	333	335	339
345	348	350	353	356	359	360	363	368	375	377	382	385	390	391
400	408	412	416	422	428	437	439	444	448	453	459	460	462	468
475	477	482	488	492	493	502	507	511	514	522	527	531	538	545
549	552	555	564	569	573	577	586	588	590	591	600	606	611	617
622	628	633	639	641	647	658	659	664	665	671	676	680	683	685
694	699	703	705	710	716	727	721	722	738	739	745	746	752	753
764	769	770	772	773	782	788	791	795	800	801	815	816	820	823
830	832	841	843	853	854	864	865	870	879	886	887	892	895	908
909	912	917	925	928	931	934	936	943	944	950	952	967	968	969
974	975	977	983	985	988	989	991	994	999	1000	1001	1012	1173	1853

Write the 20 numbers your partner chose here:

Reading Charts, Tables, and Graphs

Directions: Use the chart, table, and graph below to answer the questions.

Grades from Grade Book						
Student	Quiz 1	Quiz 2	Report	Project	Quiz 3	Exam
Joel Nicke	24	32	135	200	20	56
Sindy Soll	32	32	142	155	32	63

Room Assignments

5th Graders: Rm 235

6th Graders: Rm 220

7th Graders: Rm 209

8th Graders: Rm 112

9th Graders: Rm 100

10th Graders: Rm 155

11th Graders: Rm 83

12th Graders: Rm 22

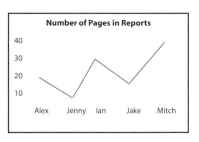

1. What grade did Sindy Soll receive on her project? _____
2. Did Sindy Soll or Joel Nicke do better on the report? _____
3. To what room are the 8th graders assigned? _____
4. Which grades are assigned to the second floor? _____
5. About how many pages are in Ian's report? _____
6. Whose report has the least number of pages? _____

Reading Roman Numerals

Directions: Use the key to help you fill in the table.

| Key: | I = 1 | V = 5 | X = 10 | L = 50 |
| | C = 100 | D = 500 | M = 1000 | |

Roman Numerals	Cardinal Numerals
III	
	5
VII	
	12
IX	
	40
CXL	
	300
DCCXV	
	630
MDCLXVII	
	2000

Reading the Speedometer and Gas Gauge

Directions: Use the sign and speedometer to decide if the car is speeding. Use the gas gauge to decide if the car needs gas.

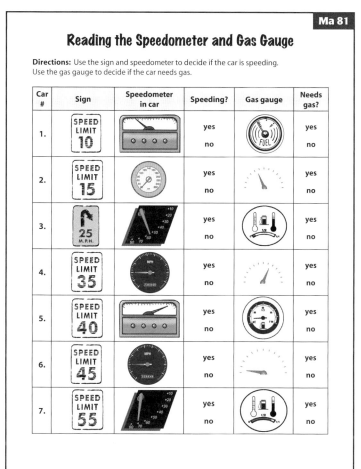

Car #	Sign	Speedometer in car	Speeding?	Gas gauge	Needs gas?
1.	SPEED LIMIT 10		yes / no		yes / no
2.	SPEED LIMIT 15		yes / no		yes / no
3.	25 M.P.H.		yes / no		yes / no
4.	SPEED LIMIT 35		yes / no		yes / no
5.	SPEED LIMIT 40		yes / no		yes / no
6.	SPEED LIMIT 45		yes / no		yes / no
7.	SPEED LIMIT 55		yes / no		yes / no

Recognizing Letter and Legal Sizes

Directions: For each pair of items below, circle the one that is letter-size and explain how you know.

How do you know the circled one is letter-size?

How do you know the circled one is letter-size?

How do you know the circled one is letter-size?

How do you know the circled one is letter-size?

How do you know the circled one is letter-size?

How do you know the circled one is letter-size?

Recognizing Standard Measurements

Directions: Measure the items in your house and fill out the table.

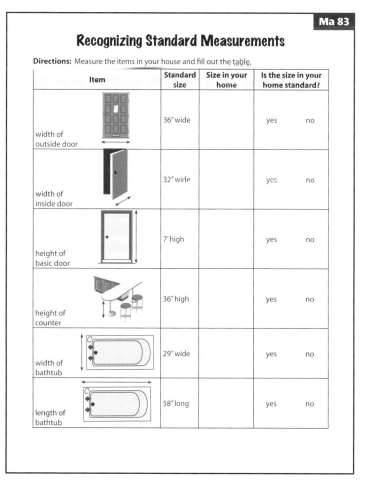

Item	Standard size	Size in your home	Is the size in your home standard?
width of outside door	36" wide		yes / no
width of inside door	32" wide		yes / no
height of basic door	7' high		yes / no
height of counter	36" high		yes / no
width of bathtub	29" wide		yes / no
length of bathtub	58" long		yes / no

Scheduling Errands

Directions: Susie is a student. She has volleyball practice after school each day until 6:00. She needs to complete the errands below in one week. Make a plan for her using your school hours.

Errand	Time Needed (with Travel)	Business Hours
Pick up shirt at Grandma's	2 hours	Awake 7:00 A.M.– 9:00 P.M.
Get a new pair of shoes	1 hour	9:00 A.M.– 9:00 P.M.
Look in attic for costume	1 hour	Anytime (24/7)
Pick up duffle bag at gym	30 minutes	6:00 A.M.– 11:00 P.M.
Get therapy on sore arm	1 hour	11:00 A.M.– 8:00 P.M.
Have nails done for dance	45 minutes	10:00 A.M.– 7:00 P.M.
Buy snacks for party	1 hour	Anytime (24/7)
Get a hair cut	1 hour	9:00 A.M.– 6:00 P.M.

Monday	
Tuesday	
Wednesday	
Thursday	
Friday	
Saturday	
Sunday	

Scoring Sports

Directions: Find the score for each sport.

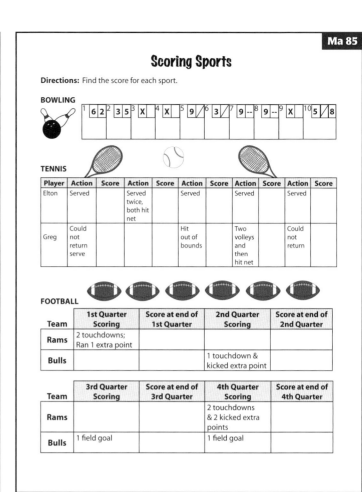

BOWLING

| 1 | 6 2 | 2 3 5 | 3 X | 4 X | 5 9 / | 6 3 / | 7 9 -- | 8 9 -- | 9 X | 10 5 / 8 |

TENNIS

Player	Action	Score	Action	Score	Action	Score	Action	Score	Action	Score
Elton	Served		Served twice, both hit net		Served		Served		Served	
Greg	Could not return serve				Hit out of bounds		Two volleys and then hit net		Could not return	

FOOTBALL

Team	1st Quarter Scoring	Score at end of 1st Quarter	2nd Quarter Scoring	Score at end of 2nd Quarter
Rams	2 touchdowns; Ran 1 extra point			
Bulls			1 touchdown & kicked extra point	

Team	3rd Quarter Scoring	Score at end of 3rd Quarter	4th Quarter Scoring	Score at end of 4th Quarter
Rams			2 touchdowns & 2 kicked extra points	
Bulls	1 field goal		1 field goal	

Setting the Alarm on a Clock

Directions: Study the buttons on the clocks below.
Then take a guess how you would set the alarm on each clock.

Clocks with Buttons	Explanations telling how to set the alarms
Snooze PM **12:21** Time set AL Set AL on AL off Hour Minute	
ALARM PM **7:54** SNOOZE HOUR MINUTE TIME ALARM ON OFF	
Radio Side Panel Radio On/Off Alarm On/Off Time Set Slow Time Set Fast **Top of Radio** Alarm Alarm Reset Slumber Reset Alarm	

Setting the Time on a Clock

Directions: Study the buttons on the clocks below.
Then explain how you would set the time on each clock.

Clocks with Buttons	Explanations telling how to set the time
Snooze PM **12:21** Time set AL Set AL on AL off Hour Minute	
ALARM PM **7:54** SNOOZE HOUR MINUTE TIME ALARM ON OFF	
(analog clock face)	

Sewing by Hand

Directions: Choosing the right needle is important when sewing by hand. Match the needles below to the BEST use.

Answers	Needles	Uses for Needles
	1. 2" long thin needle with small eye	**A.** Weave a loose yarn into a sweater.
	2. 3" long thick needle with large eye and dull tip	**B.** Using a thick cord to sew a button onto a jacket
	3. 4" long thin needle with medium eye and sharp tip	**C.** Using common thread to sew a button on a shirt
	4. 2" long thin needle with large eye	**D.** Using yarn to make decorative tips on a dish towel
	5. 3" long thick needle with large eye and sharp tip	**E.** Using a thick string and a button to create a tuck in the middle of a pillow

Shopping for Clothes

Directions: Choose a shopping option for each shopping need. Explain your choice.

Shopping Need	Shopping Option (circle)	Explanation
Shoes to wear wading in a creek	Nicer department store / Budget department store / Speciality store: socks / 2nd-hand store	
A jacket by your favorite designer	Nicer department store / Budget department store / Speciality store: socks / 2nd-hand store	
A high-quality pair of white socks	Nicer department store / Budget department store / Speciality store: socks / 2nd-hand store	
Green sweatshirt for a stage costume	Nicer department store / Budget department store / Speciality store: socks / 2nd-hand store	
A pair of scocks with a non-local college logo	Nicer department store / Budget department store / Speciality store: socks / 2nd-hand store	
A large-size belt	Nicer department store / Budget department store / Speciality store: socks / 2nd-hand store	

Sizing Recipes

Directions: Triple this recipe

Cranberry Relish

12 oz. chopped cranberries
1 apple, cored & sliced
1 orange, peeled & chopped
1 1/2 cup coarsely chopped walnuts
1/2 cup sugar
1/3 cup horseradish

Chop cranberries and apples in blender. Add remaining ingredients and toss. Serve with turkey.

Cranberry Relish (tripled)

Telling Time

Directions: Match the times that are the same.

Answers	Standard Clocks	Digital Clocks
	1.	**A.** 8:00
	2.	**B.** 1:54
	3.	**C.** 1:00 SAT PM
	4.	**D.** 12:19
	5.	**E.** 10:00

Math   41

Translating a Phone Number from Words to Numbers

Directions: Use numbers to rewrite the phone numbers below.

| 1-800-Buy Tree | dial **Mr. Clown** |
| | |

| **Call: Fix Sink** | call **Dr. 4 Pets** |
| | |

| 1-800-Run Race | 1-555-Car Deal |
| | |

| **Call: Mow Yard** | **Phone: Ms Tutor** |
| | |

Translating Sales Percents Into Dollars

Directions: Find the sale prices.

Amount of sale	Before-Sale Price of Item	After-Sale Price of Item
10% off	$15.00	
15% off	$45.50	
20% off	$95.00	
25% off	$10.00	
30% off	$150.00	
35% off	$15.00	
40% off	$45.50	
50% off	$95.00	
60% off	$10.00	
75% off	$150.00	

Understanding A.M. and P.M.

Directions: Use times to answer these questions. Include A.M. and P.M.

A.M. = from midnight through
1 second before noon

P.M. = from noon through
1 second before midnight

1. What time do you get up in the morning? _____
2. What time do you usually get to school? _____
3. What time do you have math class? _____
4. What time does your second class end? _____
5. What time do you have lunch? _____
6. What time do you usually get home after school? _____
7. What time do you usually eat at night? _____
8. What time is your favorite show on TV? _____
9. What time do you usually go to sleep at night? _____
10. About what time will the sun rise tomorrow? _____

Understanding Costs of Owning a Car

Directions: Talk to an adult who owns a car and ask him or her to estimate the following costs.

Car Issue	Estimated Cost
Car payment for a $15,000 car with $200 down	
20 gallons of gas	
Oil change	
Quick wash at a car wash	
Inside, outside, and wax at a car wash	
Tune-up	
Four new tires	
Windshield wiper solution	
License plates	
Insurance payment for 3 months	

Understanding Costs of Personal Hygiene Products

Directions: Go to an actual grocery or department store and find prices for each of these personal hygiene products.

Personal Hygiene Products	Prices	Personal Hygiene Products	Prices
Four rolls of toilet paper		Bar soap	
Box of facial tissue		Deodorant	
Mouthwash		Shaving cream	
Toothpaste		Squirt hand soap	
Shampoo		Hand lotion	

Understanding Counterclockwise

Directions: Complete each task.

Starting at the dot, draw an arrow showing counterclockwise.	Starting at the dot, draw an arrow showing counterclockwise.
Starting at the dot, draw an arrow showing counterclockwise.	Starting at the dot, draw an arrow showing counterclockwise.
Starting at the dot and going counterclockwise, create a large letter O. Do you usually go in a counterclockwise direction when you make a letter O?	Starting at the dot and going counterclockwise, draw half of a square.

Understanding Credit History

Directions: Match the credit terms to the descriptions.

Answers	Descriptions	Credit Terms
	1. summary of whether, over time, you pay your bills on time or late	**A.** late payment
	2. buying things with borrowed money	**B.** on-time payment
	3. money paid after the due date	**C.** credit history
	4. set dates when payments on borrowed money are to be paid	**D.** buying on credit
	5. money paid on or before the due date	**E.** payment schedule

Answers	Descriptions	Credit Terms
	6. created by paying bills on time	**F.** bad credit history
	7. borrowed money	**G.** good credit history
	8. created by paying bills late	**H.** getting a car loan
	9. summary of whether you pay your bills on time or late	**I.** credit report
	10. will be difficult if you have a bad credit history	**J.** credit

Understanding Household Meters and Gauges

Directions: Answer each question with numbers, a drawing, or words.

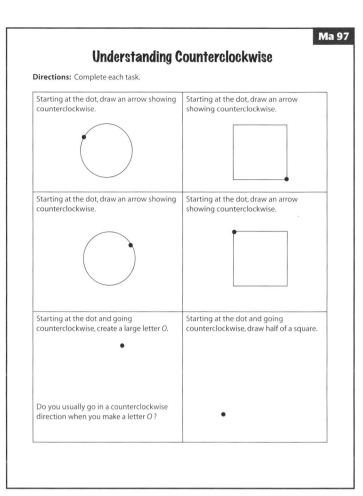

Look at this meter. Write the numbers that the meter reader would write:

_____

Add dials to these meter gauges so they show this meter reading number:

74308

Look at this meter. Explain why people often do not know when the meter reader reads the meter.

Where might these meters be located? Explain.

Math   43

Understanding How to Use Credit

Directions: Complete each sentence.

1. Even if you do not use a credit card very often, you might want to have one because

   _____
   _____
   _____

2. If you are staying in a hotel, it is a good idea to use a credit card because

   _____
   _____

3. If you cannot afford to pay your credit card each month you are probably

   _____
   _____

4. Due to the cost of the interest,

   _____
   _____

5. Say you get a credit card offer in the mail and do not want to accept it. You should make sure to shred the offer and the card because

   _____
   _____

Understanding Interest Rates

Directions: Study these two statements and then answer the questions.

Mortgage Statement

Account Number	8347205324SY234
Current Statement Date	May 07, 2007
Maturity Date	October 01, 2018
Interest Rate	5.500000
Current Principal Balance	$103,438.81
Interest Paid Year-to-Date	$2,409.64

Account Activity Since Last Statement

Description	Due Date	Tran. Date	Tran. Total	Principal	Interest
Payment	5/01	5/07	$1,050	$573.28	$476.72

1. How much interest was paid with this house payment? _____

2. Look at this calculation 5.5% x 103,438.81 = $5,689.13. The $5,689.13 is the amount of

   _____ that is due on this house in one _____.

3. The amount being paid off on this loan this month is (about twice as much / about $100 more

   / about half as much) as the amount of interest.

Bank Statement

Balance Forward	Number of Credits	Deposits (Credits)	Number of Debits	Withdrawals (Debits)	Closing Balance
7,399.02	2	156.54	0	0.00	7,555.56

Credits

12/20	Deposit 11083452		150.00
12/31	Interest Earned this Period		6.54
Average Collected Balance	7,447.41	Average Statement Balance	7,418.66
Lowest Balance This Period	7,399.02	Interest Paid This Period	6.54
Days in Interest Period	92	Annual Percentage Yield Earned	0.35
Interest Period	09/30 to 12/31		
Interest Paid This Period	6.54	Interest Paid Previous Year	3.40
Interest Paid Year to Date	31.37		

4. The amount of interest that this bank account earns is (more than / less than) 2%.

5. How much interest did the bank pay this account this month? _____

6. How can you tell that this account has had more money in it this year than last year?

   _____

Understanding Logical Sequences

Directions: Each row is a separte sequence. Fill in the blanks.
Do not use the shaded boxes.

2	4	6	8		12
Monday	Tuesday		Thursday	Friday	
d	e		g		
July 1	July 2				
morning	afternoon				
March			June		
Put these cities in ABC order: Cleveland, Omaha, Toledo Helena, Anaheim					
Put these numbers in order: 104, 22, 67, 41, 82					
Put these dates in order: Nov. 7, April 15, Feb. 26, Oct. 31, Mar. 17					

Understanding Measurement Equivalents

Directions: Fill in the blanks with equal measurements.

1 foot	= ____ inches	36 inches	= ____ feet
1 yard	= ____ inches	72 inches	= ____ yards
1 yard	= ____ feet	9 feet	= ____ yards
1 gallon	= ____ quarts	12 quarts	= ____ gallon
1 quart	= ____ cups	16 cups	= ____ quarts
1 gallon	= ____ cups	32 cups	= ____ gallons
1 cup	= ____ ounces	24 ounces	= ____ cups
1 dozen	= ____ things	36 things	= ____ dozen
1 gross	= ____ things	288 things	= ____ gross

Understanding Net and Gross Pay

Directions: Use the two paycheck deduction slips to answer the questions below.

Name: Jenna Wynn					Date: March 12			Check # 5867	
Regular Hours Worked	Regular Hourly Wages	Overtime Hours Worked	Overtime Wage	Gross Wages	Federal Tax	State Tax	FICA	Insurance	Net Wages
40	10.00	5	15.00	475.00	95.00	23.75	36.10	0.00	320.15

Name: Diego Diaz					Date: March 12			Check # 5898	
Regular Hours Worked	Regular Hourly Wages	Overtime Hours Worked	Overtime Wage	Gross Wages	Federal Tax	State Tax	FICA	Insurance	Net Wages
40	13.00	0	0.00	520.00	104.00	26.00	39.52	50.00	300.48

1. How much money did Jenna earn altogether? _____ Diego? _____

2. How much is Jenna's "take home pay"? In other words, how much money does she actually have

   to spend? _____ Diego? _____

3. Fill in this math problem to show how Jenna can check to see if her take home pay is correct.

   (40 x _____) + (5 x _____) = $475

   $475 – _____ – 23.75 – _____ = $320.15

4. Fill in this math problem to show how Diego can check to see if his take home pay is correct.

   (_____ x _____) = $520

   _____ – _____ – _____ – _____ – _____ = $300.48

5. Even though Diego earned more gross wages than Jenna did, Diego has less

   _____   _____   _____

   because he had money withdrawn for _____ .

Understanding Quantity Relationships

Directions: Number these containers from the one that will hold the most (#1) to the one that will hold the least (#5). Think only of having containers level full, not piled high.

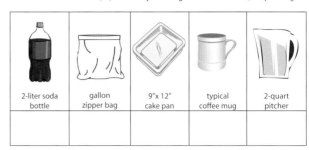

2-liter soda bottle	gallon zipper bag	9"x 12" cake pan	typical coffee mug	2-quart pitcher

Directions: Number these substances from the one that would require the largest container (#1) to the one that would require the smallest container (5).

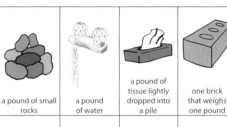

a pound of small rocks	a pound of water	a pound of tissue lightly dropped into a pile	one brick that weighs one pound	a pound of blown-up balloons

Understanding Ratios

Directions: Match the ratios and situations by writing answers A, B, or C in the answer blanks.

Answers	Situations	Ratios
	Three of Angie's friends have blonde hair and two have black hair.	**A.** 3/5
	Bethany ate three of the five apples.	**B.** 3 : 2
	Dago scored two of the teams five goals.	**C.** 2/5

Directions: Write ratios for these situations.

Situations	Ratios
There are seven kids in LeRoy's family, and five of them are boys.	
Emily has four green pencils and seven pink ones.	
Jonah got six new shirts, and four of them are blue.	

Directions: Write situations for these ratios.

Situations	Ratios
	7 : 10
	5/6
	4 : 1

Understanding Sports Statistics

Directions: Sports statistics charts usually give a lot of information in a little space. Gather facts from the charts below to fill the table at the bottom of the page.

High School Baseball

Panthers 8 & Tigers 3

Panthers	AB	R	H	BI	Tigers	AB	R	H	BI
Dorn cf	4	3	2	0	Owens cf	3	0	0	0
Smith 2b	4	1	1	1	Taro cf	0	0	0	0
Pye dh	3	0	2	2	Jenk lf	3	0	1	0
Gark 1b	4	1	2	2	Thom dh	4	0	0	0
Pearla ss	3	0	0	1	Kone 1b	4	0	1	0
Suess rf	4	0	2	0	Duke rf	4	1	0	0
Toms lf	4	1	1	0	Urby ss	3	2	2	3
Blake 3b	5	1	1	0	Rice 2b	4	0	2	0
Nint c	4	1	0	1	Gona 2b	2	0	0	0
					Terry c	3	0	0	0
Totals	35	8	11	8	Totals	31	3	6	3
Panthers		012		003		200			8
Tigers		010		200		000			3

E–Nint (3), DP–Panthers 1 ,Tigers 1, LOB–Panthers 12, Tigers 4, 2B–Smith (7), Suess (11), Blake (33), Rice (6) HR–Gark (18), Urby 2 (18), SB–Dorn (32), Toms (3), Jenk (12), CS–Rice (3), S–Smith

Professional Tennis

Singles first round

Igor Andreez (5) Russia, def. Peter Luczak, Australia, 6-4, 3–6, 6-4

Albert Montanes (8), Spain, def. Nicolas Devilder, France, 6–3, 6-1.

Gilles, Simon (6), France, def. Guillermo Garcia-Lopez, Spain, 7-6 (3), 6-4.

Martin Vassallo Arguello, Argentina, def. Werner Eschauer, Austria, 6-4, 6-4.

Andreas Seppi, Italy, def. Jurgen Melzer (4), Austria, 4–6, 7–5, 6-4.

Evgeny Korolev, Russia, def. Florent Serra, Italy, 4–6, 6-5, retired.

Ivan Navarro Pastor, Spain, def. Chris Guccione, Australia, 6-4, 7-6 (4).

College Football

Rank	Team	Record	Pts	Pvs
1.	Southern Cal (42)	1-0	1,476	1
2.	LSU (11)	2-0	1,437	2
3.	Florida (7)	2-0	1,353	3
4.	West Virginia	2-0	1,269	4
5.	Oklahoma	2-0	1,264	6
6.	Texas	2-0	1,156	7
7.	Wisconsin	2-0	1,141	5
8.	California	2-0	1,038	10
9.	Lousiville	2-0	972	11
10.	Ohio State	2-0	1,020	8
11.	UCLA	2-0	837	14
12.	Penn State	2-0	804	15
13.	Rutgers	2-0	699	16
14.	Nebraska	2-0	677	17
15.	Georgia Tech	2-0	582	21
16.	Arkansas	1-0	493	18
17.	Virginia Tech	1-1	371	9
18.	Texas A&M	2-0	325	23
19.	Boston College	2-0	315	25
20.	Clemson	2-0	311	-
21.	Oregon	2-0	309	-
22.	Hawaii	2-0	308	22
23.	South Carolina	2-0	294	-
24.	Tennesee	1-1	237	24
25.	Georgia	1-1	199	12

Which tennis player was ranked 6th at the start of this tournament?	What country is tennis player Andreas Seppi from?	How many of the tennis matches went three sets?	How many tennis players were from Spain?
Which college football team received 677 points in the rankings?	Last week, where was the sixth ranked college football team ranked?	Which college football team received 11 first-place votes?	How many of the ranked college football teams have only played one game so far?
Which one of the Tigers' baseball players had the best game?	Who plays left field for the Panthers' baseball team?	Which baseball team's designated hitter had the best game?	Which player batted the most during the baseball game?

Understanding Types of Taxes

Directions: Match the situations to the types of taxes. Each type of tax has three answers.

Answers		Types of Taxes		Situations
	1		A	Will be taken out of your paychecks
	2	income tax	B	Homeowners have to pay each year
	3		C	Will be added onto the cost of a car and can be hundreds of dollars
	4		D	You need to add to the cost of a shirt you are buying
	5	property tax	E	You might have to pay more or get some back at the end of each year
	6		F	You will have to pay if you buy a house
	7		G	Is money that workers pay and that is used for government expenses
	8	sales tax	H	Is charged by most retail stores
	9		I	Needs to be added onto the costs when you are deciding if you can afford to buy a house

Understanding Years and Decades

Directions: Write the letter answers to match the years and the decades.
(Hint: Decades go from 0 to 9. Example: 1900–1909)

Answers	Decades	Years
	2000–2009	**A.** 1942
	1920–1929	**B.** 1927
	1940–1949	**C.** 2005
	1960–1969	**D.** 1961

Answers	Years	Decades
	2004	**E.** 2010–2019
	1998	**F.** 1990–1999
	2010	**G.** 2020–2029
	2021	**H.** 2000–2009

Directions: Write the decade to which each of these dates belong.

1994	2016	2007	1989

Using a Calculator

Directions: Look at a hand-held calculator keyboard and draw it in the middle of this page. Then, draw lines from the descriptions to the correct buttons.

- Push to add
- Push to clear and start over
- Push to subtract
- Push to turn off
- Push to turn on
- Push to find percent
- Push to put into memory
- Push to divide
- Push to multiply
- Push to find answer
- Push to add decimal
- Push to delete last entry

Use a Calendar as a Reminder to Pay Bills

Directions: Write the bills below on this calendar so you could pay them in time. Remember to allow at least five days to mail a bill.

August

Sunday	Monday	Tuesday	Wednesday	Thursday	Friday	Saturday
		1	2	3	4	5
6	7	8	9	10	11	12
13	14	15	16	17	18	19
20	21	22	23	24	25	26
27	28	29	30	31		

Bill	Date Due	How You Will Pay It
credit card	August 28th	by mail
car payment	August 17th	online
phone bill	August 19th	by mail
electric bill	August 23rd	in person
garbage bill	September 3rd	by mail
rent	August 1st	in person
water bill	August 10th	online

Using a Debit Card Wisely

Directions: Match sentence beginnings to sentence endings to create statements about using debit cards.

Answers	Sentence Beginnings	Sentence Ending Choices
	1. When you use your debit card, you need to always be very careful to remember	**A.** if you lose it or it is stolen, you are protected from losing money.
	2. Using a debit card is safer than using cash since	**B.** is a good way to help make sure you do not get too far into debt.
	3. Using a debit card instead of a credit card	**C.** you will most likely be rejected since it is easy for stores to check your balance.
	4. If you try to use a debit card to spend more money than you have in the bank,	**D.** to write all purchases in your register.
Answers	**Sentence Beginnings**	**Sentence Ending Choices**
	5. If you have $200 in your bank account,	**E.** you should have someone with you and make sure the area is well lighted.
	6. For your debit card, you should create a pin number that you can remember	**F.** keep it mostly in your head and never in the same place as your debit card.
	7. If you use your debit card to get cash at an ATM machine at night,	**G.** you cannot use your debit card to buy a music player that costs $210.
	8. As far as where you should keep your pin number for your debit card,	**H.** and make sure not to give it to anyone else.

Using a Grid to Arrange Furniture

Directions: Measure the length and width of the student desks in your classroom. Using a scale of 1 square = 1 foot, use this grid to make a new arrangement for the classroom. If needed, use two or more grids taped together.

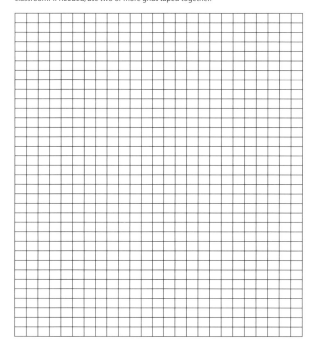

Using a Microwave

Directions: Create the four lists.

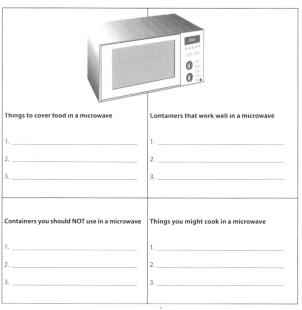

Things to cover food in a microwave

1. _____
2. _____
3. _____

Containers that work well in a microwave

1. _____
2. _____
3. _____

Containers you should NOT use in a microwave

1. _____
2. _____
3. _____

Things you might cook in a microwave

1. _____
2. _____
3. _____

Using a Padlock

Directions: Use colored pencils to show how you would turn the padlock for each padlock number. Use arrows on the end. Use this pattern:
- Go forward to the number.
- Go in reverse and go all the way around the start number and then to the second number.
- Go in reverse and go straight to the third number without going all the way around.

The first one is done as an example.

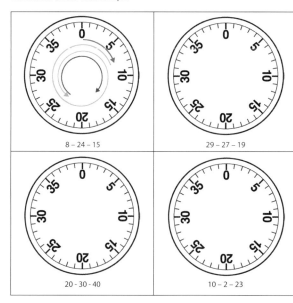

8 – 24 – 15

29 – 27 – 19

20 - 30 - 40

10 – 2 – 23

Using an Oven

Directions: Match the oven vocabulary words and the definitions.

Answers	Definitions	Oven Vocabulary Words
	1. to turn an oven on some minutes before ready to use it	A. dial
	2. to cook only on the top side	B. preheat
	3. coil in the bottom of the oven that gets very hot	C. broil
	4. ovens settings that are not computerized	D. element

Answers	Definitions	Oven Vocabulary Words
	5. where things bake more evenly	E. bottom rack
	6. a high oven temperature	F. 450°
	7. where things get dark on the bottom faster	G. 200°
	8. a low oven temperature	H. top rack

Using an Oven Timer

Directions: Connect the lines with dots to lines with arrows (•——→) to make the statements point at the correct parts of an oven timer.

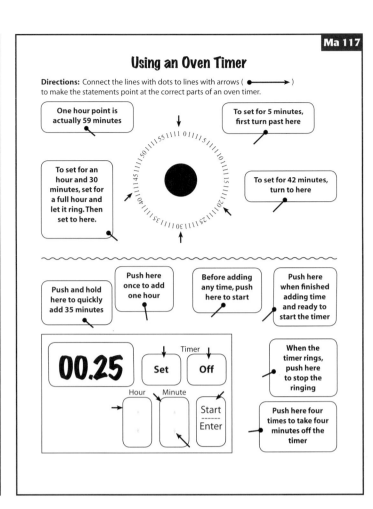

One hour point is actually 59 minutes

To set for 5 minutes, first turn past here

To set for an hour and 30 minutes, set for a full hour and let it ring. Then set to here.

To set for 42 minutes, turn to here

Push and hold here to quickly add 35 minutes

Push here once to add one hour

Before adding any time, push here to start

Push here when finished adding time and ready to start the timer

When the timer rings, push here to stop the ringing

Push here four times to take four minutes off the timer

00.25 — Set — Off — Timer — Hour — Minute — Start / Enter

Using Burners

Directions: Match each burner setting to one of the cooking needs.

Answers	Burner Settings	Cooking Needs
1	(dial: High, Med-High, Med, Med-Low, Low, Off)	A. Your soup is finished and you want to keep it on a very low temperature to keep it warm until it is time to eat.
2	(dial: High, Med-High, Med, Med-Low, Low, Off)	B. You are boiling water.
3	(dial: High, Med-High, Med, Med-Low, Low, Off)	C. You are grilling a cheese sandwich and want it hot enough to brown the bread, but not so hot that the bread will burn before the cheese melts.
4	(dial: High, Med-High, Med, Med-Low, Low, Off)	D. You are finished cooking and want the burner turned off.

Using Counting Words

Directions: Use the words from the Word Box to fill in the blanks. There are no correct answers. Just create sentences that make sense. Cross out the words as you use them. Then, use the unused words in sentences of your own.

Word Box				
biggest	double	few	first	last
least	many	medium	middle	more
most	next	none	octagon	oldest
once	quadruplets	second	several	single
smallest	triple	triplets	twice	twins

1. Since they are the same age, the two brothers are _____.

2. Avery has _____ pencils than Henry has, but Lucy has the _____ pencils of the three of them.

3. The _____ person in the room will probably choose the _____ chair and the _____ person will probably end up with the _____ chair.

4. Grace played tennis _____ week and she plans to play again _____ week.

5. I have a _____ ideas about things to do tonight, but _____ of them are thing you like to do.

6. Jordan made that mistake _____, but I doubt he will make the same mistake _____.

Using Non-Traditional Measuring Devices

Directions: Use a piece of standard paper to measure the items below. Write your measurements in "papers" and then estimate the measurements in inches or feet. Remember that a standard piece of paper is 8 1/2" wide and 11" long.

Items	Measurement in Papers	Estimate in Inches or Feet
Height of the chair you are sitting in		
Length of your shoe		
Height of the classroom door		
Width of a window in the classroom		
Width of the table or desk you are using		

Using Prescription Medication Properly

Directions: Choose the correct timing for taking each medication.

1. Take four times a day with food.
   _____ Take at 9:00 A.M., at 10:00 A.M., at 3:00 P.M., and at 5:00 P.M.
   _____ Take at 8:00 A.M., at noon, at 5:00 P.M., and at 9:00 P.M.

2. Take in the morning and in the evening.
   _____ Take at 9:00 A.M. and at 10:00 P.M.
   _____ Take at 8:00 A.M. and at 5:00 P.M.

3. Take as needed, not to exceed one every four hours.
   _____ Take at 7:00 A.M., at 11:00 A.M., at 3:00 P.M., and at 7:00 P.M.
   _____ Take at 7:00 A.M., at noon, at 2:00 P.M., and at 9:00 P.M.

4. Take every three hours as needed, not to exceed five within 24 hours.
   _____ Take at 6:00 A.M., at 9:00 A.M., at noon, at 3:00 P.M., at 6:00 P.M., and at 9:00 P.M.
   _____ Take at 6:00 A.M., at 11:00 A.M., at 2:00 P.M., at 5:00 P.M., and at 9:00 P.M.

5. Take 2–4 times per day as needed, being sure to take them at least three hours apart.
   _____ Take at 6:00 A.M., at 10:00 A.M., at 3:00 P.M., and at 7:00 P.M.
   _____ Take at 6:00 A.M., at 9:00 A.M., at noon, at 3:00 P.M., at 6:00 P.M., at 9:00 P.M., and at midnight

Using Rulers, Yard Sticks, and Meter Sticks

Directions: Use a ruler, a yard stick, and a meter stick to make each of the measurements below. In each case, circle the one of the three choices that you think works best for making that measurement.

Item to Measure	Ruler	Yard Stick	Meter Stick
Length of one of your backpack straps			
Length of one of your fingers			
Width of the classroom			
Height of the blackboard or whiteboard			
Length of your leg			

Using Shapes

Directions: Find objects to trace to create the shapes below.

Trace something to create a circle.	**Trace something to create a square.**
Describe items you could trace to create each shape in this image.	**Find some items to trace and arrange them to create an image.**

Math   49

Using Tallies

Directions: Use tallies as described below.

1. **Use tallies to count every "e" in these sentences.**

Sentences	Tallies
Knock, Knock. Who's There? Deanna. Deanna who? Deanna-mals are restless. Don't open the cage!	

2. **Use tallies to count the words in these sentences.**

Sentences	Tallies
Antwon works at the fish market. He is 6'4" tall, wears a size 12 shoe, has a 38" waist, and wears size XL shirts. What does he weigh? *Answer: Fish*	

3. **Use tallies to count every "a" in these sentences.**

Sentences	Tallies
Miss Myers: How many minutes are there in an hour? *Hannah:* 60. *Miss Myers:* Good! How many seconds in a minute? *Hannah:* 60 *Miss Myers:* Good! Get ready for a hard one now! How many seconds in a year? *Hannah:* 12 *Miss Myers:* Only 12? *Hannah:* That's right! January 2nd, February 2nd, March 2nd, ...	

4. **Use tallies to count the letters in these sentences.**

Sentences	Tallies
Teacher: Can anyone tell me the longest word in the English langauge? *Ben:* S-M-I-L-E-S *Teacher:* But, "smiles" only has six letters. *Ben:* That's right. But, look.....there is a mile between the first and last letter.	

Using Tax Tables

Directions: Use this tax table to fill in the chart below.

If line 43		And you are—					If line 43		Single	Married filing jointly	Married filing separately	Head of a household
At least	But less than	Single	Married filing jointly	Married filing separately	Head of a household		At least	But less than				
23,000		**Your tax is**					**26,000**		**Your tax is**			
23,000	23,050	3,076	2,699	3,076	2,916		26,000	26,050	3,526	3,149	3,526	3,366
23,050	23,100	3,084	2,706	3,084	2,924		26,050	26,100	3,534	3,156	3,534	3,374
23,100	23,150	3,091	2,714	3,091	2,931		26,100	26,150	3,541	3,164	3,541	3,381
23,150	23,200	3,099	2,721	3,099	2,939		26,150	26,200	3,549	3,171	3,549	3,389
23,200	23,250	3,106	2,729	3,106	2,946		26,200	26,250	3,556	3,179	3,556	3,396
23,250	23,300	3,114	2,736	3,114	2,954		26,250	26,300	3,564	3,186	3,564	3,404
23,300	23,350	3,121	2,744	3,121	2,961		26,300	26,350	3,571	3,194	3,571	3,411
23,350	23,400	3,129	2,751	3,129	2,969		26,350	26,400	3,579	3,201	3,579	3,419
23,400	23,450	3,136	2,759	3,136	2,976		26,400	26,450	3,586	3,209	3,586	3,426
23,450	23,500	3,144	2,766	3,144	2,984		26,450	26,500	3,594	3,216	3,594	3,434
23,500	23,550	3,151	2,774	3,151	2,991		26,500	26,550	3,601	3,224	3,601	3,441
23,550	23,600	3,159	2,781	3,159	2,999		26,550	26,600	3,609	3,231	3,609	3,449
23,600	23,650	3,166	2,789	3,166	3,006		26,600	26,650	3,616	3,239	3,616	3,456
23,650	23,700	3,174	2,796	3,174	3,014		26,650	26,700	3,624	3,246	3,624	3,464
23,700	23,750	3,181	2,804	3,181	3,021		26,700	26,750	3,631	3,254	3,631	3,471
23,750	23,800	3,189	2,811	3,189	3,029		26,750	26,800	3,639	3,261	3,639	3,479
23,800	23,850	3,196	2,819	3,196	3,036		26,800	26,850	3,646	3,269	3,646	3,486
23,850	23,900	3,204	2,826	3,204	3,044		26,850	26,900	3,654	3,276	3,654	3,494
23,900	23,950	3,211	2,834	3,211	3,051		26,900	26,950	3,661	3,284	3,661	3,501
23,950	24,000	3,219	2,841	3,219	3,059		26,950	27,000	3,669	3,291	3,669	3,509

Income Amount	Situation	Tax Due
$26,638	Married filing jointly	
$23,234	Single	
$26,871	Married filing separately	
$26,400	Head of a Household	
$23,700	Person: Never been married, has no children	
$23,909	Person: Never been married, has one young child	
$23,125	Person: Married, but does not file taxes with his or her spouse	
$26,201	Person: Married, is main income maker, has three young children	
$26,999	Person: Married, has no children	
$23,001	Person: Divorced and has no children	

Watching for Good Shopping Deals

Directions: Use the "shopping deal" words in the Word Boxes to fill in the blanks.

> **Word Box**
> original price — sale aisle — sale price
> two for one — half price — discount at the register
> bin or shelf with special deals

1. As long as you need two of an item, a _____ deal is as good as a _____ deal.

2. If you do not know what the _____ was, it is hard to tell if the _____ is actually a good deal.

3. Even if you do not know about a sale when you go to a store, you might find a sale in the _____, by looking for a _____, or by getting a _____ that you do not even know about until the clerk rings it up.

> **Word Box**
> newspaper ad — 20% off — signs on the racks or shelves
> 75% off — discount coupon — buy one and get one half off

4. If you need two of an item, it is better to _____ than to get _____.

5. If you look in a newspaper, you might see a _____ for a sale or you might see a _____ that you can cut out and use.

6. Stores often advertise their cheapest prices by putting some of their older items together and placing _____ that say _____.

Watching Refrigerator and Freezer Temperatures

Directions: Match each thermometer temperature to its likely location.

Answers	Thermometer Readings	Thermometer Location
1	Freezer-Refrigerator	**A.** in a freezer that is working well
2	Freezer-Refrigerator	**B.** in a refrigerator that is probably forming some ice in spots
3	Freezer-Refrigerator	**C.** in a freezer or refrigerator that is not working at all
4	Freezer-Refrigerator	**D.** in a refrigerator that is working well

Working at a Rate that Shows Effort

Directions: Read each situation and decide if it shows effort. Remember that "effort" means a person is trying to do well. Circle the correct answer.

1. Even though Janie was the slowest runner in the group, she kept running to the very end of the race.	shows effort	shows someone not trying
2. Matt studied for the test for two hours.	shows effort	shows someone not trying
3. Cory didn't think he could paint very well, so he didn't help his brother paint the wall.	shows effort	shows someone not trying
4. Darcy was tired at the end of the day, so she just pretended to work for the last hour before quitting time.	shows effort	shows someone not trying
5. Marta watched TV instead of cleaning her room, so her room was a mess when Taye came over.	shows effort	shows someone not trying
6. When Daniel finished mowing the yard, he noticed some long grasses along the fence, so he cut them with the hand trimmer.	shows effort	shows someone not trying
7. The teacher asked the students to put their names, the date, and the subject at the top of the page. Jing-Wei just put his name there.	shows effort	shows someone not trying
8. Minyi saw that Rosa was about to drop her books and stopped to help her.	shows effort	shows someone not trying
9. Jenna is a waitress. She saw two new groups come in and sit down. She let them wait for about five minutes so she could finish talking to her friend.	shows effort	shows someone not trying
10. Mitchell revised his paper three times until he thought it sounded just right.	shows effort	shows someone not trying

Working with a Bus Schedule

Directions: Use this early-morning airport bus schedule to answer the questions.

From BURIEN, WA to Sea-Tac Airport (Weekday):

S 2nd & Burnett Av S	S Grady Way & Shattuck Av S	Tukwila Station	Andover Pk W & Baker	Sea-Tac (Bag Claim) Bay-2	4th Av SW & SW 150th
5:34am	5:40am	---	5:50am	6:04am	6:16am
5:54am	6:00am	---	6:10am	6:24am	6:36am
6:05am	6:12am	6:18am	6:22am	6:36am	6:48am
6:19am	6:26am	6:32amB	6:36am	6:50am	7:02am
6:35am	6:42am	6:48amB	6:52am	7:07am	7:20am
6:50am	6:57am	7:03amB	7:08am	7:23am	7:36am
7:03am	7:11am	7:18amB	7:23am	7:38am	7:51am
7:17am	7:25am	7:33amB	7:38am	7:53am	8:06am
7:32am	7:40am	7:48amB	7:53am	8:08am	8:21am
7:48am	7:56am	8:04amB	8:09am	8:24am	8:37am
8:05am	8:12am	---	8:23am	8:38am	8:51am
8:20am	8:27am	---	8:38am	8:53am	9:06am
8:35am	8:42am	---	8:53am	9:08am	9:20am
8:50am	8:57am	---	9:08am	9:23am	9:35am
9:05am	9:12am	---	9:23am	9:38am	9:50am
9:20am	9:27am	---	9:38am	9:53am	10:05am
9:35am	9:42am	---	9:53am	10:08am	10:20am
9:50am	9:57am	---	10:08am	10:23am	10:35am
10:05am	10:12am	---	10:23am	10:38am	10:50am

1. About how long does it take to get from S. 2nd and Burnett Ave. S. to the airport baggage claim?

   _____

2. What time should you get on the bus at S. Grady Way if you want to be at 4th Ave SW by 8:45?

   _____

3. If you are getting on the bus at Tukwila Station, and you need to be at the Bay-2 at the airport by 9:38, what is the latest time you can get on the bus? _____

4. Say you have a flight at noon and you want to be at the airport two hours before your flight. What is the latest bus you can catch at Andover Pk W & Baker? _____

5. Say you board the 6:35 A.M. bus at S. 2nd & Burnett Ave. S., and your flight is at 9:00. If you get off at Baggage claim, how much time will you have before your flight? _____

Wrapping a Gift

Directions: On the left are four gifts that you have to wrap. On the right are some gift wrapping materials. Make the best possible matches by writing the letters in the blanks.

Answers	Gifts	Gift Wrapping Materials
1		**A.** Use a paper gift bag since the gift is small and light.
2		**B.** Use rolled paper since the gift is big, but easy to wrap.
3		**C.** Just put a bow on it since it is too big to wrap in any way.
4		**D.** Use a tight-fitting cardboard box to help make sure the gift doesn't break.

Writing Money Amounts in Numbers and Words

Directions: Write each of the money amounts in words. Fit the words for each amount on one line.

1. 31¢ _____

2. 95¢ _____

3. $1.50 _____

4. $5.43 _____

5. $7.88 _____

6. $12.34 _____

7. $13.45 _____

8. $16.22 _____

9. $27.00 _____

10. $35.81 _____

11. $40.00 _____

12. $52.26 _____

13. $63.07 _____

14. $76.19 _____

15. $88.20 _____

16. $99.99 _____

17. $107.28 _____

Math   51

Social Studies

Adjusting Behavior for Different Situations

Directions: Match each behavior to a situation where it would be appropriate.

Answers	Situations	Behaviors
	1. You are in the cafeteria when you see someone is about to back into another person and both will likely drop their trays.	A. talking about someone
	2. You are watching a funny show with a friend.	B. eating while you talk
	3. Someone you know wants you to help him by distracting a salesperson while he steals something.	C. refusing to help someone
	4. Your friend is really sad about moving away and you want others to be extra nice to her.	D. laughing aloud

Answers	Situations	Behaviors
	5. A friend you really like wants to do something that you know you will get in trouble for doing.	E. saying "no" to an authority figure
	6. You are out for dinner with a friend when she suddenly passes out.	F. going barefoot
	7. Your teacher asks you to take your shoes off and stand on her desk to reach something. As you start to take off your shoes, you see broken glass on the floor.	G. arguing with a friend
	8. You are playing kickball in your yard with a friend.	H. talking on a cell phone in a restaurant

Apologizing When You Hurt or Inconvenience Others

Directions: Working with a partner, take turns giving and accepting apologies for the following situations. Use the space to plan what you will say.

1. You accidently knocked a classmate's backpack onto the floor as you tried to squish past his or her desk. _____

2. You promised to call a friend back, but you forgot. _____

3. You told a friend's secret to others. Now everyone knows the secret, and your friend is upset with you. _____

4. Your parents told you to put the clean dishes away, but you didn't. _____

5. You told your grandmother you would help her on Saturday, and now you remember that you have a ball game on Saturday. _____

Asking a Person for a Date

Directions: Working with a partner, practice asking a person to go on a date to do each named activity. Begin by planning what you would say in the chart below.

Activity for Date	What would you say?
go ice skating	
play video games at your house	
go to a school ball game	
play a board game with some other friends	

Assembling a First Aid Kit

Directions: Match these first aid kit items with their purposes.

Answers	Purposes	Items
	1. to pull the edges of a small cut together	A. general band-aids
	2. to soothe a sore throat	B. butterfly band-aids
	3. to help with a headache	C. cough drops
	4. to wrap a wound	D. disinfectant cream
	5. to put on a cut to prevent infection	E. gauze
	6. to cover a small cut	F. over-the-counter pain medication

Answers	Purposes	Items
	7. to pull slivers out	G. scissors
	8. to fasten gauze in place	H. stretch wrap
	9. to cut gauze to size	I. tape
	10. to protect gauze from dirt	J. thermometer
	11. to clean blood from around a cut	K. tissue
	12. to check for a fever	L. tweezers

Becoming Familiar with a New Community

Directions: Use the Internet to research a new community. Find the information to fill in the chart.

Community (Choose a city or town in a different state):		
How many public high schools?	Name(s) of major park(s) in or near the city or town	How many movie theaters?
Names of 3 grocery stores 1. 2. 3.	Names of 3 restaurants 1. 2. 3.	Names of 3 banks 1. 2. 3.
Names of 3 places to get your hair cut 1. 2. 3.	Names of 3 computer stores 1. 2. 3.	Names of 3 car repair shops 1. 2. 3.

Behaving Appropriately for the Weather

Directions: Draw or name something you would and would not do in each of these weather conditions.

Weather Condition	Something You Would Do	Something You Would Not Do
Sleet storm	Example: shut window	Example: sit outside
Bright and sunny summer day		
Bright and sunny winter day		
cold and snowy day		
rainy day		

Being Honest

Directions: Decide if each situation is "dishonest" or "all in fun" by placing a check mark in the correct column.

Situation	Dishonest ☑	All in Fun ☑
1. Andy waited until his mother wasn't looking and then threw his peas in the trash.		
2. Mollie planned a surprise party for Joanie and told Joanie three lies about what was going on.		
3. Demetri hid Kyle's backpack in the trash can and it took Kyle 10 minutes to find it.		
4. Michelle told Shammie that she was tired and wanted Shammie to go home. As soon as Shammie left, Michelle went outside with some other friends.		
5. Mr. Mitchell asked his students to write a short, funny story. Darryl found a story on the Internet, printed it, and turned it in.		
6. At a costume party, Dana had a mask on and no one knew who she was. Keisha asked Dana, "Should I know you?" Dana shook her head "no" even though Keisha is a good friend of hers.		

Being Part of a Team

Directions: Draw two pictures as described below.

Draw a picture of a person being a good team member.

Draw a picture of a person who is not being a good team member.

Being Responsible at Work

Directions: Describe what you think each worker below is doing and tell whether or not you think the worker is being responsible.

	What is the worker doing?		What is the worker doing?
	Responsible?		Responsible?
	What is the worker doing?		What is the worker doing?
	Responsible?		Responsible?
	What is the worker doing?		What is the worker doing?
	Responsible?		Responsible?

Being Sensitive to Others

Directions: What would you do or say in each of these situations?

Situation	What would you do or say?
1. You are excited to go out with your friend on Saturday night, but your friend's grandmother is really sick and your friend just wants to sit around home.	
2. You are choosing a movie to watch with your sister. You like scary movies, but she does not.	
3. You and your friend both tried out for the volleyball team. Your friend made it, but you did not.	
4. Your friend is really excited about an upcoming party, but you know your friend is not going to be invited.	
5. You and your father planned to play basketball at 6:00. Your father comes home from work, isn't feeling well, and wants to play a different day. You are really disappointed.	

Calling 911

Directions: Assume you are in the following emergencies. Decide if you would call 911 and write what you would say when the 911 service answers.

Emergencies	Would you call 911? If yes, What would you say?	
	Yes	No
1. You walk out of your house to go to school and see flames coming from the neighbor's roof.		
	Yes	No
2. You are sitting in your back yard when you see bees flying all around you.		
	Yes	No
3. You are riding in the car with your mother and are about a block from school. Your mother suddenly pulls over to the side of the road and then passes out.		
	Yes	No
4. Your whole family has the flu. Everyone is dizzy and vomiting.		
	Yes	No
5. You are driving a car and get a flat tire.		
	Yes	No
6. A car comes speeding down the street in front of your house, swerves to miss a dog, and slams into a parked car. The driver is bleeding badly and saying, "Help me."		

Carrying Money Safely

Directions: Study each method of carrying money. Circle "Safe" or "Not Safe" for each. Explain why you do or do not think each is a safe way.

	Safe Not Safe		Safe Not Safe
	Explain		Explain
	Safe Not Safe		Safe Not Safe
	Explain		Explain
	Safe Not Safe		Safe Not Safe
	Explain		Explain

Choosing an Apartment

Directions: For each situation, circle the best apartment choice.

1. A single mother with two grade school-aged daughters:

   one bedroom   three bedrooms   five bedrooms

2. A family with a seventh-grade boy and a ninth-grade girl and two parents:

   one bedroom   two bedrooms   three bedrooms

3. Two college students:

   large living room   two bedrooms   single garage

4. A newly-married couple who do not plan to have children soon and who like to entertain:

   two bedrooms &   one bedroom &   large garage &
   small living room   large dining room   kitchen with only a
                                                    microwave and sink

5. Two 23-year-old girls:

   washer and dryer   large bedrooms   two microwaves

6. An elderly couple:

   large kitchen   one floor   built-in TV center

Choosing People to Ask for References

Directions: In each category, list one or two adults you could use for references.

Teacher	Neighbor	Family Friend
1.	1.	1.
2.	2.	2.
Employer (such as someone you baby-sat for or a regular job)	**Community Leader**	**Coach or Club Leader**
1.	1.	1.
2.	2.	2.
Mentor (someone you have learned from)	**School Administrator**	**Parent of a Friend**
1.	1.	1.
2.	2.	2.

Choosing the Best Route

Directions: As a group, choose a common location in town. Draw a map showing the best way to get from school to the location. Include street names. Share your map and agree on which route is best.

Map from School to _____

Choosing to Have Fresh Breath

Directions: Write the numbers in the correct columns.

1. When you are on a date	5. While you are sleeping	9. Use mouthwash	13. Suck on a mint
2. While you are doing laundry	6. While you are at school	10. Eat fish	14. Eat garlic bread
3. While you are at your job	7. While you work in your computer	11. Brush your teeth	15. Chew a piece of gum
4. While you jog	8. While you are on a job interview	12. Sleep all night	16. Go without water all day

Situations Where Fresh Breath Matters	Situations Where Fresh Breath Does NOT Matter	Ways to Get Fresh Breath	Ways to Get Bad Breath

---

Comparing Leases, Floorplans, etc.

Directions: Look at these floorplans. Explain which one you prefer and why.

#1

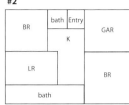

#2

#3

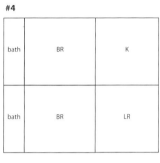

#4

Which floor plan to you prefer? _____ Why? _____

_____

_____

_____

Crossing the Street Safely

Directions: Match the sentence beginnings and endings.

Answers	Sentence Beginnings	Sentence Endings
	1. You could trip and fall if you	**A.** quickly finish crossing if you have already started, but don't start crossing.
	2. When a walk sign starts blinking	**B.** watch the cars to make sure it is safe to cross.
	3. Even if no cars are coming, you should not	**C.** make eye contact with drivers so you know they see you.
	4. Even if you have a "walk" sign, you should	**D.** run to beat oncoming cars.
	5. If you are crossing a street that has no street light, you should	**E.** cross a street by walking in the crosswalk.
	6. Since drivers are expecting you to only be there, you should always	**F.** cross the street when "Don't Walk" is showing.

Dealing with Conflict

Directions: Complete these sentences.

1. If I see someone take my pencil off my desk, _____

_____

_____

2. If I am watching a TV show and someone walked into the room and changed the channel without

saying a word to me, _____

3. If I am walking down the hall and someone bumps into me on purpose causing me to drop my

books, _____

_____

_____

4. If I am talking in class and the teacher asks me what I have to say that is so important,

_____

_____

5. If I am IMing with a friend and my mother tells me to get off the computer,

_____

_____

Dealing with Job Issues

Directions: Tell how you would handle each situation.

1. You think your paycheck is $100 short. What should you say and/or do?	**4.** People at work take your sodas from the refrigerator even though your name is on them. What will you say and/or do?
2. You feel sick if you don't eat a little something every hour or so. But, at your job, you only get one break every four hours and food is not allowed at your work station. What will you say and/or do?	**5.** You overslept yesterday and were late for work. Your boss was upset and said not to do it again. Today, your bus had a flat tire and you are late again. Your boss is quite angry when he sees you walk in. What will you say and/or do?
3. You have a piercing on your face that your boss does not like. She says you have to remove your pierced jewelry while you are at work. You are worried that your holes will close. What will you say and/or do?	**6.** For three hours, you worked hard straightening up a filing cabinet. Your boss comes in, sees the tidy drawer, assumes the girl next to you cleaned it up, and says, "Good job with the filing cabinet, Anna." Anna smiles and says, "Thanks." What are you going to say and/or do?

Differentiating Between Obvious Male and Female Names

Directions: Circle "male," "female," or "both" for each name.

1. Angela	male female both	**13.** Ian	male female both
2. Cliff	male female both	**14.** Frank	male female both
3. Lynn	male female both	**15.** Diego	male female both
4. Daisy	male female both	**16.** Alicia	male female both
5. Omar	male female both	**17.** Sam	male female both
6. Jan	male female both	**18.** Elena	male female both
7. Mi-Ling	male female both	**19.** Ben	male female both
8. Barb	male female both	**20.** Ashley	male female both
9. Emilio	male female both	**21.** Zina	male female both
10. Elaine	male female both	**22.** Toni	male female both
11. Jeff	male female both	**23.** Jordan	male female both
12. Mika	male female both	**24.** Emily	male female both

Discussing Current Events

Directions: Attach a newspaper headline in each box. List three points you could discuss about each headline.

Headline:

1. _____
2. _____
3. _____

Headline:

1. _____
2. _____
3. _____

Headline:

1. _____
2. _____
3. _____

Drawing Directions

Directions: Draw a map showing the best way to get from your house to the closest grocery store. Include street names.

Map from School to Closest Grocery Store

Evaluating Your Own Attitudes

Directions: Carefully think about the following situations and then describe your attitude issues.

1. Describe a time when your attitude helped a situation with a parent.

2. Describe a time when your attitude worsened a situation with a parent.

3. Describe a time when your attitude helped a situation with a teacher.

4. Describe a time when your attitude worsened a situation with a teacher.

Explaining Why Hitching Is Not Safe

Directions: Use the words in the Word Box to fill in the blanks to create a list of reasons why hitching is not safe.

Word Box			
road	odd	hit	dangerous
criminal	swerve	sunburnt	stranger
life	injury	do	night
dropped	hot	control	stress

1. There are some _____ people in the world, so you never know what

   a stranger will _____.

2. A stranger could be a _____ who is wanted by the police and is

   _____.

3. If you ride with a stranger, you do not have any _____ over where

   you are _____ off.

4. You might end up not getting a ride and spending all _____ alone

   alongside a _____.

5. A driver might _____ off the road and

   _____ you.

6. If it is a _____ day, you could get

   _____ while you are waiting for a ride.

7. You could get in a vehicle with a person who turns out to be a bad driver and who causes you

   great _____ or even _____.

8. You would be putting your _____ in the hands of a

   _____.

Finding Weather Reports for Varying Locations

Directions: Use a current newspaper weather map to fill in the boxes.

Name one place where each weather condition is expected today.		
rain	sunny and cool	warm
cloudy, but no rain	hot	cool and windy

Describe the weather that is expected in each of these locations.		
New York City, New York	Detroit, Michigan	Chicago, Illinois
San Francisco, California	Denver, Colorado	San Antonio, Texas

Following Neighborhood Guidelines

Directions: Match the neighborhood guidelines with possible purposes for the guidelines.

Answers	Possible Guideline Purposes	Neighborhood Guidelines
	1. People want their neighborhoods to look tidy and for their visitors to be able to park.	A. Keep pets inside, fenced, or on a leash.
	2. You must find out where the pipes and wires are located so you don't hit them.	B. Do not dig in your yard without a permit.
	3. People want to help keep their property values up by making sure all houses meet certain requirements.	C. Campers, boats, and semi-trucks cannot be parked by a house for more than 24 hours without moving.
	4. Dogs are not predictable, and some people just do not want other people's dogs in their yards.	D. All houses in a neighborhood must be at least 2600 sq. ft.

Answers	Possible Guideline Purposes	Neighborhood Guidelines
	5. The city wants no building over buried pipes or wires, and they want building plans to meet requirements.	E. Clean up all pet waste.
	6. People want their neighborhoods to look tidy.	F. You must have a permit for all building projects.
	7. Your neighbors will not want your smelly piles in their yards.	G. Approval is required for paint-color choices.
	8. People often want houses to blend in, so colors like purple are not allowed for the outside of houses.	H. You must mow your yard regularly.

Following Through

Directions: In each situation, circle the choice that shows an example of following through for that situation.

1. Alice cleared the table after dinner and then she

watched TV	wiped the table top	made a phone call

2. Tonya said she wanted to do well on the math test, so she

studied and went to bed early.	studied, went out to a party, and got home late.	watched TV and went to bed early.

3. Jamal volunteered to take tickets at the basketball game, so he

got to the game late and just helped a little.	called the woman in charge since he decided to stay home instead.	went to the game 30 minutes early to be ready when people started coming.

4. Heather went out for the basketball team, and she

quit when it got cold outside.	finished the season even though she didn't like it that much.	went to all the games even though she missed half the practices.

5. Bethany said she would call Tony at 4:00, and she

called right at 4:00.	decided to take a nap at 3:30 and called at 7:00 instead.	got busy and forgot to call.

Getting a Birth Certificate

Directions: Answer the questions to determine which Web page links will help you get a copy of a birth certificate. Use one or more of the Web page links for each answer.

Links to Web page information:

A. How to order a birth certificate
B. How to order online
C. How to order by mail
D. How to order by fax
E. How to order in person

- All methods require this information: city, county, and state of birth, reason you need the birth certificate, your birth name (first, middle, and last), gender, father's name (first, middle, and last), Mother's maiden name (first, middle, and maiden name)

- To the $15 for the certificate, add $8.50 for handling and $16 for delivery.
- Allow 3-5 business days plus shipping time.
- Type the information in the form and click on purchase.
- Enter credit card information.

- Drop the completed form (typed or hand written) off in the Public Health office.
- Show a picture ID.
- Pay $15
- Provide mailing address
- Will mail within two business days

- Fill in form including credit card number (type or write)
- Fax to 217-555-2648
- Cost: $15 plus $8.50 for handling and $16 for delivery
- Include phone #, signature, and copy of photo ID
- Allow 3-5 business days plus shipping time

- Fill in form (type or write)
- Include a check or money order for $15.00
- Include copy of photo ID
- Put in stamped envelope and mail it.
- Allow six weeks.

1. How would you order a birth certificate if you need it very quickly? _____

2. If you want to hand write the information on the form, which way would you NOT want to use to order the birth certificate? _____

3. Which two ways of ordering cost the most? _____
   The least? _____

4. How would you write your mother's name if you were filling out an order form for a birth certificate? _____

Getting Along with a Roommate

Directions: Read each of the roommate problems below and offer solutions. Try to find solutions that will solve the problems without ruining your relationship with your roommate.

1. Your roommate stays up until 3:00 A.M. or 4:00 A.M. listening to loud music. You want to sleep, but can't. What will you say or do? _____

2. You come home from class and find your roommate trying on some of your clothes. _____

3. Your roommate thinks it is funny to sing loudly whenever you get a phone call. Due to the singing, you have a hard time hearing your callers. _____

4. Your roommate eats your snacks without asking and doesn't replace them. _____

5. Your roommate leaves clothes, food, and open drinks on the floor. The food and drinks are often under the clothes, so you and your roommate sometimes step on the food and spill the drinks. _____

Getting Along With Others

Directions: Write "yes" or "no" in each box to show the result you think each situation will cause.

	Could help people get along	Will probably make sense when think about it later	Is the way you would want someone to react to you
1. Janda doesn't feel well, so she just ignores Kelly's "Hi Janda" as she walks by Kelly's locker.			
2. Collin sees Ping drop her book because her hands are so full. Collin picks up Ping's book, gives it to her, and smiles as he walks by.			
3. Gary wants to start on the basketball team tonight, so he hides Keith's uniform.			
4. Dante is hurrying down the hall when he bumps into Sierra and knocks her down. So he won't be late, Dante says nothing and keeps on going.			
5. Ashton has a bag of candy. He sees Ward looking at it and offers Ward a piece.			
6. Tory accidentally spills soda on Magalee's book. Magalee is upset, so she pours some soda on Tory's book.			

Getting Ready to Go to Bed

Directions: Rewrite this story so that it is a realistically possible explanation of what a person might do to get ready to go to bed. Change at least one word in each sentence.

Jamie turned up the television and left the room. As she left the room, she turned on the light. She went to the closet and got a drink of water. Then she went upstairs and brushed her coat. She went into her livingroom and turned on her bed-side lamp. She put on her blue jeans and snuggled into bed. Then she picked up her book and read for about 2000 minutes. When she started to get tired, she put her popsickle down and turned out the light. She closed her elbows and rested on her pillow. Soon, she was sound awake.

_____

Giving Directions to a Driver

Directions: Tell whether each direction would be helpful and explain why or why not.

1. **Turn left at the blue house.**

   Helpful? Why or why not? _____

   _____

2. **Turn right onto the street right before you get to Parkside Blvd.**

   Helpful? Why or why not? _____

   _____

3. **Turn right between the Freshness Grocery Store and the PressRight Dry Cleaners.**

   Helpful? Why or why not? _____

   _____

4. **Go straight through the lights at Wilson Lane and Strawberry Avenue and turn left at Shiny Street.**

   Helpful? Why or why not? _____

   _____

5. **Turn left when you see the big semi-truck parked in front of the yellow house.**

   Helpful? Why or why not? _____

   _____

6. **Go straight past the garden with all the huge sunflowers and turn at the next street.**

   Helpful? Why or why not? _____

   _____

7. **Go through the stoplight at Washington St. and turn onto Jefferson Ave.**

   Helpful? Why or why not? _____

   _____

Handling Peer Pressure

Directions: Explain how you would handle the peer pressure in the following situations.

1. You are tired and want to go to bed, but your friends want you to go to a party.

   _____

   _____

2. You are studying for a test when three different friends IM you and want to talk.

   _____

   _____

3. Some friends at school are picking on another student. One friend asks you if you have ever seen anyone with a more ridiculous haircut.

   _____

   _____

4. You have promised your parents you will not ride in a car with people who are drinking. But, some of your friends have been drinking and are going to drive out to a lake to swim, and you want to go with them.

   _____

   _____

5. You are walking home with two friends when one of them breaks off a neighbor's flowers. The other friend breaks one of the neighbor's flower pots. They tell you to kick the back out of the neighbor's lawn chair.

   _____

   _____

Having a Working Knowledge of the 50 States

Directions: Circle the correct answers. Research to find the answers if you are not sure.

1. Circle the largest of these three states (land area).

   Georgia   **Iowa**   **Idaho**

2. Circle the smallest of these three states (land area).

   California   **Illinois**   **Florida**

3. Circle a state that is on the West Coast.

   Arizona   **Oregon**   **Montana**

4. Circle a state that is on the East Coast.

   South Dakota   **West Virginia** **South Carolina**

5. Circle a state that borders Canada.

   Colorado   **North Dakota**   **Wyoming**

6. Circle a state that borders Mexico.

   Texas   **New Mexico**   **Louisiana**

7. Circle two states that are next to each other.

   Ohio & Tennessee **Kentucky & Georgia** **Arkansas & Oklahoma**

8. Circle a state that is on the Mississippi River.

   Missouri   **Nebraska**   **Indiana**

9. Circle a state that is NOT a mainland state.

   Michigan   **Hawaii**   **New York**

10. Circle a state that does NOT border one of the Great Lakes.

    Pennsylvania   **Maryland**   **Wisconsin**

Identifying Actions that Are Criminal

Directions: Circle "True" or "False" for each statement.

Statements	True	False
1. Since road signs belong to the state, as long as you live in that state, it is OK to take a stop sign to decorate your room.	True	False
2. Even if you are just clowning around, it is against the law to open bags of candy in the store and leave them on the store shelf.	True	False
3. As long as you only wear it once and then take it back, it is OK to sneak a shirt out of a store.	True	False
4. If you are in a hurry and will only be in a store for a few minutes, it is OK to park in a handicapped space even if you do not have a handicapped sticker.	True	False
5. If you are a really good driver, it is OK to drive without a seatbelt.	True	False
6. It is against the law to break windows and set fires in abandoned buildings.	True	False
7. It is messy, but not illegal, to toilet paper the trees in a friend's yard.	True	False
8. If you hit a parked car with your car, it is OK to leave the scene as long as you leave your contact information.	True	False
9. If someone steals your music player, it is OK for you to steal one from someone else.	True	False
10. It is OK to tell a police officer that you do not agree with what he or she is saying.	True	False
11. In a grocery store, it is OK to taste the grapes to see if they are sour.	True	False
12. As long as it is just a joke, there is nothing wrong with spray painting words on a car.	True	False
13. You can take your neighbor's mail and read it as long as you eventually give it to him or her.	True	False
14. It will be frowned upon, but it is not illegal to go to the courthouse without shoes on.	True	False
15. When the community pool is closed, it is OK to climb the fence and go swimming.	True	False

Identifying Cities

Directions: Write city names to respond to the following requests.

Requests	City Names
1. Name the largest city in Illinois.	
2. Name a city that is larger than the city/town where you live.	
3. Name a city that is smaller than Minneapolis, MN.	
4. Name a city in Washington state.	
5. Name a city in Pennsylvania.	
6. Name a city in Ohio.	
7. Name a city in Florida.	
8. Name a city in Spain.	
9. Name a city in Japan.	
10. Name a city in Mexico.	

Identifying Directions (North, South, East, West)

Directions: Use these direction words and the diagrams below to fill in the blanks:

- **North**
- **South**
- **East**
- **West**

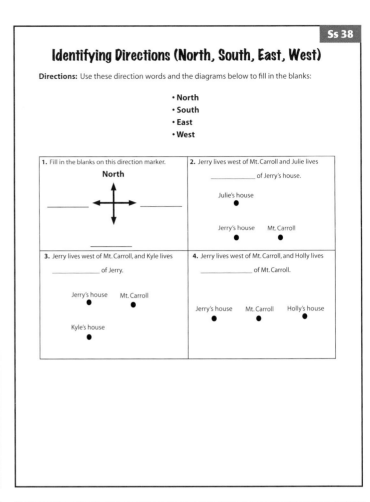

1. Fill in the blanks on this direction marker.

North

2. Jerry lives west of Mt. Carroll and Julie lives _____ of Jerry's house.

Julie's house

Jerry's house   Mt. Carroll

3. Jerry lives west of Mt. Carroll, and Kyle lives _____ of Jerry.

Jerry's house   Mt. Carroll

Kyle's house

4. Jerry lives west of Mt. Carroll, and Holly lives _____ of Mt. Carroll.

Jerry's house   Mt. Carroll   Holly's house

Identifying Ethnic Foods

Directions: Match the types of ethnic foods with the common ingredients.

Answers	Types of Ethnic Foods	Common Ingredients
	1. Mexican	**A.** garlic
	2. French	**B.** cilantro
	3. Chinese	**C.** hollandaise sauce
	4. Italian	**D.** rice
Answers	**Types of Ethnic Foods**	**Common Ingredients**
	5. German	**E.** grape leaves
	6. American	**F.** sauerkraut
	7. Greek	**G.** cheddar cheese
	8. Indian	**H.** cumin

Identifying Foreign Countries on a Map

Directions: Use the country names in the top box to fill in the names around the map.

Australia	Brazil	Canada
China	Japan	Mexico
Russia	South Africa	Spain
United States		

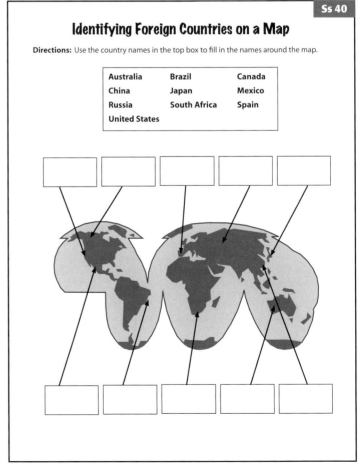

Identifying Jobs that are Well-Matched to Personal Strengths

Directions: Complete the sentences in the boxes in the outer circle. Use each response only once. Then research to find a matching job to write in the center.

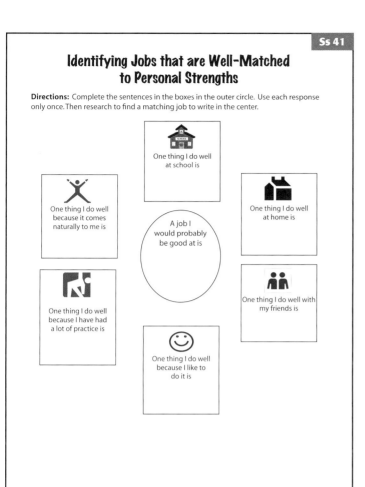

Identifying Nearby Cities

Directions: In the center, write the city or town where you live. Then write one city or town in each of the other boxes.

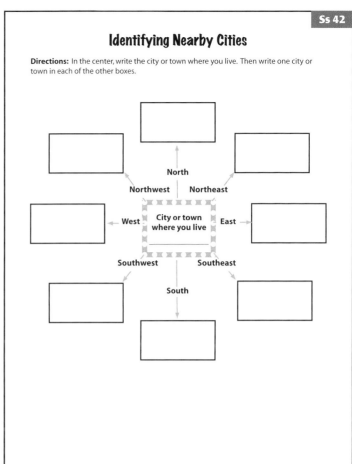

Identifying Realistic Job Possibilities

Directions: Explain why you could or could not do each of the jobs below.

babysit	
milk cows	
mow lawns	
drive a school bus	
make phone sales calls	
waitress	
paint houses	

Interacting in the Community

Directions: Use the business and community options to answer each question.

Business and Community Options		
department store	park	school
library	pharmacy	bank
emergency room	dry cleaner	exterminator

1. Where could you go if you want to ride a bike without riding on the streets?	
2. What type of business should you call if you want to get rid of bugs that are in your home?	
3. Where could you go to get books to read without having to buy them?	
4. Where could you go if you wanted to volunteer to help coach a kids' ball team?	
5. Where could you take a coat to have a stain removed?	
6. Where could you go if you fall and think you have broken a bone?	
7. Where could you go to buy a pair of slippers?	
8. Where could you go to get a prescription filled?	
9. Where should you go to open a savings account?	

Social Studies   65

Keeping Commitments

Directions: List three things you would like to do and can commit to and three things you would like to do and cannot commit to.

Three things I would like to do and can commit to
Example: I'll make three dozen cookies for the bake sale on Saturday.
1.
2.
3.

Three things I would like to do but don't know for sure I can do so I cannot commit to them
Example: I'd like to be in charge of the concession stand at the game, but I do not know for sure that I have enough time to get everything done.
1.
2.
3.

Keeping Hands in Appropriate Places When in Public

Directions: Check the answers in #1 and complete the sentences in 2–7.

1. Check each situation that is an example of being in public.

alone in your bedroom	alone in the park
in your living room with friends	at a grocery store
at a restaurant	in your bedroom
watching TV with your family	riding in your car with a friend
alone in the kitchen having cereal	walking alone on a sidewalk

2. When I'm in public and my crotch itches, I should _____

_____

3. When I'm in public and I feel something in my nose, I should _____

_____

4. When I'm in public and I'm just standing around, I should put my hands _____

_____

5. When I'm in public and I'm talking to someone, I should put my hands _____

_____

6. If I have my arms crossed at my chest, I should put my hands _____

_____

7. If I'm in public and I see a rough spot on my foot that I'd like to pick at, I should _____

_____

Knowing and Following Driving Rules

Directions: Match the driving signs to the rules.

Answers	Driving Rules		Signs	
	1.	You should not drive in the direction of this sign.	A.	(airplane sign)
	2.	You are coming to a bump in the road.	B.	(deer crossing sign)
	3.	An airport is nearby.	C.	DIP
	4.	Be careful of deer that might be crossing the road.	D.	DO NOT ENTER
	5.	Other drivers may be coming onto the road at this point.	E.	(merge sign)

Answers	Driving Rules		Signs	
	6.	Be prepared to stop for people who are crossing the street.	F.	(no left turn sign)
	7.	Left turns are not allowed here.	G.	(no parking sign)
	8.	Drivers must come to a complete stop.	H.	(pedestrian crossing sign)
	9.	The road curves to the right.	I.	(curve right arrow)
	10.	Parking is not allowed here.	J.	STOP

Knowing Family Relationships

Directions: Use the words in the box to complete Column 1. In Column 2, if you have a family member with that relationship, write the person's name. If you have no such family member, write N/A.

Family Relationships			
aunt	brother-in-law	niece	sibling
uncle	grandfather	nephew	parent
cousin	great aunt	step-brother	grandson

Family Relationship Words from Box	Definitions	Your Family Members (Names or N/A)
	Your sister's male child	
	Your mother's father	
	The child of your father's new wife	
	Your sister's husband	
	Your father's brother's wife	
	Your child's child	
	Your brother or sister	
	Your mother's brother	
	Your grandmother's sister	
	Your brother's female child	
	Your mother or father	
	Any child of your mother's sister	

Knowing Holiday Dates and Traditions

Directions: Write the date and a common decoration for each holiday.

Holiday	Date	Common Decoration
New Year's Day		
Matin Luther King Day		
Valentine's Day		
Presidents' Day		
St. Patrick's Day		
Easter		
Mother's Day		
Memorial Day		
Flag Day		
Father's Day		
4th of July		
Labor Day		
Columbus Day		
Halloween		
Veterans Day		
Thanksgiving		
Christmas		

Knowing How Current Events Relate to You

Directions: From a current newspaper, choose an article that relates to you and attach it in the box below (fold it if you need to). On the lines below, explain how the information in the article relates to you.

Knowing Languages Spoken in Different Countries

Directions: Use the words in the two boxes to fill in the chart. Do an Internet search if you need help.

Languages		Ways to Say "Hello"	
Spanish Chinese German Norwegian	Japanese English English	hola goddag konnichi wa hallo	Nǐ hǎo hello hello

Countries	Languages	Ways to say "Hello"
Mexico		
Norway		
Japan		
China		
Scotland		
Australia		
Austria		

Knowing Left and Right

Directions: Use the clue box and follow the directions to write a joke below.

		Clue Box					
	Place a(n)	to the	of the		Place a(n)	to the	of the
1.	i	left	t	10.	i	right	a
2.	a	right	w	11.	d	right	n
3.	t	right	u	12.	n	right	i
4.	h	left	s	13.	s	right	i
5.	o	right	d	14.	r	left	e
6.	t	left	a	15.	l	right	l
7.	u	right	j	16.	h	left	o
8.	h	right	s	17.	l	left	d
9.	a	right	e	18.	o	right	h

Clue Numbers (for each line)

A   D a c___s___u n___   4, 8, 11

w___t___o u___   a   ___a___l   1, 3, 6, 10, 16

i___   ___e___l___y   j___s t   a   7, 9, 13, 14, 15

w___l k i___g   h___   ___g!   2, 5, 12, 17, 18

Knowing People at Your School

Directions: Ask your teacher for a list of names of 10 people who work at your school. Write the names on the left. On the right, list each person's job.

	Names of People Who Work in Your School	Job Titles
1		
2		
3		
4		
5		
6		
7		
8		
9		
10		

Knowing Personal Choices

Directions: Complete these sentences.

It's all about me!

1. My favorite vegetable is _____

2. My favorite sport is _____

3. My favorite flower is _____

4. My favorite actor/actress is _____

5. My favorite kind of music is _____

6. My favorite school subject is _____

7. My favorite dessert is _____

8. My favorite TV show is _____

9. My favorite childhood toy was _____

10. My favorite thing for breakfast is _____

Knowing Personal Facts

Directions: Fill in this form.

First Name		Middle		Last	
Street Address					
City		State	Zip	County	
Country of Residence			Are you a U.S. citizen?		
Birth Month	Day	Year	Birth City		State
Home Phone # ( )			Cell Phone # ( )		
E-mail Address					
Sex M F	Height		Weight	Marital Status S D M W	
Hair Color		Eye Color		Age	
Food Allergies					
Exercise Habits					
Name of Physician					
Name of current (or last) school attended					
Blood type		Mother's maiden name			

Knowing Recent U.S. Presidents

Directions: Circle the names of the U.S. presidents in this list.

Ronald Reagan	Johnny Cash	George H. Bush
Colin Powell	Jimmy Carter	Ted Kennedy
Winston Churchill	George W. Bush	Nicole Kidman
Condaleeza Rice	Michael Douglas	Bill Clinton

Write the presidents you circled above in the order that they were president.

_____ _____

_____

_____

_____

_____

Write the names of any U.S. presidents who have been in office after the last person on your list.

_____ _____

_____

_____

_____

Knowing the Area Where You Live

Directions: Fill in the circles to show where you live.

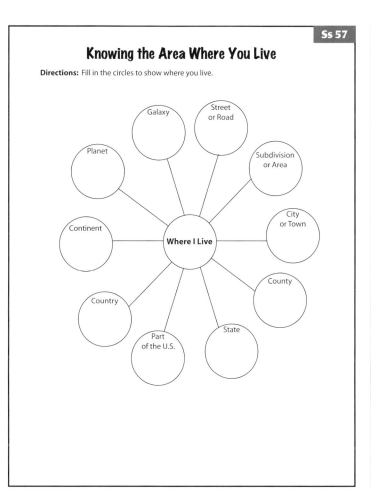

Knowing What You Will Do After High School

Directions: Finish each sentence.

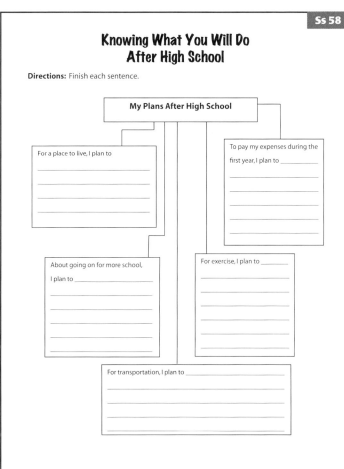

Knowing When and How to Use Travelers Checks

Directions: For each question, choose the most logical situation for using travelers checks.

1. You are going to buy a vase
   _____ **a.** in your town
   _____ **b.** on a trip to city that is a five-hour trip from where you live
   _____ **c.** in a city that is about 100 miles away and in another state

2. You are staying in a hotel, and
   _____ **a.** it is expensive
   _____ **b.** you do not have a credit card
   _____ **c.** your whole family is staying there

3. You are on vacation and you are
   _____ **a.** going on a guided tour of the area
   _____ **b.** taking a walk
   _____ **c.** leaving a tip for a bellman

4. You are back from vacation and still have a travelers' check to use, so you will
   _____ **a.** use it to buy lunch at school
   _____ **b.** use it to pay a friend back the $2.00 you borrowed
   _____ **c.** use it to eat at a restaurant

Knowing Your Legal Rights

Directions: Mark each action with an "L" for "Legal" or an "N" for "Not Legal" within the United States.

L (Legal) OR N (Not Legal)	Action
	1. You are a minor and you drink alcohol in your front yard but in no one else's yard.
	2. You drive without a license since you are just going to the grocery store and right back.
	3. You plan to vote at age 18.
	4. When you are accused of a crime, you decide not to show up for your court date.
	5. You ignore temporary stop signs that are set up in a parking lot.
	6. You are kept in jail for 10 years while waiting for a trial.
	7. In a local newspaper, you say that you disagree with some of the U.S. president's main policies.
	8. You tear a page out of a magazine at the doctor's office.
	9. You sneak out of a restaurant without paying.
	10. You tell your teacher that you lost your homework when you really never did it.

Knowing Your Mother's Maiden Name

Directions: Fill in the blanks in your family tree.

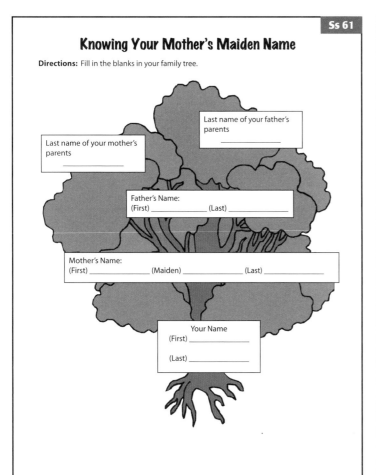

Last name of your father's parents
_____

Last name of your mother's parents
_____

Father's Name:
(First) _____ (Last) _____

Mother's Name:
(First) _____ (Maiden) _____ (Last) _____

Your Name
(First) _____

(Last) _____

Knowing Your Neighbors

Directions: Fill in the boxes with the names of six of your nearest neighbors.

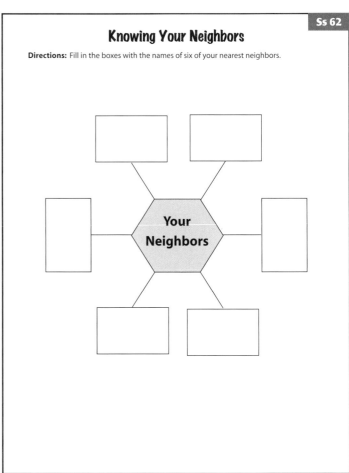

Your Neighbors

Listing Pros and Cons

Directions: Choose one of the topics below and use it to create a pros and cons list.

Topics
(Choose One)

1. Should I start exercising at an exercise club?
2. Should I eat more vegetables?
3. Should I go to bed by 9:00 on school nights?

Topic:	
Pros	**Cons**

Maintaining Quality Work for Eight Hours

Directions: For each work situation on the right, circle one of the two descriptions on the left.

Descriptions	Work Situations
quality work habit poor work habit	1. You go to the copy room to make a copy. Your boss is there and starts talking to you. You end up staying in the copy room and having a personal conversation for 30 minutes.
quality work habit poor work habit	2. You go to the copy room to make a copy. Your friend from the shipping department is there. You end up staying and having a personal conversation for 30 minutes.
quality work habit poor work habit	3. Three of your friends call, so you spend an hour on the phone and do not have the report ready when your boss asks for it.
quality work habit poor work habit	4. Three of your friends call, so you spend an hour on the phone. You work during your lunch hour so that the report is ready when your boss asks for it.
quality work habit poor work habit	5. Your boss gives you an hour to file some papers. You do not get done, so you put the papers in the trash and tell your boss you are finished.
quality work habit poor work habit	6. Your boss gives you an hour to file some papers. You do not get done, so you tell your boss that you just couldn't get done that quickly, but will gladly finish them later.
quality work habit poor work habit	7. A customer says that her hamburger isn't cooked enough. You tell her that it won't hurt and she might even like it.
quality work habit poor work habit	8. A customers says that her hamburger isn't cooked enough. You tell her that you will get her a new one.
quality work habit poor work habit	9. You are unloading window at a construction site when you drop and break one. You call your boss and tell her what happend.
quality work habit poor work habit	10. You are unloading windows at a construction site when you drop and break one. Since no one saw you, you put the broken window with the other windows and leave.

Making and Carrying Out Plans

Directions: Order the sentences below to show a logical plan for getting ready for school in the morning. Use the numbers 1–10 to show the correct order.

Plan for Getting Ready for School in the Morning	
Numbers 1–10	**Step in Plan**
	Get dressed
	Make your bed
	Comb your hair
	Get your back pack ready
	Decide what to wear
	Get out of bed
	Eat breakfast
	Leave for school
	Brush your teeth
	Pack your lunch
Try to follow this plan yourself!	

Making Assumptions

Directions: Assumptions are guesses based on facts. Make an assumption about each of the following situations.

1. Jordy walked into school crying and with mud all over her coat and hair. What do you think happened? _____

2. When Hank did not show up for soccer practice this morning, Coach Vinna called him. The coach could hardly understand Shawn because Shawn was talking very quietly and saying only a few nonsense words. Why do you think Shawn was not at practice? _____

3. Lavita was in class getting her math homework out when she stopped and said, "Oh, no!" Why do you think she said that? _____

4. Malik sat down to dinner and said to his mother, "Did you really make that lasagna?" What do you think Malke was thinking about the lasagna? _____

5. Justin quietly sat and listened to the student council candidates talk. As Marcie talked, Justin started nodding his head gently up and down. What do you think Justin was thinking? _____

Making Decisions

Directions: Make and explain each decision below.

Situation	Your Decision	Why You Think Your Decision is Correct
1. For dinner, your parents say you can either make meatloaf and mashed potatoes for the whole family or you can have canned soup by yourself. What will you decide to do?		
2. In social studies class, you can either take the final exam or write a 10-page paper. What will you decide to do?		
3. You can paint your room yourself using whatever color you want or you can have a painter paint your room ivory white with the rest of the house. What will you decide to do?		
4. You can go with your best friend to a movie you have already seen or you can go with a so-so friend to a movie you haven't seen yet. What will you decide to do?		

Making Friends

Directions: Cut out the "friend ideas" below and tape them into the correct columns.

Very Important	Sort of Important	Not Important

Friend Ideas		
Make friends with people who like to do the same things you like to do.	Make friends with people who are nice to you.	Make friends with people who are close to your age.
Make friends with people who live close to you.	Make friends with people who are good looking.	Avoid making friends with people who do not like the foods you like.
Avoid making friends with people who are always in trouble.	Make friends with people who are funny.	Make friends with people who understand and enjoy your humor.
Make friends with people with whom you can easily talk.	Make friends with people who have a schedule similar to yours.	Make friends with people who dress like you do.

Social Studies 71

Making Leisure Choices

Directions: Identify each leisure activity. Circle those that look like fun to you.

Identify:	Identify:	Identify:
Identify:	Identify:	Identify:
Identify:	Identify:	Identify:
Identify:	Identify:	Identify:

Make Safe Choices When Out at Night

Directions: Match the sentence beginnings with the sentence endings.

Answers	Sentence Beginnings	Sentence Endings
	1. If you work late at night,	A. try to go into a restaurant or a store.
	2. If you are walking at night, and you hear someone behind you,	B. leave with the crowd. Don't hang around.
	3. Even if a dark alley is a short cut,	C. walk to your car with a co-worker or a guard.
	4. When you leave a school activity at night and go into the parking lot,	D. always stay on well-lit sidewalks.

Answers	Sentence Beginnings	Sentence Endings
	5. If you know you have to walk home after dark,	E. call someone on your cell phone.
	6. If you are out at night and see some questionable people,	F. say "thanks," but don't hang around and talk.
	7. If you are out alone at night and feel a little frightened,	G. plan to walk with someone.
	8. If you drop some groceries in the dark and a stranger stops to help you,	H. cross to the other side of the street.

Making Travel Decisions Based on Typical Climate

Directions: Fill in the short blanks with the 12 months of the year. Use each month only once. Then complete the sentences.

1. I would like to visit Florida in _____ or _____ because _____

2. I would like to visit Alaska in _____ or _____ because _____

3. I would like to visit Maine in _____ or _____ because _____

4. I would like to visit South Texas in _____ or _____ because _____

5. I would like to visit Minnesota in _____ or _____ because _____

6. I would like to visit Colorado in _____ or _____ because _____

Naming Elected Officials

Directions: Fill in the chart with names of elected officials.

Your mayor	Area senator to the state congress	Area representative to the state congress
Member of your local school board	Person on your local county board	Person on your local city council
One U.S. senator from your state	The second U.S. senator from your state	Member of the U.S. House of Representatives from your area
Governor of your state	Current U.S. Vice president	Current U.S. president

Naming Major Local Intersections

Directions: In each sentence, fill in the first blank with a major local intersection (Example: Cherry and Washington Streets. Fill in the second blank with a description of a specific house, building, or business that can be used to help describe the intersection.

Example:

One thing at the intersection of **Cherry and Washington Streets**

is **the public library, which is a gray, brick building.**

1. One thing at the intersection of _____ is
   _____

2. One thing at the intersection of _____ is
   _____

3. One thing at the intersection of _____ is
   _____

4. One thing at the intersection of _____ is
   _____

5. One thing at the intersection of _____ is
   _____

Packing to Move

Directions: The following words are often abbreviated on packing boxes when people are moving. For each word, write an abbreviation on the packing box.

1. Kitchen	2. Bedroom	3. Livingroom	4. Family Room
5. Bathroom	6. Garage	7. Office	8. Attic

Directions: Complete the sentences about packing to move.

9. One way to keep dishes from breaking is to _____
   _____

10. You can get boxes for moving from _____
    _____

11. You will need to get help to move bigger items such as _____
    _____

12. One way to make sure you don't lose your labeling marker as you are packing is to _____
    _____

Parenting

Directions: Write possible solutions to each of these parenting problems.

Problems	Possible Solutions
1. Your 5-year-old gets out of bed about 10 times before going to sleep.	
2. Your 8-year-old wants to wear the same shirt every day even when it is dirty.	
3. Your 10-year-old has stolen candy from the drug store three times in the past month.	
4. Your 12-year-old told you he was at a friend's house. You find out he was really at the park where you have told him not to go.	
5. Your 14-year-old took $20 out of your wallet without your knowledge.	
6. Your 16-year-old stayed out an hour past the time you told her to be home.	

Planning a Picnic

Directions: Explain how each of the following items could fit into a plan for a picnic.

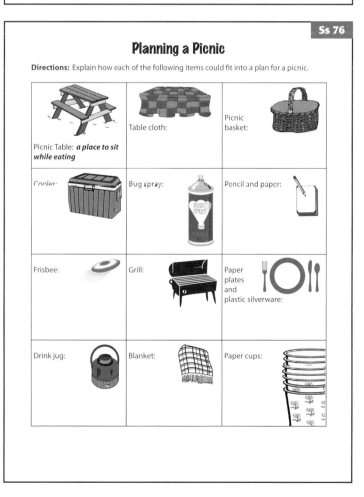

Picnic Table: *a place to sit while eating*

Table cloth:

Picnic basket:

Cooler:

Bug spray:

Pencil and paper:

Frisbee:

Grill:

Paper plates and plastic silverware:

Drink jug:

Blanket:

Paper cups:

Planning a Vacation

Directions: Use the boxes below to plan a vacation you would enjoy.

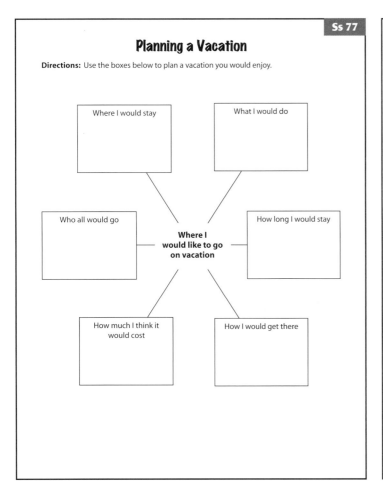

Where I would stay

What I would do

Who all would go

Where I would like to go on vacation

How long I would stay

How much I think it would cost

How I would get there

Preparing to Get Married

Directions: For each situation, put an X in the correct column.

Things You and Your Spouse-to-Be Should Agree on Before Getting Married		Things That It Isn't Important if You Agree on Before Getting Married
	If you will ever start your own business	
	Who will cook the meals	
	Where you will spend holidays	
	What the wedding will be like	
	Who will clean the house	
	How many kids you would like to have	
	Whether steaks or porkchops are better	
	How you will budget your money	
	Where you will live	
	What kind of car you will buy next year	

Protecting Your Identity

Directions: Roleplay each situation with a partner. If you are role playing the part in the third column, write what you will say before starting.

Situation #1: Giving social security numbers.	Caller: Could I please have your social security number so I can look up your record?	Callee:
Situation #2: Throwing things away	Student A: Could you throw these old checks in the trash for me, please? I got some new pretty ones, so I don't need these plain ones any more.	Student B:
Situation #3: Sharing house codes	Student A on a cell phone: I'm right by your house. If you give me the code, I can run in and get your backpack and bring it to you.	Student B:
Situation #4: Sharing computer passwords	Student A: Hey! What's your password? I'll check your e-mail for you.	Student B:

Providing Identification

Directions: Write the needed type of identification for each situation.

Types of Identification

Picture ID (Such as a school ID, State ID, or driver's license)

In-person identification (Someone vouches that you are who you say you are.)

Social Security Card

Birth Certificate

Situations	Needed Type of Identification
1. Fly on an airplane	
2. Sign up at a new school	
3. Start a new job	
4. Meet a friend of a friend	
5. Get a discount at a movie	
6. Get a passport	
7. Make a purchase with a check or credit card	
8. Move into a new apartment	

Putting Utilities in Your Name

Directions: Find the local phone numbers you would call to get each of the following utilities put in your name (or to open a new account).

Utility	Phone #
gas	
electricity	
water	
phone (land line)	
Internet	
garbage pick-up	
TV service	
Pest control	

Reacting to Strangers

Directions: Choose the youngest age at which it is OK to make each of the following choices.

Ages to Choose From

Grade Schooler

Teenager

Adult

Never

Choice	Youngest Age OK
1. Talk to strangers on dark streets alone at night.	
2. Talk to strangers at the grocery store.	
3. Talk to strangers on the phone.	
4. Talk to a stranger in the classroom with the teacher.	
5. Talk to a stranger who is next to you at a concert.	
6. Talk to a stranger who continually drives slowly past your house.	
7. Talk to a stranger in a parking lot at night.	
8. Talk to a stranger who knocks on your door at home.	

Reading a Map

Directions: Use the map to answer the questions. For each answer, include street names and whether each turn is to the left or to the right.

1. What streets would you take to get from A to G? _____

2. What streets would you take to get from C to E? _____

3. What streets would you take to get from F to I? _____

4. What streets would you take to get from H to L? _____

5. What streets would you take to get from D to K? _____

6. What streets would you take to get from B to J? _____

Reading a Map While in the Car

Directions: Complete these sentences about problems caused by looking at a map while driving.

1. When in a car, instead of the driver, a passenger should read a map because _____

2. If you are alone in a car and need to read a map, you should _____

3. When a person tries to read a map while driving, _____

4. When a passenger reads a map while in the car, it helps to position the map so that north on the map is _____

5. When you are going somewhere that is unfamiliar to you, a good plan is to read the map before you start driving and make a list of _____

Recognizing Area Types

Directions: Match the cities and towns to the descriptions. If you need help, use the Internet or an atlas to find out about the cities and towns.

Answers	Cities and Towns	Descriptions
	1. Carol Stream, Illinois	A. rural
	2. Stockton, Illinois	B. urban
	3. Cicero, Illinois	C. suburban
	4. Franklin Park, Illinois	D. inner city

Answers	Cities and Towns	Descriptions
	5. Lovington, New Mexico	E. small city
	6. Las Cruces, New Mexico	F. small town
	7. Albuquerque, New Mexico	G. large town
	8. Silver City, New Mexico	H. large city

Reconizing Areas of Town or City by Streeet Categories

Directions: Find three areas in your town or city that have category street names. For each area, write the category name on the left and three sample street names on the right.

Example	
Category Name	**Sample Street Names**
Fruits	Apple Street
	Cherry Avenue
	Lemon Boulevard

Category Name	Sample Street Names

Recognizing Colors in Your World

Directions: For each color listed below, identify something that you can see.

Colors	Things You Can See
1. red	
2. maroon	
3. pink	
4. lime green	
5. olive green	
6. true green	
7. aqua	
8. light blue	
9. royal blue	
10. navy blue	
11. yellow	
12. gold	
13. tan	
14. brown	
15. purple	

Recognizing Famous People

Directions: Find a picture of a famous person in each category below.
For each person, tape the person's picture in the box and write the person's name.

elected official	actor
Name:_____	Name:_____
singer	professional athlete/
Name:_____	Name:_____
author or artist	person from another country/
Name:_____	Name:_____

Recognizing Geographical Differences

Directions: Match the geographic descriptions to the terms.

Answers	Geographic Descriptions	Terms
	1. water that flows from a mountain to an ocean	A. ocean
	2. big enough for boating and surrounded by land	B. pond
	3. bigger than a puddle and smaller than a lake	C. lake
	4. huge body of salt water	D. river

Answers	Geographic Descriptions	Descriptions
	5. hilly areas at the base of mountains	E. canyon
	6. flat land that is not as high as surrounding land	F. valley
	7. deep valley, often with rocky sides and a river running through	G. lowlands
	8. a small mound of land surrounded by flatter land	H. hills
	9. grassy area between two hills or mountains	I. foothills

Answers	Geographic Descriptions	Descriptions
	10. flat, grassy land	J. mountains
	11. land covered with trees	K. plateau
	12. the highest land on Earth	L. forest
	13. high, flat land	M. desert
	15. land that is too dry to grow many plants or trees	N. meadow

Recognizing House Styles

Directions: Match the pictures to the house styles.

Answers	House Pictures	House Styles
	1.	A. ranch
	2.	B. two-story
	3.	C. split level
	4.	D. trailer

Answers	Sentence Beginnings	Sentence Endings
	5.	E. A-frame
	6.	F. duplex
	7.	G. three-story
	8.	H. raised ranch

Respecting Cultural Diversity

Directions: The United States is made up of people from many different cultures. Identify friends, classmates, relatives, neighbors, and acquaintances from each culture listed below.

Culture	Person You Know
African American	
Asian American	
Caucasian	
Hispanic	
Other race:	
Jewish	
Christian	
Other religion:	
Indian	
English	
French	
Other nationality:	

Respecting Individuals with Physical/Mental Challenges

Directions: Answer the questions.

1. Think of someone who cannot walk well: _____

   What is something that person can do well? _____

2. Think of someone who is not good at math: _____

   What is something that person can do well? _____

3. Think of someone who cannot talk well: _____

   What is something that person can do well? _____

4. Think of someone who cannot read well: _____

   What is something that person can do well? _____

5. Think of someone who has trouble following school rules: _____

   What is something that person can do well? _____

Respecting Others' Privacy

Directions: Answer each question.

1. You know your friend Jason writes great stories. You want to read his latest story, but he doesn't want you to read it. What will you say or do? _____

_____

_____

2. You have gotten your math tests back and you did well. You want to know how your friend Leslie did, but she turned her test upside down. What will you say or do? _____

_____

_____

3. Your cousin has a secret and won't tell you. You really want to know the secret. What will you say or do? _____

_____

4. You find your sister crying in her room. She won't say what is wrong. What will you say or do?

_____

_____

5. You see that some of your neighbor's mail is in your mailbox. You wonder what is in one of the envelopes. What will you say or do? _____

_____

_____

Respecting Others' Property

Directions: For each situation, give an example of both respecting property and disrespecting property.

Example of Respecting Property	Situations	Example of Disrepsecting Property
	You are getting a ride home with your neighbor. You have very muddy shoes.	
	You see a classmate's backpack in the hall and you wonder what all is in it.	
	You see that someone drew a picture on a fence by the school. You are a good artist and would like to draw a picture too.	

Searching for Service Providers

Directions: Use the local phone book to fill in possible names, addresses, and phone numbers for these service providers.

Service Provider	Name	Address	Phone Number
doctor			
lawyer			
hair dresser			
dentist			
painter			
window washer			
repairman			
dry cleaner			
house-cleaning service			
yard service			

Serving on a Jury

Directions: Complete this juror questionnaire.

___ M ___F	Race (required by State Law):		Age	Religion		U.S. Citizen ___Y ___N
How long have you been a resident of this county?		Your Occupation		Employer		How long?
Highest level of education completed		Current marital status S M D W		Number of children	Ages of children	
Spouse's Name		Spouse's Occupation		Spouse's Employer		How long?

Has any accidental bodily ___Y ___N If so, what type?
injury requiring medical By your family? ___Y ___N
attention ever been Is so, what type?
sustained by you?

Ask your teacher for a label with your name and address on it and place it here.

If the above address is incorrect, correct here

Have you ever served on a
Civil Jury? ___Y ___N   Criminal Jury? ___Y ___N

Have you ever been party to a civil lawsuit? ___Y ___N
If yes, what type?

Have you ever been the accused, the complainant, or a witness in a criminal case? ___Y ___N

Are any of your relatives law enforcement officers? ___Y ___N

I CERTIFY THAT ALL ANSWERS ARE TRUE AND CORRECT.
Please sign here:

Directions: Read and answer the questions.

General Qualifications for Jury Service*	Exemptions from Jury Service*
To serve as a juror you MUST 1. be at least 18 years old. 2. be a citizen of this state and a resident of this county. 3. be qualified by law to vote in this county. 4. be of sound mind and good moral character. 5. be able to read and write. 6. not have served as a juror for six days during the last three months in the county court or during the last six months in the district court. 7. not have been convicted of theft or any felony. 8. not be under indictment of a midemeanor theft, felony theft, or any other felony charge. *based on the State of TX juror information	**You MIGHT be excused from jury service if** 1. you are over 70 years of age. 2. you have legal custody of one or more children under 10 and they will be unsupervised if you are gone all day. 3. you are a student at a public or private high school. 4. you are enrolled and attend college. 5. you are an officer or an employee of the senate or the house of representatives or work for the legislative branch of the state government. 6. you are the primary caretaker of an invalid. 7. you have served as a juror in the district courts or county courts of this county within the last 36 months. *You are not required to claim an exemption even if you qualify.

1. Are you qualified to serve as a juror? _____

2. Can you choose not to serve as a juror? _____

Showing a Positive Attitude

Directions: For each situation, give an example of a positive attitude and a negative attitude.

Positive Attitudes	Situations	Negative Attitudes
	1. You have to study for a science test tonight.	
	2. Your mom asked you to scrub the kitchen floor.	
	3. You have to wait until next week to go shopping for the new clothes your parents said you could have.	

Showing Country Loyalty

Directions: Finish these sentences.

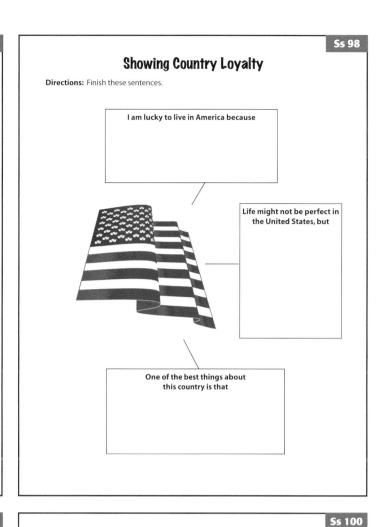

I am lucky to live in America because

Life might not be perfect in the United States, but

One of the best things about this country is that

Showing Family Loyalty

Directions: Finish these sentences.

1. Even though my (sister, brother) makes me mad sometimes _____

2. I'm not always happy about everything my parents say, but _____

3. One really good thing about my family is _____

4. Another really good thing about my family is _____

5. When it comes down to supporting a family member in a difficult situation _____

Showing Good Sportsmanship

Directions: Put an "X" next to each example that shows bad sportsmanship.

1. Your high school football team loses to your cousin's team, so you do not answer your cousin's IMs for one week.	**6.** You are shooting baskets with a friend and you aren't doing very well. Each time your friend gets ready to shoot, you yell something like "You look stupid" or "Are you bleeding?"
2. Your high school basketball team loses to a rival high school. As you are leaving the gym, you call out to some students from the other team, "We'll be back next year."	**7.** You are playing doubles tennis and you don't think your partner is trying very hard. So, on purpose, you swing at balls that come to him and hit him with your racket several times.
3. You are in a bike race and you have a problem with your bike. You get it fixed, but quit the race since you have fallen so far behind.	**8.** You are on the debate team and in the middle of a competion. Your partner keeps forgetting when to say his parts, so you lightly kick him under the table when it is his turn.
4. You are swimming in a swim meet. You see that the person in the lane next to you is two laps ahead of you. You know you can't catch up, so you stop and get out of the pool.	**9.** You are playing basketball and are up to bat. You have two strikes. The pitch comes and you think it is a ball, so you do not swing. The umpire calls it a strike. You get out and throw the bat as hard as you can.
5. You are bowling with some friends (guys against girls), and the other team is way ahead. Each time one of the them gets a strike, you yell things like "Lucky" and "Hope you get a gutter ball next."	**10.** You are golfing and you have just hit a really bad shot. On your next turn, you are determined to hit the ball soundly. You swing and follow through. The ball soars, but you lose your grip on your club and it flies through the air and hits your golfing partner on the shoulder.

Showing Public Courtesy

Directions: Circle "**is**" or "is **not**" in each sentence and then complete the sentence.

1. Itching my feet (**is** / **is not**) a rude thing to do in public because _____
   _____

2. Humming (**is** / **is not**) a rude thing to do in public because _____
   _____

3. Crying when you get hurt (**is** / **is not**) a rude thing to do in public because _____
   _____

4. Sitting in a crowded room and silently reading a book (**is** / **is not**) a rude thing to do in public
   because _____
   _____

5. Talking on a cell phone in a restaurant (**is** / **is not**) a rude thing to do in public because _____
   _____

6. Using a toothpick to remove a piece of food that is caught in your teeth (**is** / **is not**) a rude
   thing to do in public because _____
   _____

7. Sitting quietly without starting a converstation (**is** / **is not**) a rude thing to do in public
   because _____
   _____

8. Doing most of the talking (**is** / **is not**) a rude thing to do in public because _____
   _____

Showing Self Control

Directions: Give examples of reasons for self control in each of the following situations.

Situations	Examples of Self Control	Reasons for Using Self Control
1. Debbie is sitting in study hall when Micah walks by. Micah bumps Debbie's purse, knocks the purse on the floor, and spills everything out of it.		
2. Rob is watching TV when his dad walks in and changes the channel.		
3. Terry (17) is giving Seth, (12) a ride from school. Terry is frustrated because Seth is talking nonstop and looking through Terry's things.		
4. Sally and Donna are sharing an order of French fries. Donna is eating way more than her share, because she eats three at a time.		
5. Estelle and Daryl are eating at a fancy restaurant. Daryl chews most bites with his mouth open so the chewed food shows.		

Showing Two IDs

Directions: Answer the questions about having to show two IDs.

Some Possible IDs		
driver's license	credit card	school ID
debit card	social security card	insurance card
state non-driving ID		

1. What two IDs would you use if the directions said a school ID could not be used?
   _____   _____

2. Name two IDs that usually have photos.
   _____   _____

3. Which ID would you use if you needed a picture ID and did not have a driver's license.
   _____   _____

4. What are two IDs that you could use over the phone?
   _____   _____

   What information would you give from the IDs? _____
   _____

5. What two IDs could you use to prove where you live?
   _____   _____

6. What two IDs could you use as identification when you fly on an airplane?
   _____   _____

Sorting Bodies of Water

Directions: Identify each body of water as a pond, lake, river, or ocean.

1. _____ Erie
   pond   lake   river   ocean

2. Atlantic _____
   pond   lake   river   ocean

3. _____ Mead
   pond   lake   river   ocean

4. Missouri _____
   pond   lake   river   ocean

5. Great Salt _____
   pond   lake   river   ocean

6. Arctic _____
   pond   lake   river   ocean

7. Seine _____
   pond   lake   river   ocean

8. Mississippi _____
   pond   lake   river   ocean

9. Euphrates _____
   pond   lake   river   ocean

10. a frog _____
    pond   lake   river   ocean

11. Indian _____
    pond   lake   river   ocean

12. Walden _____
    pond   lake   river   ocean

13. Colorado _____
    pond   lake   river   ocean

14. Karl's _____
    pond   lake   river   ocean

Sorting Land Types

Directions: Match the land type descriptions to the terms.

Answers	Land Type Descriptions	Terms
	1. land covered with trees	A. canyon
	2. land that is much higher than the land around it	B. desert
	3. land surrounded by water	C. forest
	4. land at a slightly higher level than the land around it	D. hill
	5. flat, grassy land	E. island
	6. land that is too dry to grow many plants or trees	F. meadow
	7. deep valley, often with rocky sides and a river running through	G. mountain

Answers	Land Type Descriptions	Terms
	8. very wet land; like a "thick" body of water	H. peninsula
	9. a great many acres that are all flat	I. plain
	10. cold land where very little grows	J. plateau
	11. high land with a flat top	K. river bed
	12. very rich land lining a river	L. swamp
	13. land with water on three sides	M. tundra
	14. grassy area between two hills or mountains	N. valley

Sorting Societal Structures

Directions: Sort the places into the correct columns.

PLACES

Asia	Miami	Utah	Missouri
Denver	Europe	Boise	Spain
Antarctica	Egypt	China	Charleston
Illinois	Stockton	Pennsylvania	Georgia
Africa	America	Canada	United States

Cities and Towns	Countries

States	Continents

Storing Important Papers Safely

Directions: Complete the sentences.

1. I should not keep important papers in a pile in the kitchen because _____

_____

2. The glove box in a car is not a good place for important papers because _____

_____

3. A good place to keep an apartment lease is _____

_____

4. Between a birth certificate and a high school diploma, it is more important to keep the birth

certificate in a safe place because _____

5. A filing cabinet in your house is a good place for very important papers, but a better place is

_____

6. Five examples of important papers are _____

_____

_____

Taking Action When Lost

Directions: Match the sentence beginnings with the sentence endings.

Answers	Sentence Beginnings	Sentence Endings
	1. If you are shopping in a grocery store with your mom and can't find her,	A. try to see if your remote key can cause the lights to blink.
	2. If you can't find your car in a parking lot,	B. remember that you are a stranger to him or her and take care not to frighten him or her.
	3. If you see a small child who is lost,	C. stay in well-lighted areas
	4. If you get lost walking on a sidewalk at night,	D. try walking across and looking down each aisle.

Answers	Sentence Beginnings	Sentence Endings
	5. If you are lost and someone you don't know offers you a ride,	E. stand in a place where you can easily be seen and watch for them.
	6. If you are at the fair with some friends and suddenly realize you have lost them,	F. follow the seating guide signs or ask for directions from someone who works there.
	7. If you are shopping in a mall and lose track of where you are,	G. say "No, thanks," but ask for directions.
	8. If you are in a large football stadium and cannot remmeber how to get back to your seat,	H. find the closest mall directory or ask a store clerk.

Taking Care of Things You Borrow

Directions: Choose the correct choice for each situation.

Answers	If you borrow some (a)......	You should.......
1.		**A.** make sure not to bend it or get it wet
2.		**B.** clean it before you return it
3.		**C.** buy the person some new ones
4.		**D.** fill it up before you return it

Answers	If you borrow some (a).......	You should.......
5.		**E.** make sure not to change any settings
6.		**F.** make sure not to sleep or shower with it
7.		**G.** give the person some of yours at a later time
8.		**H.** return it before you leave the person so you will remember

Taking Part in Leisure Activities

Directions: Fill in the chart with activities you would enjoy.

Amount of Time	Activity
10 minutes	
20 minutes	
1/2 hour	
45 minutes	
1 hour	
2 hours	
3 hours	
all morning	
all afternoon	
all evening	
all day	

Taking Responsibility for One's Own Actions

Directions: Fill in the chart with one possible answer for each situation.

If you.......	How could you take responsibility for your actions?
1. were gooofing around and broke a friend's backpack.	
2. were angry with a family member, threw a shoe at him or her, and broke a lamp.	
3. didn't study for a math test, failed the test, had to miss three basketball games, and your team lost them all.	
4. are looking at a jar of applesauce in the grocery store, you drop the jar, and it breaks.	
5. are talking about your friend, she hears you, and is hurt.	
6. eat some leftover pasta you see in the refrigerator, and a family member comes home and is looking for his or her leftovers.	

Talking to Bereaved Friends and Relatives

Directions: Choose the best thing to say or do.

1. You are at your grandmother's funeral and you see your mother crying
   _____ **a.** Hug your mother without saying anything.
   _____ **b.** Say "Can I get you something?"
   _____ **c.** Quickly move away so she doesn't know you saw her crying.

2. A classmate, Kyle, died in an accident and you are at the funeral.
   You are in the greeting line by Kyle's mother.
   _____ **a.** Say "I'm sure you will soon forget this day and hten things won't seem so bad."
   _____ **b.** Say "Kyle always made class fun. He could make both students and teachers laugh.
   _____ **c.** Smile and say nothing.

3. Your 50-year-old neighbor died of a heart attack. You see his wife in the driveway the next day.
   _____ **a.** Say "Hi Mrs. Wilson. I'm going to mow our lawn this afternoon, so I'll mow yours, too."
   _____ **b.** Say "Did you know he had a heart problem?"
   _____ **c.** Keep your eyes lowered and quickly go into your house.

4. Your uncle died and you are at the visitation. You see your cousin (your uncle's son) sitting by himself staring out the window.
   _____ **a.** Say "What are you looking at, Abe?"
   _____ **b.** Say "Hi Abe. I know this is going to be a hard time.
   How about if we shoot some baskets later this week?"
   _____ **c.** Sit down and quietly stare out the window with him.

5. Your best friend's mother died and you are sitting with your friend at an after-funeral lunch.
   _____ **a.** Say "You look nice in that dress."
   _____ **b.** Say "My mom said to tell you that she will be happy to help you with "Mom" things.
   _____ **c.** Just eat and be quiet.

Talking to the Boss

Directions: Answer each question.

1. You are late to work because you got stuck behind an accident on the freeway.

   When you walk in, your boss is clearly angry with you for being late. What should you say or do?

   _____

   _____

2. You are eating in the company kitchen when your boss comes in and asks, "Why is this place such

   a mess?" It is messy, but you did not make the mess and it is not your job to clean it.

   What should you say or do? _____

   _____

   _____

3. You get to work and realize you left your brief case at home and your work computer is in it.

   You live an hour from work, so it will take you two hours of work time to drive home and get it.

   What will you say or do? _____

   _____

   _____

4. You are at work when a friend calls you and says that an article about another friend and his

   family is in the newspaper. You get a newspaper and are reading the article at your desk. Your

   boss comes by and just stops and stares at you.

   What will you say or do? _____

   _____

   _____

Understanding About Candidates and Voting

Directions: Explain what each picture has to do with candidates and voting.

#		What do these pictures have to do with candidates and voting?	#		What do these pictures have to do with candidates and voting?
1.			8.		
2.			9.		
3.			10.		
4.			11.		
5.			12.		
6.			13.		
7.			14.		

Understanding About Alcohol/Drugs and Driving

Directions: From a local newspaper, cut out headlines about driving and alcohol/drug situations. Tape the headlines in Column 1 and fold them if needed. Then fill in Column 2.

	Headlines	What is one thing you should remember about this article?
1		
2		
3		
4		

Understanding and Dealing with Inappropriate Words and Touches from Others

Directions: Put a check by each situation that is inappropriate.

Inappropriate ✓	Situations
	1. A relative comes up behind you, squeezes your shoulders, and says, "Nice to see you."
	2. A neighbor sees you coming home from school, meets you in your garage, and tries to kiss you.
	3. A teachers asks you to stay after class and then tells you that you are so hot.
	4. A minister tells you that you are growing up into a fine young lady or young man.
	5. An older student tells you to come behind the stage curtains. When you do, he or she rubs up against you and tells you that you are special.
	6. A relative calls you into a closet and touches your private areas.
	7. A teacher tells you that you are a lucky kid to have such pretty, thick hair.
	8. A bus driver pinches your rear end and tells you he would sure like to take you for a night ride.
	9. A coach tells you that you are the prettiest girl (or best-looking guy) on the team and that you deserve special treatment.
	10. Your step-parent often goes in the bathroom when you are naked and says things like "you sure are growing a beautiful body."

Understanding General History Timelines

Directions: Use the timeline to answer the questions.

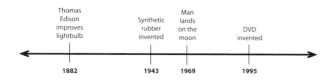

Thomas Edison improves lightbulb — 1882
Synthetic rubber invented — 1943
Man lands on the moon — 1969
DVD invented — 1995

1. On this timeline, which event took place first? _____

2. How do you know whether or not Thomas Edison used synthetic rubber in any of his intentions?

   _____

3. Is it possible that the synthetic rubber was part of the moon landing equipment?

   Explain _____

   _____

4. Do you think Thomas Edison helped invent items for the moon landing?

   Explain. _____

   _____

Directions: Add these events to the above timeline.

5. **1932:** Franklin D. Roosevelt elected president of the U.S.

6. **late 1980s:** Cell phones become common

7. **1914:** First commercial airline flight in the U.S.

8. **1959:** Hawaii became a state

Understanding Good Customer Service

Directions: Read each customer-service situation and then write what you would expect the employee to do or say.

Situations	What would you expect the employee to do or say?
1. You are in a grocery store and you ask an employee where to find the deli.	
2. You are in a department store. You asked where to find sleeping bags, went where you were told, but couldn't find them. You see the same employee and say you couldn't find the sleeping bags.	
3. You call the phone company because you are paying for call-waiting, and it is not working.	
4. You are getting a hair cut and the creative styliest would like to cut your hair differently than you want.	
5. You are eating at a restaurant and have been waiting for your food for 45 minutes. When it finally comes, it is not what you ordered.	

Understanding Living Location Options

Directions: Match the places people live with the descriptions.

Answers	Places People Live	Descriptions
	1. in a half-way house	**A.** housing provided by the Army or Air Force
	2. in a supported living program	**B.** housing where you live alone and have to pay all the bills
	3. with your parents	**C.** childhood housing
	4. in an apartment on your own	**D.** housing for a person who has just gotten out of jail
	5. in military housing	**E.** housing where you get help with cooking, cleaning, and budgeting

Answers	Places People Live	Descriptions
	6. in a group home	**F.** housing where you split the bills with another person
	7. with relatives other than parents	**G.** housing with many individual rooms in a row and without kitchens
	8. in an apartment with a roommate	**H.** temporary housing while the owner is on a trip
	9. in a college dormitory	**I.** housing where several people live together and careworkers make sure everything is going OK
	10. in a house you are house sitting	**J.** housing where you probably have your own bedroom, but share the rest of the space with people you know well.

Understanding Local, State, and National

Directions: Use the numbers to sort the situations into local, state, and national.

1. Northern, Eastern, Western, and Southern Universities all four had more students this year.

2. In Washington D.C. today, the Senate passed a new tax law.

3. The mayor has asked four volunteers to work on SummerFest.

4. The school principals from 20 counties met for a meeting.

5. Car sales are up in 30 states

6. The article in the paper says that your school was evacuated due to a problem with a science experiment.

7. The President held a news conference.

8. your governor is running for reelection.

9. During winter snowplowing season, park on the left side of the street on odd days and on the right side on even days.

Local

State

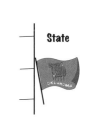

National

---

84 **Social Studies**

Understanding Parking Options

Directions: Use the parking options to fill in the blanks.

Parking Options	
large parking lot	parking spot on a street some distance away
small parking lot	parking ramp
underground parking lot	parking spot on the street in front

1. If you want your car to stay dry in the rain, you should park in a(n)

   _____ or a(n) _____ .

2. If you want to be as close to a small store as possible, you should use a(n)

   _____ .

3. If you park in a(n) _____ , you could be several stories up in the air.

4. If you park in a(n) _____ , you might be able to take an elevator up

   to the street.

5. A(n) _____ will often have signs, such as with pictures of animals, to

   help people remember where they parked.

6. A(n) _____ works well for a small store as long

   as people come and go rather quickly.

7. You will definitely have to walk a ways if all you can find is a(n) _____

   _____ .

Understanding Registrations and Licenses

Directions: A registration is like formally signing up for something. A license gives you a legal right to do something. Sort these actions into the three columns.

Actions	
to bowl on a bowling league	to join a chat room
to drive a car	to sign up for a big event
to have a picnic in a city park	to become a parent
to have a garage sale	to sell real estate
to get a haircut	to wash clothes at a laundromat
to get married	to cut hair

Registration Needed	License Needed	No Registration or License Needed

---

Understanding Special Needs Assistance Options

Directions: Tell what assistance you think each of the following people should ask for.

Situations	Special Needs Assistance He or She Should Ask For
1. Mitch cannot read very well and he is signing a lease for an apartment.	
2. Mya wants to play on a softball team and she has a foot problem that keeps her from being able to run.	
3. Axel wants to get a job, but he has an impulsive disorder that causes him to say things that make it hard for him to get and keep a job.	
4. Heather is blind. She has to take a history test.	
5. Mike is in a wheelchair and he has to take PE.	
6. Benito is deaf and he is taking a lecture class.	
7. Wenyi has a sever shaking disorder, so she has trouble writing and typing, and she has to turn in some long papers.	
8. Adam has trouble comprehending ideas and he has to take the state high school exit exam.	
9. Abigail has casts on both hands. She has to take notes on some articles and share the notes with her group by pasting the notes on an online site.	
10. Taye can't see and each day she has to walk the three blocks between her apartment and her work.	

Understand the 3-Day Right to Rescind a Contract

Directions: Use the October calendar to answer the questions.

OCTOBER						
S	M	T	W	Th	F	S
		1	2	3	4	5
6	7	8	9	10	11	12
13	14	15	16	17	18	19
20	21	22	23	24	25	26
27	28	29	30	31		

1. If you sign a contract on October 17th, when is the last day you can rescind it? _____

2. If you sign a contract on October 1st, when is the last day you can rescind it? _____

3. If you sign a contract on October 7th, when is the last day you can rescind it? _____

4. If you sign a contract on October 23rd, when is the last day you can rescind it? _____

5. If you sign a contract on October 11th, when is the last day you can rescind it? _____

6. If you sign a contract on October 26th, when is the last day you can rescind it? _____

7. If you sign a contract on October 6th, when is the last day you can rescind it? _____

8. If you sign a contract on October 31st, when is the last day you can rescind it? _____

Understanding the Skills Needed to Perform a Desired Job

Directions: Match each school subject to a job where the skill is needed.

Answers	Jobs	School Subjects
	1. mail deliverer	A. English
	2. taxi driver	B. Science
	3. construction worker	C. Social Studies
	4. greenhouse worker	D. Math
	5. secretary	E. Reading

Answers	Jobs	School Subjects
	6. cleaning person	F. Art
	7. tour guide	G. PE
	8. architect	H. Home Ec
	9. dance instructor	I. Speech
	10. bus driver	J. Driver's Ed

Understanding U.S. Road Systems

Directions: Match the road types to the definitions.

Answers	Definitions	Road Types
	1. a road that goes around a city	A. U.S. highway
	2. a road that drivers can't get onto from all roads in the area	B. gravel road
	3. a road that passes through more than one state	C. paved road
	4. any local road not covered in gravel	D. by-pass
	5. any small country road	E. limited-access road

Answers	Definitions	Road Types
	6. a highway that requires a fee from each vehicle	F. local road
	7. a road that passes through more than one state	G. interstate highway
	8. a road that is not a highway	H. two-lane road
	9. a road that is wide enough for two cars—one going each direction	I. four-lane road
	10. a road that is wide enough for four cars—two going each direction	J. toll road

Understanding Wants versus Needs

Directions: Identify each item below as a want or a need.

Wants	Needs	Items
		1. popcorn during a movie
		2. cell phone
		3. shoes
		4. ice cream for dessert
		5. vegetables with your meals
		6. friends
		7. school
		8. brand-name tennis shoes
		9. water
		10. clean sheets

Wants	Needs	Items
		11. candy
		12. vacation
		13. own bedroom
		14. clean house
		15. good grades
		16. backpack
		17. TV
		18. popular clothes
		19. a shower or bath on a regular basis
		20. the right hair style

Understanding Why the U.S. Government Needs Taxes

Directions: Use checkmarks to tell whether or not each thing or location is paid for or supported by taxes.

Supported by Taxes Yes	No	Things or Locations
		1. The school you attend
		2. the local theater
		3. the park that is closest to your house
		4. the roads in your area
		5. food for your meals
		6. your clothes
		7. your car
		8. the local bus system
		9. the local court system
		10. your teachers

Supported by Taxes Yes	No	Things or Locations
		11. the local drugstore
		12. the local newspaper
		13. the college that is closest to you
		14. a local pet shelter
		15. the expenses for your local mayor
		16. the local electric company
		17. a local museum
		18. holiday street decorations for your city or town
		19. a local senior-citizen center
		20. a local homeless shelter

Understanding Your Values

Directions: In each pair, circle the thing that matters most to you and explain why.

The thing that matters most to you is.....		because......
a pet	friends	1.
playing sports	watching sports	2.
having free time	having a great job	3.
money	love	4.
being warm	doing winter sports in the cold	5.
meat	vegetables	6.
being popular	being friendly	7.
having new clothes	going to lots of movies	8.
haivng a class with friends	having an interesting class	9.
seeing pretty or interesting things	hearing good music	10.

Using a Globe

Directions: Use a globe to answer these questions.

1. Tennessee is (**closer to / farther from**) Wisconsin than it is to (from) North Dakota.
2. India is (**closer to / farther from**) Egypt than it is to (from) Spain.
3. China is (**closer to / farther from**) Viet Nam than it is to (from) Japan.
4. Brazil is (**closer to / farther from**) Chile than it is to (from) Columbia.
5. London is (**closer to / farther from**) Paris than it is to (from) Stockholm.
6. The United States is (**closer to / farther from**) Japan than it is to (from) Germany.
7. Los Angeles is (**closer to / farther from**) New York than it is to (from) Tokyo.
8. Moscow is (**closer to / farther from**) Glasgow than it is to (from) Warsau.
9. Australia is (**closer to / farther from**) Thailand than it is to (from) Brazil.
10. Dublin is (**closer to / farther from**) Madrid than it is to (from) Rome.

Using a Mall Directory

Directions: Use the mall directory to answer the questions.

Oscar Department Store | Bo Shoes | Candy & Spirits | Souvenir City | Frames For All | Working Woman | Hats and Socks | Kiddie's Corner | Wilson's Department Store

Pretzel Pit Stop | Rest Room | Bill's Photography Studio | East Entrance | Cute Cards | Teen Tops | Chains and Baubles | Jeans and Skirts | Books Galore | West Entrance | Movies Music & More | Darwin Shoes | Ice Cream Bar | Formal Wear

1. If you are at *Cute Cards* and you want to go to both *Kiddie Clothes* and *Teen Tops,* which one would it make sense to go to first (you are parked by the West Entrance).

   _____

2. You are at the *Oscar Store* and want to go to *Darwin Shoes.* Does it make more sense to go to the rest room now or when you get down by *Darwin Shoes?* _____

3. If you are facing *Hats and Socks,* should you go left or right ot get to *Movies, Music, and More?*

   _____

4. Which shoe store is closest to *Books Galore?* _____

5. Which store is closest to the East Entrance, *Bo Shoes* or *Formal Wear?* _____

6. Where should you look for a necklace? _____

7. Where would you look for something to wear to a prom? _____

Using a Map Legend

Directions: Match the map legend items with the descriptions.

Answers	Descriptions	Map Legend Items
	1. U.S. highway	A.
	2. railroad	B.
	3. two lanes of traffic in each direction	C.
	4. standard two-lane highway	D.
	5. small roads	E.
	6. road under construction	F.
Answers	**Descriptions**	**Map Legend Items**
	7. interstate highway	G.
	8. airport	H.
	9. park	I.
	10. picnic area	J.
	11. campground	K.
	12. rest stop	L.

Using a Road Map or Atlas

Directions: Use a map of the state of Wisconsin to answer the questions.

1. Which highway(s) would you take to get from Green Bay to Milwaukee? _____

2. What city is the capital of Wisconsin? _____

3. What is the longest river in Wisconsin? _____

4. Name the cities in Wisconsin with over 500,000 people.

_____

5. Name a city with under 5000 people. _____

6. Name a state park in Wisconsin. _____

7. Name a national forest or national park in Wisconsin. _____

8. Fill in this chart

City	Is there an airport?	If there is an airport, what is its name?
Madison		
Beloit		
Milwaukee		
Hazel Green		
Oshkosh		

9. Name a four-lane state highway in Wisconsin. _____

10. Name a four-lane national highway in Wisconsin. _____

11. Name an interstate highway in Wisconsin. _____

Using Community Resources

Directions: Fill in the second column with resources in your community.

If I needed or wanted to......	I would go to ....
1. wash my car	
2. get a book to read	
3. play golf	
4. go on a picnic	
5. get a haircut	
6. see some original art	
7. get my computer repaired	
8. get my teeth cleaned	
9. have my wool coat cleaned	
10. get a massage	
11. rent a carpet cleaner	
12. play raquetball	

Using Mailing and Shipping Services

Directions: Match the mailing and shipping terms and pictures to the definitions.

Answers	Definitions	Mailing and Shipping Terms
	1. a private shipping service called United Parcel Service	**A.** C.O.D.
	2. a second private shipping service	**B.** U.S. mail
	3. shipping service that requires the receiver to pay for the shipping when the package is delivered	**C.** U.P.S.
	4. a small locker where you can receive mail	**D.** Fed Ex
	5. government shipping service	**E.** P.O. Box

Answers	Definitions	Mailing and Shipping Pictures
	6. bubble wrap	**F.**
	7. corrigated cardboard	**G.**
	8. flimsy cardboard	**H.**
	9. label	**I.**
	10. return address	**J.**

Using Proper Eating Manners

Directions: Use the words in the box to fill in the ovals.

butter knife	coffee cup	dessert fork	dessert spoon
dinner fork	dinner plate	dinner spoon	salad fork
salad plate	saucer	soup bowl	soup spoon
water glass			

Using Public Transportation

Directions: Use this map of the Washington D.C. Metro to answer the questions

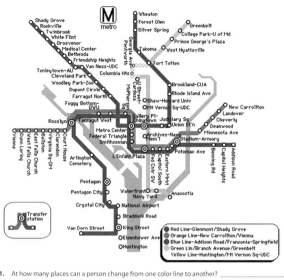

1. At how many places can a person change from one color line to another? _____

2. Use the color letters R (red), O (orange) B (blue), G (green), and Y (yellow) to tell which line or lines you should use to travel between each pair of locations.

Shady Grove to Silver Spring _____   Rosslyn to Minnesota Ave _____

Medical Center to Eisenhower Ave _____   Takoma to Benning Rd _____

the Smithsonian to the Pentagon _____   National Airport to Howard Univ _____

Volunteering in the Community

Directions: List 10 places in your community where you could volunteer. For each, list a task a volunteer might do.

10 Places You could Volunteer	Possible Volunteer Tasks
1.	
2.	
3.	
4.	
5.	
6.	
7.	
8.	
9.	
10.	

Waiting in Line Calmly

Directions: Respond to each possible behavior with checkmarks in two columns.

Possible Waiting-In-Line Behavior	I Have NEVER Done	I Have Done in the Past	A Good Idea	Not a Good Idea
1. Talking to people around you				
2. Yelling things like "Let's go." and "What's taking so long?"				
3. Constantly muttering to yourself "I can't believe this line."				
4. Telling people around you to be quiet.				
5. When others are not looking, trying to move up in the line.				
6. Asking a person by you to save your spot and then leaving the line and sitting down so you are more comfortable.				
7. Sitting on the floor when the line is not moving.				
8. Playing a word game with other people in the line.				
9. Looking at your watch every two minutes and then louding announcing how long you have been waiting.				
10. Reading a book.				

Walking and Driving in Parking Lots

Directions: Use this drawing of a parking lot to answer the questions. Each question matches a numbered circle.

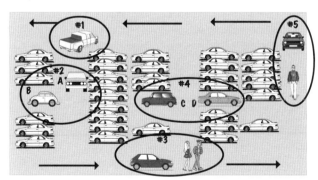

1. The problem with the truck is that it is

    _____ **a.** turning the wrong way

    _____ **b.** driving too slowly

    _____ **c.** driving where cars want to park

2. What should happen here?

    _____ **a.** Car B should wait for Car A.

    _____ **b.** Car A should wait for Car B.

    _____ **c.** The first to move should go first.

3. What should happen here?

    _____ **a.** The people should wait.

    _____ **b.** The car should wait.

    _____ **c.** The car should back up.

4. Who should yield here?

    _____ **a.** Car C

    _____ **b.** Car D

    _____ **c.** the car that started moving last

5. What should happen here?

    _____ **a.** The car should wait for the person who is walking.

    _____ **b.** The person should move to the side so the car can drive.

    _____ **c.** The person in the car should offer a ride to the person who is walking.

Working in a Group

Directions: Put a checkmark next to each idea that is a good group-work plan.

Good Plan ✓	Group-Work Ideas
	1. Let the people with most of the ideas do all the work.
	2. Decide what part of the work you would be best at and offer to do that right away before all the jobs are taken.
	3. Tell your group members that you are busy and need them to cover for you.
	4. Make a written plan including deadlines and who is doing what.
	5. When you finish the part you are working on, quit—even if there is more work to do. This way, you can make sure you do not do more than your share.
	6. If someone in the group is bossy, tell him or her to stop being bossy.
	7. If you are falling behind on the schedule, make a plan to meet and make one last big push to finish on time.
	8. If you want to be the leader, refuse to help unless they agree to let you be the leader.
	9. Brainstorm as a group to figure out what you will do and how you will do it.
	10. If you do not like part of the group plan, refuse to work on that part.

Science

Adapting to Workplace Conditions

Directions: Complete the Sentences

1. If I find that I get cold everyday at work, _____
_____

2. If I am always warm in the afternoon at work, _____
_____

3. If the dust at work makes me cough and choke. _____
_____

4. If the sun coming in the windows next to my desk bothers me, _____
_____

5. If the people I work by talk so much that it is hard to get my work done, _____
_____

6. If my feet get sore from standing all day at work, _____
_____

7. If my work chair is in bad shape and is very uncomfortable, _____
_____

Adjusting Ring Sizes

Directions: Using modeling clay or firmly-twisted pipe cleaners make rings to match the sizes shown. Then fill in the table.

Ring Sizes	Fits Well	Too large	Too small		Ring Sizes	Fits Well	Too large	Too small
Size 4					Size 9			
Size 5					Size 10			
Size 6					Size 11			
Size 7					Size 12			
Size 8					Size 13			

Name of one local business that could size a ring for you:

Asking for Gardening Advice

Directions: Using the Internet, find gardening advice to answer the questions.

1. When should you plant tomatoes in your area? (month and week) _____
_____

2. How do you know that asparagus is ready to pick? _____
_____

3. How do you cut rhubarb from a patch? _____
_____

4. How do you plant peas? _____
_____

5. How can you control pickle vines? _____
_____

6. How much, if any, water should you put in a potato hole when planting potatoes?
_____
_____

Avoiding Bug, Bee, Snake, Mosquito, and Spider Bites

Directions: Explain what each person below could have done to prevent the bites or bugginess.

Situation	What He or She Could Have Done
1. Janie was walking on a path in a forest when she left the path to watch a squirrel and got bit by a snake. What could she have done to lessen her chances of getting bit?	
2. Kevin saw a bee and started swatting at it. He was really upset when the bee stung him. What should he have done to keep from being stung?	
3. Maggie got 15 mosquito bites during the picnic. How could she have prevented the bites?	
4. While sleeping, Brendan has gotten spider bites the last three nights. What could he do so he doesn't get anymore?	
5. Melinda wants to sit on her patio, but it is too buggy. What can she do to make it more pleasant?	

Science/Health 93

Avoiding Unplanned Pregnancies

Directions: Work in a group to list at least five ways to make sure you are not involved in an unplanned pregnancy.

1. _____
2. _____
3. _____
4. _____
5. _____
6. _____
7. _____
8. _____
9. _____
10. _____

Being a Responsible Driver/Car Owner

Directions: Complete the sentences as if you were a car owner. If necessary, ask an adult for help.

1. You should check the oil in your car every

   month   3 months   year

2. You should change the oil in your car every

   month   3 months   year

3. You will need to renew your driver's license every

   year   five years   depends on your state

4. You will need to get new license plates or stickers every

   year   five years   depends on your state

5. You need to have car insurance in case of

   an accident   bad weather   serious illness

6. You need to have new tires about every

   10,000 miles   20,000 miles   30,000 miles

7. On most cars, you should have your brakes checked every

   2000 miles   10,000 miles   50,000 miles

Being Patient with Expectations of Self and Others

Directions: Tell whether or not you can perform each action. If you can't perform an action, tell how you feel about it.

Can you....			If not, how do you feel about it?
1. sing well?	yes	no	
2. run fast?	yes	no	
3. dance well?	yes	no	
4. do math easily?	yes	no	
5. say funny things?	yes	no	
6. sit quietly for a long time?	yes	no	
7. read fast?	yes	no	
8. laugh at yourself easily?	yes	no	
9. do well in sports?	yes	no	

Being Socially Aware

Directions: For each situation, identify the social mistake the person made.

Situations	What mistake did the person make?
1. Darcy wore a sleeveless dress to her cousin's wedding. It was a warm day, and Darcy was hot. Every half hour, she used a paper napkin to wipe the sweat from her underarms so that she wouldn't get her dress wet.	
2. In history class, Jared told Kyle and Dago that he had heard that some idiot had run over two dogs on Milton Avenue. He said the driver should go to jail. Kyle looked upset and said, "I wasn't driving badly. The dogs were chasing a deer and they ran out into the street. I didn't have a chance to stop."	
3. Eva was walking to her next class, and everyone on her side of the hall was going the other direction. They were making faces at her and asking her what she thought she was doing.	
4. Andy got a job as a bus boy in a fancy restaurant. The person who hired him told him to dress all in black. So, on his first day, Andy wore stretch biking shorts, a black t-shirt, and black flip-flops. He was upset that he had to work in the backroom instead of cleaning tables.	
5. Connie heard that Adele was haivng a party. Connie went up to Adele and asked, "Can I come to your party?" Adele looked at Connie and walked away.	
6. George was telling Paul how much he liked last night's game. Paul interrupted and started talking about a movie he had seen. After talking about the movie for a while, George said he was looking forward to Saturday because his cousin was coming. Paul responded by saying, "I have two favorite cousins." He proceeded to tell George all about the two cousins.	

Believing in Yourself (Work and Personal)

Directions: Give this piece of paper to three other students and ask them to write something positive about you. Then, write how you feel about their comments.

Your Name:	
Comments from Classmates	**How do you feel about their comments?**
1.	
2.	
3.	

Breathing as a Way to Deal with Pain or Anger

Directions: Choose the correct answers.

1. When you are in pain, it is best to try to breathe
   _____ **a.** quickly
   _____ **b.** slowly
   _____ **c.** as little as possible

2. When you are angry, the main reason to control your breathing is to
   _____ **a.** calm down
   _____ **b.** to look tough
   _____ **c.** to get up enough nerve to say what you think

3. When you are in pain or are angry, you might have to consciously think about how you are breathing because, when you are upset, you are likely to
   _____ **a.** breathe too gently
   _____ **b.** forget to breathe
   _____ **c.** breathe in a stressful way

4. When you are trying to control your breathing, one thing you should NOT do is
   _____ **a.** listen to what others say
   _____ **b.** sit down
   _____ **c.** put food in your mouth

5. If you are around someone who is in pain or is angry, you might be MOST able to help by
   _____ **a.** reminding them to breathe slowly
   _____ **b.** leaving them alone
   _____ **c.** breathing for them

Caring for Children

Directions: In each circle, write one thing you could do to take care of children.

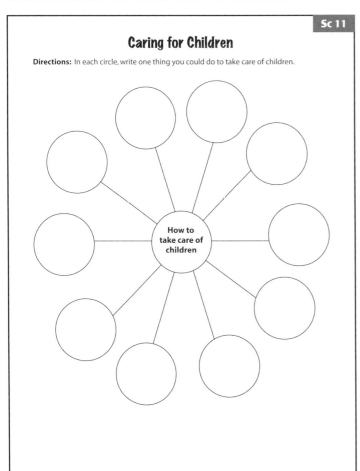

How to take care of children

Caring for Hair and Teeth

Directions: Place a large X over each statement that is a bad idea.

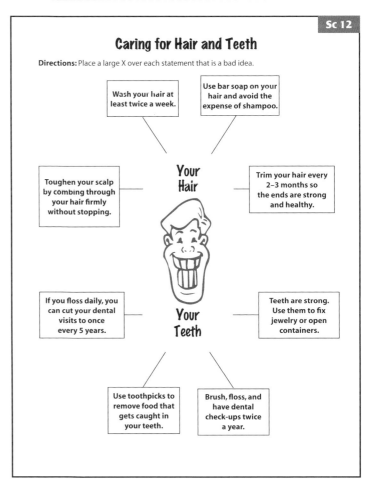

Wash your hair at least twice a week.

Use bar soap on your hair and avoid the expense of shampoo.

Toughen your scalp by combing through your hair firmly without stopping.

Your Hair

Trim your hair every 2–3 months so the ends are strong and healthy.

If you floss daily, you can cut your dental visits to once every 5 years.

Your Teeth

Teeth are strong. Use them to fix jewelry or open containers.

Use toothpicks to remove food that gets caught in your teeth.

Brush, floss, and have dental check-ups twice a year.

Caring for Pets

Directions: For each pet below, identify one example of special care needed for that type of animal.

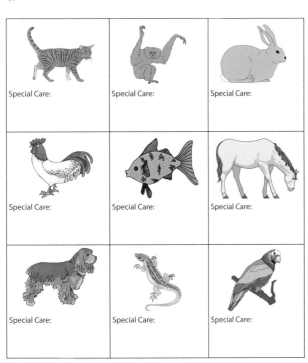

Special Care:

Special Care:

Special Care:

Special Care:

Special Care:

Special Care:

Special Care:

Special Care:

Special Care:

Caring for Self When Sick

Directions: Circle each statement that is an example of taking good care of yourself when you are sick.

1. I am going to take an extra dose of pain medication so I will have the strength to exercise.

2. I have a sore throat, so I am going to stay home tonight instead of going to the game with my friends.

3. I am really dizzy and I have a fever, but I am going to go to school this morning because I have a test.

4. I have an upset stomach, so I am going to have chicken soup for dinner instead of having pizza with the family.

5. I'm not feeling well, but I have been looking forward to this party for a week. So, I'll go to bed early tomorrow night.

6. The doctor said that I should take my medication with food, but I am on a diet, so I'm going to skip the food.

7. I have walking pnemonia, but I don't want to let the team down, so I'm going to run in the track meet today.

8. I think I have mono, but I am not going to the doctor until next week since I don't want to have to stay home this week.

9. I have a nasty cold, so I'm going to rest on the couch and watch TV. I'll wait to go shopping when I feel better.

10. I have odd bleeding, so I am going to make a doctor's appointment today.

11. The doctor said to drink a lot of water. But, I dont' like water, so I'm going to drink a lot of soda instead.

12. I have an infection on my arm, so I am going to keep it clean, put disinfectant on it, and call the doctor if it worsens.

13. I'm not feeling well, but some friends are coming over to play computer games, so I'll be up late.

14. I have the flu, but I am tough, so I am not going to eat sissy food. I'm having steak and potatoes.

15. Since I am just getting over a two-week illness, I'm scheduling short naps into each day this week.

16. I have a cold, so I am going to drink a lot of water, eat some soup, and get some extra rest.

17. I have had a nosebleed for five hours. I think I'll go to the emergency room.

18. Since I sprained my ankle last night, I am not going to take part in the Walk for Health today.

Checking Fuses and Breakers

Directions: Match the fuse and breaker descriptions to the terms

Answers	Fuse Descriptions	Fuse Terms
	1. What happens to a fuse when your toaster shorts out	**A.** melt
	2. What could happen to wires in your walls if your toaster did not have a fuse	**B.** current
	3. The part of a fuse that melts when the toaster overloads	**C.** trips
	4. What fuses prevent from getting to unsafe levels	**D.** filament
Answers	**Breaker Descriptions**	**Breaker Terms**
	5. The part of a breaker that heats up and bends when a refrigerator shorts out	**E.** trips
	6. What a breaker protects electrical wires from	**F.** reset
	7. What happens to a breaker when a refrigerator shorts out	**G.** metal strip
	8. What has to be done to a breaker before the non-working appliance will work again	**H.** surge

Chewing Food Adequately

Directions: Finish the sentences.

1. If you swallow food without chewing it enough _____

_____

_____

2. If you chew food too much _____

_____

3. Two foods that need to be chewed a lot are _____

_____

4. Two foods that do not need to be chewed much are _____

_____

_____

5. It is easier to chew food enough when _____

_____

_____

6. Not chewing food enough can cause a person to choke because _____

_____

_____

Choosing a Car

Directions: Circle each car feature that matters to you when you are buying a new or used vehicle.

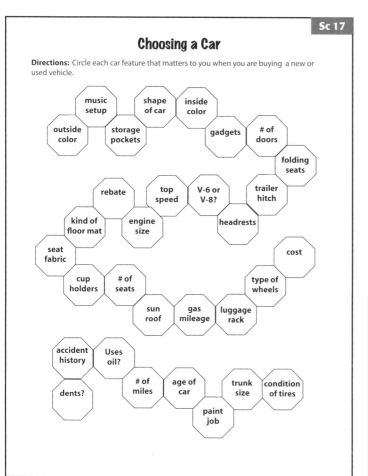

music setup · shape of car · inside color · outside color · storage pockets · gadgets · # of doors · folding seats · rebate · top speed · V-6 or V-8? · trailer hitch · kind of floor mat · engine size · headrests · seat fabric · cost · cup holders · # of seats · type of wheels · sun roof · gas mileage · luggage rack · accident history · Uses oil? · dents? · # of miles · age of car · trunk size · condition of tires · paint job

Choosing Appropriate Clothing for the Occasion

Directions: Describe or draw clothing you own that you would wear to each of the following events.

Interview at a fast-food restaurant	Typical school day	School day when you are giving a speech
Party at a friend's house	Walk on a beach	Wedding
Formal dance at school	Watching TV at home	A service-club meeting with the school principal

Choosing a Protective Place During a Storm

Directions: From each set of three choices, choose the safest place to be during a major storm.

1. • behind a bush • under a tree • behind a boulder	5. • under a bed • beside a bed • in a bed
2. • behind a couch • under a window • in a closet	6. • in a tub • in a shower • in a hamper basket
3. • in the front seat of a car • in the back seat of a car • under a car	7. • in a store inside a shopping mall • in the walkway of a shopping mall • in the parking lot of a shopping mall
4. • in the attic • in the kitchen • in the basement	8. • under a wooden table • under a glass table • under a plastic table

Choosing Comfortable Clothes

Directions: From each set of three choices, choose the item that would be most comfortable to wear.

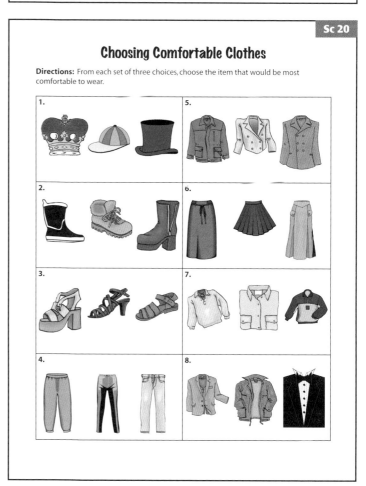

Choosing Cooking Methods

Directions: Write the items from the food box under the cooking methods you think would work well. You can put items under more than one cooking method.

Food					
steak	potatoes	carrots	hotdogs	soup	bacon
eggs	ham	broccoli	chicken	apples	beans
tacos	lasagna	cake	pie	toast	fish
squash	cabbage	pork chops	pizza	hamburger	roast

(stove–fry) (stove–boil) (stove–cook slowly)

(oven–broil) (oven–bake) (toaster)

(grill) (open fire) (slow cooker)

(toaster oven) (electric frying pan) (microwave)

Choosing Correct Battery Sizes

Directions: Match the battery pictures and battery slots to the battery sizes.

Answers	Batteries and Battery Slots	Battery Sizes
	1.	**A.** Size: C
	2.	**B.** Size: AA
	3.	**C.** Size: D
	4.	**D.** Size: 9 volt

Answers	Batteries and Battery Slots	Battery Sizes
	5.	**E.** Size: D
	6.	**F.** Size: AAA
	7.	**G.** Size: 9 volt
	8.	**H.** SIze: AA

Choosing Microwave Containers

Directions: Circle the containers that would work well in a microwave.

(metal) (plastic) (ceramic)

(glass) (glass with plastic lid) (plastic)

(metal with plastic handle) (glass) (ceramic)

(metal with glass lid) (metal with plastic handle) (metal with plastic parts)

Choosing Not to be Taken Advantage Of

Directions: Respond to the following situations by completing the chart.

Situations	Are you being taken advantage of?	What will you say or do?
1. Everytime you buy a new music CD, your friend wants to borrow it. But your friend never buys CDs so you can't ever borrow from him.		
2. Your parent tells you and your sibling to clean the kitchen while she is gone. You do it yourself because your sibling wants to watch TV.		
3. You always take detailed notes in history class. Your friend goofs off during class and then borrows your notes to copy.		
4. About once a month, your friend asks to borrow one of your shirts. She then wears it for a whole month before giving it back to you.		
5. Your friend always wants rides to school and to differnet places, but never offers to pay for any of the gas.		
6. Your neighbors asks you to babysit about once a week. They say they will pay you in a few days, but they haven't paid you for the last two months.		

Choosing not to Pollute

Directions: Choose the correct answers.

1. You are on a walk in the park and you see litter along the walking path. What would be the BEST thing to do?

_____ **a.** Pick it up and carry it home.

_____ **b.** Plan to go back the next day with gloves and a bag.

_____ **c.** Leave it alone since you didn't put it there.

2. You are walking home from school and munching on a bag of chips. When it gets empty, you do NOT want to have to hang onto it. What would be the BEST thing to do?

_____ **a.** Throw it on the ground since you know someone will pick it up later.

_____ **b.** Tear it into small pieces and eat it.

_____ **c.** Fold it and tuck it into your pocket or wasteband.

3. You are walking along the street in your neighborhood and finish eating an apple. What would be the BEST thing to do with the apple core?

_____ **a.** Throw it on the sidewalk since an animal will probably get it.

_____ **b.** Throw it under a bush where it can decay.

_____ **c.** Throw it as high and far as you can.

4. You used a toothpick after your picnic. What would be the BEST thing to do with it?

_____ **a.** Throw it on the ground since it is made of wood.

_____ **b.** Keep it in your mouth until you see a trash can.

_____ **c.** Put it in your pocket until you get home.

5. You are riding your bike down the street when a paper flies out of your backpack. What would be the BEST thing to do?

_____ **a.** Stop immediately and pick it up.

_____ **b.** Pull off to the side, check for traffic, and go back and get it.

_____ **c.** Go on since you did not do it on purpose.

Choosing Workplace Options

Directions: From each set of three choices, choose the workplace option with which you are MOST comfortable.

1.	5.
• wear dressy work clothes • wear casual work clothes • wear jeans or sweats	• work 8:00 a.m.–5:00 p.m. • work 3:00 p.m.–11:00 p.m. • work 11:00 p.m.–7:00 a.m.
2.	6.
• work inside all the time • work inside and outside • work outside all the time	• work set days and hours • work set days, but different hours • work different days, but set hours
3.	7.
• do not ever travel • travel a little • travel several days every week	• work only on weekdays • work only on weekends • work weekdays and weekends
4.	8.
• work with less than fifty people • work with 50–100 people • work with over 100 people	• work at a desk • work where you can move around • work at a facotry station

Clearing Ears in Pressurized Situations

Directions: Tell how you would clear your ears in each situation.

Situations	How would you clear your ears?
1. You are hiking in the mountains and feel yourself getting stuffed up. You have drinks and snacks in your backpack.	
2. You are flying in an airplane and your ears are starting to plug up.	
3. You are in the back seat of a car and the car is going down a steep hill. Your ears feel plugged. You do not have anything to eat or drink.	
4. You are skiing down a mountain, and your ears start to pop.	
5. You are riding in an elevator and have your hands full. Your ears suddenly plug up.	
6. You are parasailing and your ears start to pop.	

Comparing Snacks

Directions: Think of 30 snacks you could eat. Make sure you have ten that fit into each category below.

Very Healthy Snacks	Sort of Healthy Snacks	Unhealthy Snacks

Conserving Electricity

Directions: Explain what Jane could have done differently to save electricity in each situation below.

Situations	What could Joel have done differently to save electricity?
1. Jane turned the TV on at 8:00 a.m. She watched a movie from 8:00–10:30, a ball game from 1:00–4:00, and a sitcom from 6:30–7:00. She turned the TV off at 9:00.	
2. Jane preheated the oven at 5:30. It was quite hot by the time she had the pizza ready to put in at 7:00.	
3. When Jane woke up this morning, she turned the lights on in the whole house. When she went to bed tonight, she turned the lights off in the whole house.	
4. Jane likes to see her photos scroll on her computer, so she has her computer set to stay awake and scroll the pictures whenever she isn't using the computer.	
5. Jane leaves her curling iron on 24 hours a day so that it is ready to use whenever she wants to pick it up and use it.	
6. When Jane feels cold, she cranks the furnace up to 80 degrees.	

Considering Weather when Packing

Directions: Assume you are visiting each of the locations below in the month of January. Make a list of the things you own that you will pack. Use colors to identify specific items.

	Vermont	Georgia	South Texas
shoes and socks			
skirts, pants or shorts			
tank tops, shirts, or sweaters			
jacket or coat			
pajamas			
hats, mittens, and scarves			

Counting Calories

Directions: From each set of three choices, choose the food item with the least amount of calories.

1. • green beans • corn • lima beans	**5.** • water • soda • orange juice
2. • fresh strawberry pie • chocolate cream cake • sherbet ice cream	**6.** • large cheeseburger • taco • one piece of lasagna
3. • chicken • steak • ham	**7.** • popcorn • peanuts • chocolate
4. • cheese • apple • chips	**8.** • celery • potato • tomato

Dealing with Ants, etc. in a Home

Directions: Match the sentence beginnings to the sentence endings.

Answers	Sentence Beginnings	Sentence Endings
	1. If you have ants on your kitchen counter,	**A.** you should call a company that deals with termites.
	2. If you see wood shavings around the edge of the house,	**B.** You should keep the doors shut and windows/screens down and ignore the animals.
	3. If you have a lot of flies in your house,	**C.** you should keep the doors shut and the windows/screens down and use a swatter.
	4. If you have wasps in your house	**D.** you should clean the counter and use an ant spray from a department store.

Answers	Sentence Beginnings	Sentence Endings
	5. If you have maggots on foods on your counter,	**E.** have it professionally cleaned and treat your dog.
	6. If you see ants on the floor,	**F.** call a professional service to check it out.
	7. If you have fleas on your couch,	**G.** you should get rid of the food, clean off the counters, and don't leave foods out anymore.
	8. If you hear noises in your walls,	**H.** spray around the baseboards of the room.

Dealing with Death

Directions: Choose words from the Word Box to complete the sentences.

Word Box			
alone	busy	depressed	flowers
natural	sad	`times	visitation

1. It is normal to feel a little _____ when someone you love dies.

2. If you are feeling really sad because someone died, it is probably a good idea to make plans so you are not home _____.

3. As painful as it is to lose a loved one, it is important to remember that it is a _____ part of life.

4. When people stay _____, they are less likely to get depressed.

5. Sometimes, when a loved one dies, it is helpful to remember the good _____.

6. When a loved one dies, if you are the main living relative, you will probably have to send out thank you notes to people who send _____ or food.

7. When a loved one dies, the family will likely have both a _____ and a funeral.

8. It is normal for a person to feel _____ for days, weeks, or even months after a loved one dies.

Dealing with Garbage and Recycling

Directions: Circle each item that should be recycled rather than thrown in the garbage.

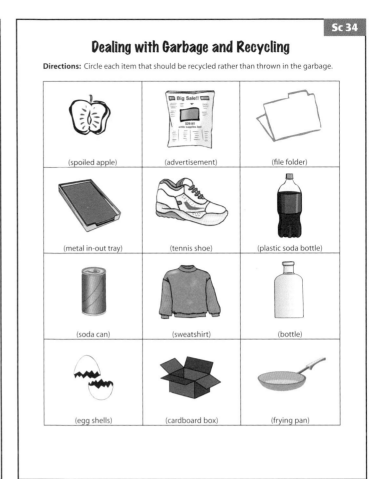

(spoiled apple)	(advertisement)	(file folder)
(metal in-out tray)	(tennis shoe)	(plastic soda bottle)
(soda can)	(sweatshirt)	(bottle)
(egg shells)	(cardboard box)	(frying pan)

Dealing with Leftover Food

Directions: For each food item below, explain how you would store leftovers. Include where you would put the food, what you would put the food in, if you would cover it, etc.

Foods	What to do with leftovers	Foods	What to do with leftovers

Dealing with Stress

Directions: Tell how you would try to deal with the stress in each situation.

Situations	How you could deal with the stress
1. You have two tests tomorrow and you have to study all night for them. Besides that, you are very nervous about doing well on the tests.	
2. It will be your turn to bat after the next two batters. You are so terrified you do not even know if you can walk out to home plate.	
3. You are applying for a job. You have an interview in 30 minutes, and you are sweating so badly that you are afraid the wetness will show.	
4. You have a date tonight, and you are very nervous. You are so afraid you won't be able to think of anything to talk about.	
5. You are in driver's training class, and you have to drive behind the wheel for the first time. You are so afraid that you cannot remember the information you have learned.	
6. You have just received a pass from the principal's office. You are afraid that you are in trouble. You are worried that your nerves will make you look guilty.	

Dealing with Teasing

Directions: Write a response you could make in each of the following teasing situations.

Situations	How you could deal with the teasing
1. You wear a new bright-colored shirt that you really like. When you walk into math class, Josh laughs and says, "Whoa, we can sure see you coming!"	
2. You are giving a speech in class when someone laughs at something that isn't intended to be funny.	
3. You are walking down the hall when someone calls out to you, "Hey fluffy hair, this isn't Halloween."	
4. You are telling a friend that you are getting pretty good at playing basketball. Your friend says, "Good one. Got another joke?"	
5. You take your shoes off at a friend's house and your friend says, "Since when did you start wearing giant shoes?"	
6. You are watching a favorite TV show when a friend calls. You say that you will call back after the show is over. Your friend says he is surprised that you are a slave to such a silly show.	

Dealing with Unusual or Dangerous Odors

Directions: Complete the following sentences.

1. If you smell something that you think might be rotten fruit, you should _____
_____
_____

2. If you think you smell gas, you should _____
_____
_____

3. If you smell something burning in the kitchen, you should _____
_____
_____

4. If you smell something hot in the living room, you should _____
_____
_____

5. If you think you smell something dead in a closet, you should _____
_____
_____

6. If you smell sewage in your house, you should _____
_____
_____

Deciding When to Open Eyes in Water

Directions: Complete the following sentences.

1. If you are taking a shower, you (**should, should not**) open your eyes because _____
_____

2. If you are swimming in a pond, you (**should, should not**) open your eyes because _____
_____

3. If you are swimming in a swimming pool, you (**should, should not**) open your eyes because _____
_____

4. If you are swimming in the ocean, you (**should, should not**) open your eyes because _____
_____

5. If you are bobbing for apples in a large tub, you (**should, should not**) open your eyes because _____
_____

6. If your head is under water in a hot tub, you (**should, should not**) open your eyes because _____
_____

Describing a Person

Directions: Choose a person you know, and use the circles at the top to brainstorm words you could use to describe the person. Then, use the ideas you have brainstormed to write a description of the person.

Person's Name:

_____
_____
_____
_____
_____

Describing Yourself

Directions: Use the circles at the top to brainstorm words you could use to describe yourself. Then, use the ideas you have brainstormed to write a description of yourself.

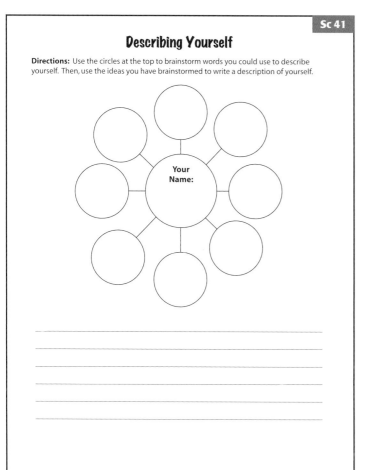

_____
_____
_____
_____
_____
_____

Detecting the Source (Direction) of Noises and Voices

Directions: Work with a partner. Take turns wearing a blindfold and identifying the direction of noises you hear. When you are not wearing the blindfold, move around the other person and make eight noises from the eight positions shown below. Record the correct and incorrect responses of your partner.

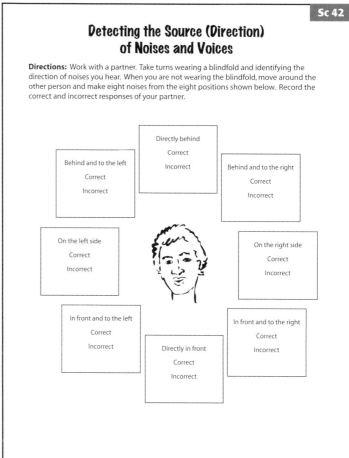

Dieting Sensibly

Directions: With a plan to lose weight, create a sensible menu for one day.

Breakfast

Lunch

Dinner

Differentiating Between Water and Permanent Markers

Directions: Decide whether you should use a water marker or a permanent marker in each of the following situations.

water marker	permanent marker	
water marker	permanent marker	**1.** You want to make a poster that you will hang outside.
water marker	permanent marker	**2.** You want to write on a t-shirt.
water marker	permanent marker	**3.** You are making drawings with a five-year-old.
water marker	permanent marker	**4.** You are writing a message on fabric and want to hang it inside, wash it, and then write a new message.
water marker	permanent marker	**5.** You are writing on plastic.
water marker	permanent marker	**6.** You are writing on paper and do not want bleed through.
water marker	permanent marker	**7.** You are marking jobs in the want ads.
water marker	permanent marker	**8.** You are labeling your gym clothes with your name.

Differentiating Between Wild and Tame Animals

Directions: Circle each animal that is typically a tame animal.

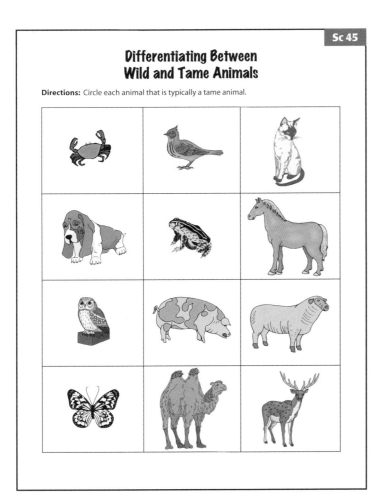

Doing Laundry

Directions: Describe clothing items you own that you would wash with each of the items below.

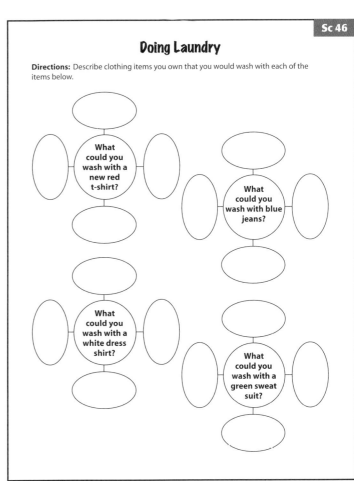

Dressing Appropriately for the Weather

Directions: Cut out the clothes and dress the dark-haired boy for winter and the light-haired boy for summer.

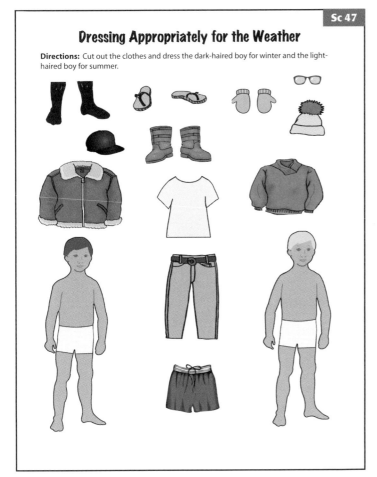

Drinking Enough Water

Directions: Work together as a class to answer the questions.

1. How many glasses or bottles of water do you drink each day? _____

2. Do you think you drink enough water? _____

3. Do you drink water with your meals? _____

4. What time of day do you usually drink your first glass of water? _____

5. What time of day do you usually drink your last glass of water? _____

6. If you were going to drink more water in a day, when would you do it? _____
_____

7. What can you do to help you remember to drink enough water? _____
_____
_____

8. Do you drink more water, less water, or about the same amount of water as the average person in your class? _____

9. Explain why drinking water is important. _____
_____
_____

10. Explain why soda, milk, and/or juice cannot take the place of drinking water. _____
_____
_____

Eating a Balanced Diet

Directions: Create a menu for one day. Make sure you have protein, dairy, fruit or vegetables, and bread or grains at each meal.

Breakfast
Lunch
Dinner

Exercising

Directions: Fill in the empty boxes with examples of ways to exercise for fun (like playing basketball), during your regular work or school day (like walking the long way around the hall to get a longer walk), and for the sake of exercising (like lifting weights).

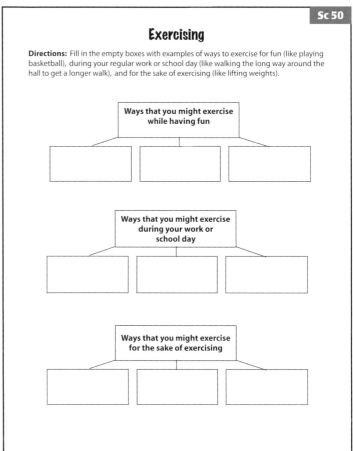

Feeling Differences in Temperatures

Directions: Imagine you are setting up an experiment to see if a blindfolded person can touch items and rank them in order by temperature. Describe the items you will use. If possible, try your experiment with a blindfolded partner.

Temperatures	Item Descriptions
almost too hot to touch	
quite warm	
room temperature	
rather cold	
frozen	

Feeling Differences in Thicknesses

Directions: Imagine you are setting up an experiment to see if a blindfolded person can touch items and rank them in order by thickness. Describe the items you will use. If possible, try your experiment with a blindfolded partner.

Temperatures	Item Descriptions
thinnest	
thin	
medium	
thick	
thickest	

Science/Health 105

Freezing Foods Properly and Safely

Directions: Choose the correct answers.

1. If you buy a frozen pizza, and you are going to put it in your freezer, you should

_____ **a.** keep it in the same package

_____ **b.** take it out of the package and put it in a plastic bag

_____ **c.** take it out of the package and leave it unwrapped

2. As a rule, it is best to freeze food in

_____ **a.** tin foil

_____ **b.** cardboard

_____ **c.** plastic wrap

3. Leftovers will usually keep well in a freezer for about

_____ **a.** one week

_____ **b.** three months

_____ **c.** three years

4. If you are going to freeze some hot soup, one thing you should NOT do is

_____ **a.** let it cool down to room temperature before putting it in the freezer

_____ **b.** put it in the freezer hot

_____ **c.** put it in the refrigerator, let it cool down for a day, and then put it in the freezer

5. Of these three choices, the BEST way to prevent freezer burn is to

_____ **a.** use both a plastic bag and tinfoil

_____ **b.** use self-stick plastic wrap

_____ **c.** use two freezer bags

Getting Enough Sleep

Directions: Getting enough sleep is important. Answer the questions to explain how you react when you are short on sleep.

1. How do you act towards other people when you are tired? _____

_____

_____

2. How do you act in class when you are tired? _____

_____

_____

3. How do you do on tests when you are tired? _____

_____

_____

4. How well do you remember things when you are tired? _____

_____

_____

5. How does being tired affect your ability to have fun? _____

_____

_____

6. How does being tired affect you when you read for fun? For school? _____

_____

_____

Getting Stains Out

Directions: On the top, match the sentence beginnings and sentence endings. On the bottom, match stains with the methods for removing stains.

Answers	Sentence Beginnings	Sentence Endings
	1. Always remove stains before putting a stained clothing item in the dryer so that	**A.** pieces of the substance can smear around and add to the stain.
	2. Remove as much of the staining substance as possible before using a stain remover because	**B.** rubbing it can cause it to spread.
	3. You should always test a stain remover in a spot that will not show because	**C.** you do not set the stain.
	4. You should always blot a stain because	**D.** that is the only way you will know how the fabric and stain will react without risking making a bigger problem.

Answers	Stains	Methods for Removing Stains
	5. ink	**E.** white wine or club soda
	6. blood	**F.** laundry stain remover
	7. grass	**G.** soap and water
	8. mud	**H.** hair spray

Getting the Roots When Pulling Weeds

Directions: Circle the weed-pulling technique that would probably work for each situation. You will likely circle more than one response for some of the situations.

1. Garden dirt the day after a big rain

2. Garden dirt a few days after a big rain

3. Garden dirt that has gone a month without rain

4. Yard dirt the day after a big rain

5. Yard dirt a few days after a big rain

6. Yard dirt that has gone a month without rain

Giving Medical Histories

Directions: Use checks to fill in this medical form. Ask your parents for help if needed.

Do you or any member of your immediate family have the following conditions?

You	Family member	Conditions
		Migraines; headaches; carpal tunnel syndrome; seizure disorder; paralysis; multiple sclerosis; neurological disorders; disorder of the central nervous system
		Attention deficit disorder; anxiety; depression; chemical imbalance; behavioral, emotional, or eating disorder; mental retardation; bipolar disorder or psychosis
		Chest pain or palpitations; heart murmur; mitral valve prolapse; heart attack; stroke; other heart or circulatory disorder or condition; hypertension/high blood pressure
		Varicose veins/spider veins; high cholesterol; anemia; blood clot; other blood disorder
		Asthma; allergies; sinusitis; bronchitis; pneumonia; tuberculosis; apnea; emphysema; respiratory disorder
		Hernia; colitis; chronic diarrhea or intestinal problems; hemorrhoids or rectal disorder; gastroesophageal reflux
		Disorder of the gallbladder, pancreas, or liver; cirrhosis, hepatitis
		Cancer; tumor; growth; cyst; polyp; enlarged lymph nodes; leukemia
		Acne; keratosis; psoriasis; basal cell carcinoma; lesions of the skin or mouth; other skin disorder
		Kidney stones; reflux; urinary incontinence; infection of disorder of the urinary tract, bladder, or kidney
		Breast cyst or nodule; breast disease or disorder
		Arthritis; bursitis; herniated, bulging, or slipped disc; gout; TMJ; injury, disease, or disorder of the spine, back, knees, jaw, bones, muscles, or joints; bunions
		Thyroid disorder; goiter; Graves disease; diabetes; lupus; pituitary or adrenal disorder
		Cataracts; glaucoma; hearing loss; deviated nasal septum; eye, ear, nose, or throat disorder
		AIDS, HIV, or ARC disorders

Guessing People's Ages

Directions: Guess the ages of these people by placing one of these ages in each box: 2, 5, 10, 14, 16, 20, 25, 40, 50, 60, 70, 80.

Age: Age: Age:

Age: Age: Age:

Age: Age: Age:

Age: Age: Age:

Handling Electricity Safely

Directions: Answer each question.

1. Why shouldn't a person pull an electric plug out of a socket by the cord?

2. Why shouldn't a person touch the plug prongs while putting a plug into a wall socket?

3. Why shouldn't a person plug several plugs into one outlet?

4. What is wrong with running an electric cord across a room?

5. Why shouldn't a person plug in a frayed cord?

Having Well Check-Ups

Directions: Answer the questions.

1. What is a well check-up? (Make sure you know this answer before you continue.) _____

2. How often should you have a well check-up with your doctor? _____

3. Why is it important for you to have well check-ups with your doctor? _____

4. How often should you have a well check-up with your dentist? _____

5. Why is it important for you to have well check-ups with your dentist? _____

Science/Health 107

Identifying and Using
Serrated- and Smooth-Bladed Knives

Directions: Circle the knife that would work BEST to cut each item.

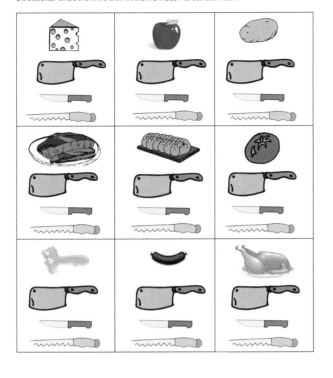

Identifying Smells

Directions: Working with a partner, number ten brown lunch bags from 1–10 and gather ten items that each have a smell. In each bag, one partner should place one of the ten items and then ask the other partner to wear a blindfold and identify the ten items by smell. Fill in the chart as you go. Switch roles and repeat with the items in different bags.

Bag #	Guess about item in bag	Actual item in bag
1		
2		
3		
4		
5		
6		
7		
8		
9		
10		

Identifying Things by Touch

Directions: Working with a partner, number ten brown lunch bags from 1–10 and gather ten items that each have a different feel. In each bag, one partner should place one of the ten items and then ask the other partner to wear a blindfold and identify the ten items by touch. Fill in the chart as you go. Switch roles and repeat with the items in different bags.

Bag #	Guess about item in bag	Actual item in bag
1		
2		
3		
4		
5		
6		
7		
8		
9		
10		

Identifying Things You Shouldn't Touch

Directions: Circle each item you should not touch and explain why the item should not be touched.

	Why should not be touched:		Why should not be touched:
Dead Bird		**Spoiled Meat**	
Keychain on the floor of a public restroom	Why should not be touched:	**Animal Feces**	Why should not be touched:
Battery Acid	Why should not be touched:	**A Beaker with an Unknown Chemical**	Why should not be touched:

Identifying Your Hair as Oily or Dry

Directions: Circle each desription that matches your hair. Cross out those that do not.

- Hair looks kind of wet when dirty
- Hair looks bad if not washed each day
- **Your Hair and Scalp**
- Hair never feels oily
- Might get oil on fingers when touching scalp
- Hair looks OK if washed twice a week
- Scalp is often dry and scaly

Directions: Answer the questions.

1. Based on your choices above, do you think you have oily or dry hair? _____

2. How often do you need to wash your hair? _____
   _____

3. What happens to your hair if you wait too long to wash it? _____
   _____
   _____

Interpreting Weather Reports

Directions: Use the weather report to answer the questions.

Sunday	Monday	Tuesday	Wednesday	Thursday	Friday	Saturday

1. According to the weather report, on which days will you definitely need an umbrella?
   _____

2. According to the weather report, on which days will you definitely NOT need an umbrella?
   _____

3. According to the weather report, on which day will the weather be the most unpleasant?
   _____

4. According to the weather report, on which days should you plan to take a long walk?
   _____

5. According to the weather report, why should you NOT wash your car this week?
   _____
   _____

6. According to the weather report, on which days will it probably be cooler and without rain.
   _____

7. What would you predict the weather will be like on Sunday of the following week?
   _____

Judging the Safety of a Surface When Walking, Running, or Driving

Directions: For each shoe and walking surface set, circle "safe" or "not safe." Then explain why you think your choice is correct.

Shoes and Surfaces	Circle One	Explain Why? or Why not?
	Safe / Not Safe	
	Safe / Not Safe	
	Safe / Not Safe	
	Safe / Not Safe	

Keeping a Car Cleaned and Tuned

Directions: Choose words from the Word Box to complete the sentences.

Word Box

wax	soap	oil
outside	rough cloth	soft cloth
battery	gauge	inside

1. You should NOT use a _____ to wash a car.

2. You should have the _____ in a vehicle changed two or three times a year.

3. You should _____ your vehicle two to four times a year.

4. Your vehicle will stay cleaner if you keep it _____ during rain storms.

5. If your vehicle is _____ during a snow storm, it will likely be quite dirty.

6. You should use _____ and water to wash your vehicle.

7. When waxing your vehicle, you should rub and rub with a very _____.

8. Every two to five years you should get a new _____ for your vehicle.

9. If a _____ is not in the normal ranges, you should have your vehicle serviced.

Keeping a Home Tidy

Directions: Identify three steps you cold take to help keep each of the different rooms clean. Try not to use ideas that could be used in any room, such as dusting.

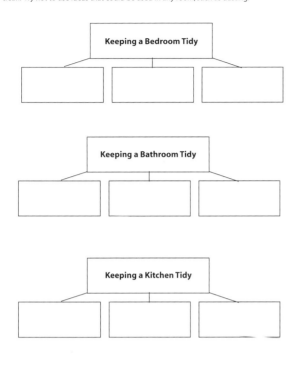

Keeping a Bedroom Tidy

Keeping a Bathroom Tidy

Keeping a Kitchen Tidy

Keeping a Yard in Good Shape

Directions: Number the steps in order of importance for the area where you live.

Order (1–10)	Steps to Keeping a Yard in Good Shape
	Mow the grass.
	Keep the weeds out.
	Trim along the sidewalk(s).
	Water the grass.
	Aerate the grass.
	Fertilize the grass.
	Rake the leaves.
	Rake the grass shavings.
	Add grass seed in thin areas.
	Keep the yard clear of litter.

Keeping Clothes from Shrinking

Directions: Circle the correct answers.

Don't let your clothes shrink because they won't fit you

1. Clothes are MOST likely to shrink in
   (**hot water,   warm water,   cold water**).

2. One way to make sure most clothes do NOT shrink is to dry them
   (**on a clothes line,   in a dryer**).

3. If you are drying clothes in a dryer, they are LESS likely to shrink
   if you take them out
   (**after they are good and dry,   just before they are completely dry**).

4. When using a dryer, (**the permanent press setting,   60 minutes**)
   is LEAST likely to cause clothes to shrink.

5. Of these two fabrics, (**denim,   lycra**) is MOST likely to shrink.

6. Of these two fabrics, (**sweat-shirt fabric,   wool**) is MOST likely to shrink.

7. Of these two fabrics, (**t-shirt fabric,   terry cloth**) is MOST likely to shrink.

8. Of these two fabrics, (**woven cotton,   double knit**) is MOST likely to shrink.

Keeping the Bathroom Mirror from Fogging Up

Directions: Choose the correct answers.

1. The fogging of bathroom mirrors is caused by
   _____ **a.** people breathing.
   _____ **b.** water condensing.
   _____ **c.** water breathing.

2. One way to stop or lessen the fogging of bathroom mirrors is to
   _____ **a.** use hotter water.
   _____ **b.** breathe with your mouth shut.
   _____ **c.** open the bathroom door.

3. One way to clear fogging in a bathroom mirror is to
   _____ **a.** blow the mirror with a blow dryer.
   _____ **b.** stand far away from the mirror.
   _____ **c.** keep the water running.

4. Another way to clear fogging in a bathroom mirror is to
   _____ **a.** stick a piece of paper to the mirror.
   _____ **b.** breathe heavily on the mirror.
   _____ **c.** wipe the mirror with a towel.

5. A third way to clear fogging in a bathroom mirror is to
   _____ **a.** leave the water off and open the bathroom door for a while.
   _____ **b.** remove the wet towels from the bathroom.
   _____ **c.** turn the water knobs so the water runs faster.

Keeping Your Fingernails Clean and Trimmed

Directions: Decide if the nails on each hand are clean and trimmed. Explain your choices.

Explain your choice
_____
_____
_____

Clean & Trimmed?
Yes   No

Explain your choice
_____
_____
_____

Clean & Trimmed?
Yes   No

Explain your choice
_____
_____
_____

Clean & Trimmed?
Yes   No

Explain your choice
_____
_____
_____

Clean & Trimmed?
Yes   No

Explain your choice
_____
_____
_____

Clean & Trimmed?
Yes   No

Explain your choice
_____
_____
_____

Clean & Trimmed?
Yes   No

Keeping Yourself Clean

Directions: Use checks to tell how often you think it would be BEST to do each activity.

Several times a day	Twice a day	Once a day	Once a week	Once every two weeks	
					1. Take a shower or bath.
					2. Put on clean clothes.
					3. Wash your hair.
					4. Brush your teeth.
					5. Floss your teeth.
					6. Wash your hands.
					7. Wash your face.
					8. Put clean sheets on your bed.
					9. Change your underwear.
					10. Wash behind your ears.

Knowing and Following Safety Rules at Work

Directions: Work with a partner to think of a safety rule that would logically be in place at each of these types of work places.

Types of Work Places	Safety Rules that Would Logically be in Place
1. House construction crew	
2. Factory that makes medicine	
3. Insurance company office	
4. High school cafeteria	
5. Roller skating rink	
6. Road construction crew	

Knowing Foods that are High in Proteins, Fats, Carbs, or Calories

Directions: Copy the foods from the Food Box into the correct columns. Use a food chart as needed. Some foods can go into more than one column.

Food Box					
eggs	steak	catfish	bread	chips	olives	cereal
almonds	crackers	cake	ice cream	chicken	baked beans	bagel
swiss cheese	green beans	broccoli	brownies	bacon	potatoes	tuna

High in Proteins (over 20 grams per serving)	High in Fats (over 10 grams per serving)	High in Carbs (over 10 grams per serving)	High in Calories (over 200 calories per serving)

Knowing How to Cook Foods so They Are Safe to Eat

Directions: Read through the Cooking Tips, and then use the information to complete the sentences below.

Cooking Tips
- Some meats, such as turkey, chicken, pork, and hamburger must be cooked completely through to be safe to eat. Other meats, such as fish and steaks, can be eaten less-well cooked.
- Eggs, whether in a mixture or alone, must be cooked well to be safe to eat.
- Vegetables and fruits are safe to eat cooked or raw.

1. It is not a good idea to eat unclooked cake batter because _____

   _____

2. It is OK to eat rare _____ but not

   rare _____ .

3. Eating sunny side up eggs is not really a great idea because _____

   _____

4. It is a problem to cut chicken on a cutting board and then use the cutting board for something

   else without washing it because _____

   _____

5. It is OK to cook vegetables only part way because _____

   _____

6. Hamburgers should be cooked until the centers are no longer pink because _____

   _____

Knowing Kinds of Dairy Foods

Directions: Circle each food on this page that is a dairy food.

Knowing Kinds of Grain Foods

Directions: Circle each food on this page that is a grain.

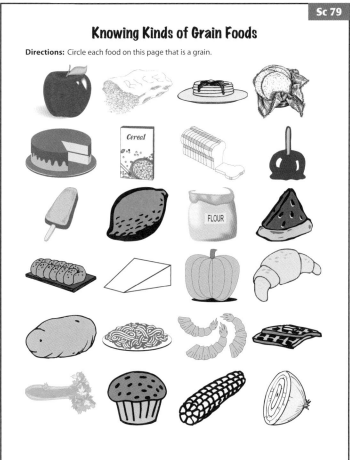

Knowing Kinds of Meat and Fish

Directions: List three different kinds of meat or fish for each category.

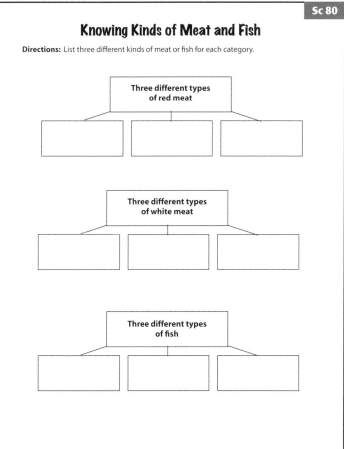

Knowning Main Car Parts

Directions: Explain the location and purpose of each car part.

Car Part	Location and Purpose
1. cruise control	
2. defroster	
3. speedometer	
4. odometer	
5. gas gauge	
6. temperature gauge	
7. radiator	
8. battery	
9. oil dipstick	
10. muffler	

Knowing Parent and Baby Animal Names

Directions: Give the father, mother, and baby names for each animal.

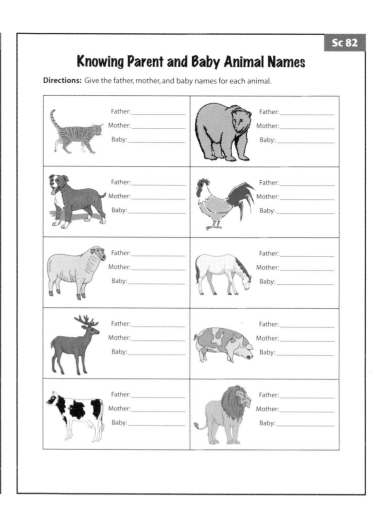

Father: _____
Mother: _____
Baby: _____

Father: _____
Mother: _____
Baby: _____

Father: _____
Mother: _____
Baby: _____

Father: _____
Mother: _____
Baby: _____

Father: _____
Mother: _____
Baby: _____

Father: _____
Mother: _____
Baby: _____

Father: _____
Mother: _____
Baby: _____

Father: _____
Mother: _____
Baby: _____

Father: _____
Mother: _____
Baby: _____

Father: _____
Mother: _____
Baby: _____

Knowing Parts of a Routine Physical

Directions: Answer the questions.

1. Explain the connection between well check-ups and routine physicals. _____

_____

_____

2. Circle each procedure that a doctor might typically include as part of a physical for a healthy person.

blood pressure check	blood test	back massage
surgery	ultra sound	temperature check
bone marrow check	heart rate count	cat scan
urine test	sonogram	lung check

3. Circle each procedure that a dentist might logically includes as part of a well check-up.

teeth cleaning	check for cavities	fill cavities
a root canal	braces application	teeth pulling

4. What can you do if you want a doctor to perform a non-routine test during a physical?

_____

_____

Knowing the Difference Between
Over-the-Counter and Prescription Medications

Directions: Sort the medications into the two columns.

Medications		
headache pills	urinary tract infection pils	cough medicine
sore throat lozenges	high-strength allergy pills	sinus decongestants
thyroid regulator	dry skin lotion	sleeping pills
low-strength allergy pills	wart remover	ear infection liquid

Over-the-Counter Medications	Prescription Medications

Knowing the Names of Fruits and Vegetables

Directions: Name each fruit and vegetable.

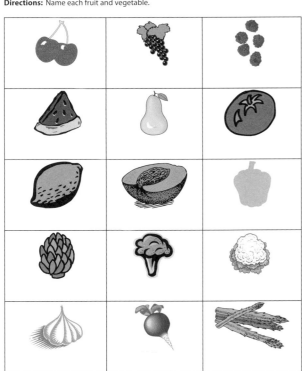

Knowing When to Get a Tetanus Shot

Directions: Use the information in the Tetanus Information Box to answer the questions.

Tetanus Information Box
- Tetanus shots protect you from getting tetanus disease from bacteria.
- As an adult with no puncture wounds, you should get a tetanus booster shot about every 10 years.
- Tetanus bacteria can get into your body through small cuts, but the bacteria is more likely to get in through deep puncture wounds. So, if you get a deep puncture wound, you need to check to make sure that your tetanus shot is current.
- If you get a puncture wound and have not had a tetanus shot in five years, you should get a new one to protect yourself.

1. Say you step on a nail with your bare foot. Your last tetanus shot was seven years ago.

   Do you need a new one? Explain. _____

   _____

2. Say you are cutting a watermelon when you drop the knife and it sticks into your foot.

   Your last tetanus shot was three years ago. Do you need a new one? Explain. _____

   _____

3. Say you were barefoot on your deck and got a sliver. Do you need to check to find out when you

   last had a tetanus shot? Explain. _____

   _____

4. If you do not remember when you last had a tetanus shot, how can you find out? _____

   _____

5. Is your tetanus shot current? (If you do not know, ask your parents.) _____

Knowing When You Need Medical Help

Directions: Decide how to BEST handle each medical situation.

Take care of it yourself	Call your doctor	Go to the emergency room	Medical Situations
			1. You are riding your bike, hit a bump, and fall. Your left knee is all scratched up and bloody.
			2. You fall down the stairs. Your right arm has an odd bend in it. You hurt a lot and are vomiting.
			3. You stub your little toe and the whole toe is black and blue.
			4. It is 11:00 a.m., and you have had a headache since you woke up.
			5. You itch and burn when you go to the bathroom.
			6. You have a sore on your leg and it won't heal. You have been putting medicine on it for four weeks.
			7. You wake up in the middle of the night and your whole pillow is covered with blood. It seems to be coming from your mouth.
			8. A cabinet falls on you and you cannot remember your name, the names of your family members, or what year it is.

Knowing Where Magnets Will Stick

Directions: Identify six surfaces in the classroom for each web below.

Surfaces to which magnets will stick

Surfaces to which magnets will not stick

Knowing Your Body Parts

Directions: Use the words in the Body Parts Box to fill in the ovals.

Body Parts Box

ankle	calf	ear	elbow	finger
forearm	genitals	heel	hip	instep
knee	nose	ribs	shin	shoulder
toe	thigh	throat	thumb	wrist

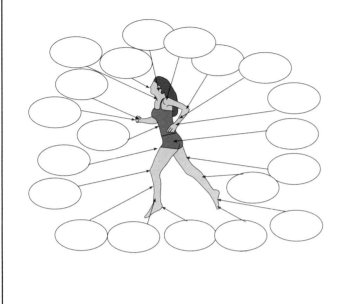

Leaving Things You See in Public Places

Directions: Imagine you saw each of the items below on the floor, on a counter, or on the ground in a public place. Explain why you should or should not pick each thing up. If you think you should pick something up, explain how you should pick it up and what you should do with it.

Items Found in Public	Pick it up? (yes/no)	If you should pick it up, how and what would you do with it?	Items Found in Public	Pick it up? (yes/no)	If you should pick it up, how and what would you do with it?

Letting Scabs Heal

Directions: Use the words from the Word Box to complete the following sentences.

Word Box

bleed	bleeding	doctor's	heal	healing
human	infection	scab	scar	slow

1. Say you have a cut that is bleeding a lot and then it finally scabs over and quits bleeding.

   You should leave the _____ in place to make sure it does not start

   _____ again.

2. Say you have a cut that is scabbed over and has a little redness around the edges. You should

   leave the scab alone to help prevent _____ .

3. Say you have a scab that starts bleeding every time you bump it.

   Your doctor tells you to keep it moist so the scab will come off and not form again.

   Even though you do not like it to _____ , you should follow

   the _____ orders.

4. Even though scabs are ugly, they should usually be left alone since they are a tool the

   _____ body uses to _____

   skin wounds.

5. Picking off a scab can _____ the body's natural

   _____ process.

6. Sometimes picking scabs off can cause a larger _____ than

   you might have had.

Loading Electrical Outlets Properly

Directions: Match the explanations to the terms.

Answers	Explanations	Terms
	1. Can cause heat to build at each joint and result in an extra load at the outlet	A. multi-plug adaptor
	2. Causes an electrical outlet to completely stop working, usually due to overload	B. electrical overload
	3. An electrical plug that has several outlets that are channeled into a single set of prongs that plugs into one socket	C. tripped breaker
	4. When too many items are plugged into one outlet	D. stringing multiple electrical cords

Answers	Explanations	Terms
	5. A warning sign that your outlet setup might be overloaded	E. surge protector
	6. Can be caused by overheating of an appliance that is not working properly or by a surge in usage	F. power strip
	7. A set of 4–6 outlets with its own protective breaker and spike protection and designed to plug into one outlet	G. high electrical demand
	8. A set of 4–6 outlets with no spike protection, with or without a protective breaker, and designed to plug into one outlet	H. warm cord or plug

Making a Regular Exercise Plan

Directions: Make a one-month plan to exercise at least three days a week.
In each time slot where you plan to exercise, write the exercise that you plan to do.

	Sunday	Monday	Tuesday	Wednesday	Thursday	Friday	Saturday
Week 1							
5:00–9:00 am							
9:00–Noon							
Noon–3:00 pm							
3:00–6:00 pm							
6:00–10:00 pm							
Week 2							
5:00–9:00 am							
9:00–Noon							
Noon–3:00 pm							
3:00–6:00 pm							
6:00–10:00 pm							
Week 3							
5:00–9:00 am							
9:00–Noon							
Noon–3:00 pm							
3:00–6:00 pm							
6:00–10:00 pm							
Week 4							
5:00–9:00 am							
9:00–Noon							
Noon–3:00 pm							
3:00–6:00 pm							
6:00–10:00 pm							

Making Choices When Pregnant

Directions: Choose True or False for each statement.

True	False	1. As long as she only has one or two drinks at a time, there is no reason for a pregnant person to stop drinking alcohol.
True	False	2. A pregnant person should plan extra time for resting.
True	False	3. If possible, a pregnant person should try to squeeze into her regular blue jeans.
True	False	4. Pregnancy is a good time to start a new exercise program.
True	False	5. A pregnant person should eat healthy food, but not worry too much about gaining a few pounds every month.
True	False	6. A preganant person should read about pregnancy and talk to other pregnant people so she understands what is going on with her body.
True	False	7. Preganant people should never eat fish, bread, or desserts.
True	False	8. A preganant person can continue doing exercises she has done before as long as she is not uncomfortable.

Making Health Decisions

Directions: Decide whether each of the students should go to school or stay home.

Go to School	Stay Home	1. Candace is very stressed about a test she is supposed to take today.
Go to School	Stay Home	2. Fabricio got hurt playing soccer, and his ankle is so swollen that he cannbot get his shoe on.
Go to School	Stay Home	3. Eddie needs some extra time to study for a big test he has tomorrow.
Go to School	Stay Home	4. Bethany woke up late and feels too tired to get ready in time to catch the bus.
Go to School	Stay Home	5. Josh has a headache and is having double vision.
Go to School	Stay Home	6. Hannah has missed two days of school this week and is still throwing up.
Go to School	Stay Home	7. Bret wants to stay home because his glasses broke and he can't see very well.
Go to School	Stay Home	8. Manu has a loose tooth that will probably come out today.

Making Non-Driving Weather-Related Decisions

Directions: Complete the sentences.

1. If you sunburn easily and are going to be out in the sun for very long, you should _____ _____

2. You should even think about sun protection on sunny winter days because _____ _____

3. When the weather report says there will be no rain, but you see dark clouds in the sky, it would make sense to _____ _____

4. Say you are planning to drive to a friend's house after you finish your homework. Before you get ready to leave, it starts to hail, so you should stay home because _____ _____

5. You are walking home on a rainy day when you come to a sidewalk that is under water and you see floating logs. You should _____ _____

6. You are golfing when you see lightning in the sky. Even though you don't mind golfing in the slight drizzle, you should stop golfing because _____ _____

7. You would like to hang some clothes outside to dry. You look out and see a blue sky with a few white clouds, so you should _____ _____

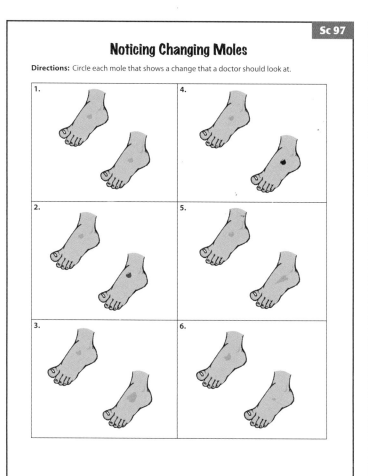

Noticing Changing Moles

Directions: Circle each mole that shows a change that a doctor should look at.

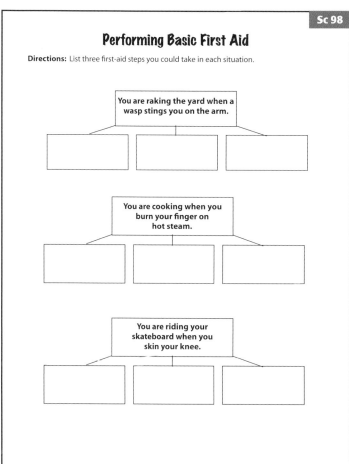

Performing Basic First Aid

Directions: List three first-aid steps you could take in each situation.

You are raking the yard when a wasp stings you on the arm.

You are cooking when you burn your finger on hot steam.

You are riding your skateboard when you skin your knee.

Planning Yard and Garden Work

Directions: For each month, list at least two typical yard work jobs in your area.

Months	First yard work job	Second yard work job
January		
February		
March		
April		
May		
June		
July		
August		
September		
October		
November		
December		

Predicting Whether an Item Will Float

Directions: Predict whether each item will float. Then, use a tub of water to test your predictions. Record your results in the table.

Items	Predict: Will It Float?	Floated	Did Not Float
1. wooden ruler			
2. empty glass jar			
3. t-shirt			
4. full can of soda			
5. empty soda can			
6. dinner fork			
7. small pebble			
8. rock the size of your hand			
9. pencil			
10. pen			

Preparing Food

Directions: Choose a food dish you know how to make. In the top box (the recipe card), write the ingredients. In the bottom box, write the steps explaining how to make the food dish.

Preparing for Season Changes

Directions: Circle the tasks you would probably have to perform for each season change where you live.

Season Changes	Tasks
Winter to Spring	Clean up leaves that were under the snow.
	Trim bushes and trees before they bud.
	Rake the yard to clean up debris that were under the snow.
	Clear debris away from flower beds so perennial flowers are free to bud.
	Plant spring flowers.
	Plant a garden.
	Clean debris from water fountains and bird baths.
Spring to Summer	Make sure the lawn mower is tuned.
	Watch the grass and begin mowing when it starts to grow.
	Plant a garden.
	Get patio furniture out.
	Fill pool.
	Put the snow blower awyay for summer.
Summer to Fall	Trim dead plants.
	Empty pool.
Fall to Winter	Put patio furniture away.
	Empty pool.
	Rake leaves.
	Put the lawn mower away for the winter.
	Make sure snow blower is ready.

Preventing Athlete's Foot

Directions: Match the questions and the answers.

Answers	Questions	Answers to Questions
	1. What type of shoes provide a warm setting that can cause athlete's foot to grow?	A. flip flops
	2. What is a damp place where athlete's foot spreads easily?	B. tennis shoes
	3. What should you wear to protect yourself from athlete's foot in a group shower?	C. locker room
	4. What is a fairly dry place where athlete's foot often spreads due to large numbers of people?	D. group showers

Answers	Questions	Answers to Questions
	5. How can you treat athlete's foot?	E. itchy
	6. What is one thing that will make athlete's foot worse?	F. keep foot dry and use special spray medicine
	7. How does athlete's foot feel?	G. wear socks that are damp from a wet floor or from sweat
	8. What does athlete's foot do that is a particular problem for sport's teams?	H. spreads easily and quickly

Preventing Household Problems

Directions: Complete the chart to explain how to prevent some household problems.

Household Problems	What could be causing the problem?	How could you prevent such a problem?
1. Your water bill is twice as high as usual.		
2. You can feel cold air coming in around the window in your bedroom.		
3. You have fallen twice because you slipped on the wet floor in front of the refrigerator.		
4. When you open the refrigerator door, a bad smell comes out.		
5. The hanging rod in your closet is so bent that you think it might break.		
6. You have two plants and they both often look droopy.		

Protecting a Kitchen Counter

Directions: Match the definitions and explanations to the terms.

Answers	Definitions	Terms
	1. Kitchen counter material made of a large sheet of rock on which hot pans can be set	**A.** formica
	2. Kitchen counter material that looks like rock, but is man-made and might be harmed by heat	**B.** granite
	3. Kitchen counter material that is the least expensive and least able to handle heat and sharp objects	**C.** tile
	4. Kitchen counter material made of small ceramic pieces on which hot pans can be set.	**D.** manufactured stone product

Answers	Explanations	Terms
	5. Must use to protect some counters from being cut	**E.** hot pad, mat, or board
	6. Should always throw away instead of leaving on counters since could cause counters to discolor.	**F.** cutting board
	7. Must use to protect some counters from heat	**G.** food colorings
	8. Should be very careful when using since could cause counters to discolor.	**H.** spoiled foods

Protecting Against Frost Bite

Directions: Explain how you could protect each identified body part from frost bite.

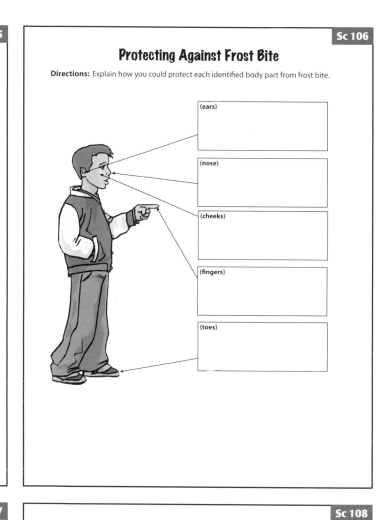

(ears)

(nose)

(cheeks)

(fingers)

(toes)

Protecting Your Ears From Loud Noises

Directions: Match the sentence beginnings to the sentence endings.

Answers	Sentence Beginnings	Sentence Endings
	1. If you pay to get into a dance, really want to be there, but find that the music is too loud,	**A.** you are most likely playing it too loudly to sit in the same room with it.
	2. If you are playing your music and you can hear it from two rooms away	**B.** you cannot adjust to loud noises and will likely lose some hearing if you do not use protection.
	3. Some people think that, if you are around loud noises a lot, your ears get used to it and it is not a problem. But, actually	**C.** you most likely have the volume too high and could damage your hearing.
	4. If you often listen to your music with ear phones and cannot hear people talking to you,	**D.** you could at least stay as far away from the speakers as possible and leave the room now and then to get a break.

Answers	Sentence Beginnings	Sentence Endings
	5. If you know ahead of time you will be in a situation with very loud noises,	**E.** you could roll a piece of the tissue and use it for ear plugs.
	6. If you are caught by surprise and find yourself in a situation with very loud noises and you have a tissue in your pocket,	**F.** you could cover your ears with your hands.
	7. If you are caught by surprise and find yourself in a situation with very loud noises and have nothing with you,	**G.** there is nothing you can do about it after the fact.
	8. If you are caught by surprise by a single very loud noise	**H.** you should take ear plugs with you.

Protecting Your Skin

Directions: Explain how you could protect your skin from each situation.

How can you protect your skin from the sun?	How can you protect your skin from daily hand and dish washing?	How can you protect your skin from possible rashes from harsh chemicals?
How can you protect your skin from dirt and mud?	How can you protect your skin from rough things?	How can you protect your skin from cold weather?
How can you protect your skin from cleaning products?	How can you protect your skin from scratchy fabrics?	How can you protect your skin from strong winds?

Putting Batteries in Correctly

Directions: In each set, circle the battery that is aligned correctly with the battery slot.

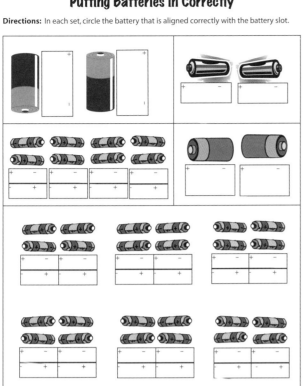

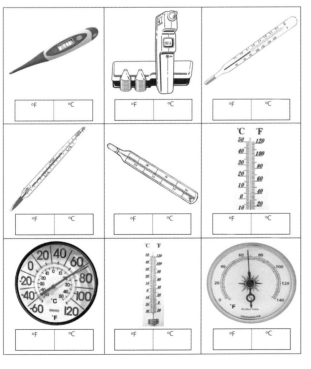

Reacting When Something Breaks or Spills

Directions: Complete these sentences.

1. Since honey is so sticky, if you spill it on the floor, you should _____

2. Even though ice doesn't seem to be much of a problem, you should always pick it up when you drop it because _____

3. If you drop a deck of cards on the floor, it doesn't really hurt anything, but you should _____

4. Say you are eating gravy when you spill a little on the floor. Even though it is near the cupboard where you won't walk in it, you should clean it up because _____

5. Say you drop some jello on a rug, but it sort of matches the rug color so it doesn't show much. You should use soap and water to clean the rug because _____

6. Since glass can shatter and pieces can fly out, if you break a glass item on the kitchen floor, you should _____

7. If you are staying in someone's house and part of the bed post breaks, you should _____

8. If you drop and break a glass bottle on a path in the park and know you won't be walking there again, you should clean it up anyhow because _____

Reading a Thermometer

Directions: Read the temperature information on each thermometer and write the temperatures in the °F and °C boxes. Mark an "X" in a box when no answer is possible.

°F	°C

°F	°C

°F	°C

°F	°C

°F	°C

°F	°C

°F	°C

°F	°C

°F	°C

Recognizing a Safe Tire Tread

Directions: Circle each tire that has tread that appears to be safe for driving.

Recognizing Common Baking Ingredients

Directions: Using either words or a drawing, describe the appearance of each common baking ingredient listed below.

shortening	flour	vanilla
soda	baking powder	cinnamon
sugar	brown sugar	powdered sugar
salt	nutmeg	cream of tartar

Recognizing Durable Materials

Directions: In each set, circle the item made of the most durable material.

thin-plastic bowl metal bowl thick-plastic bowl	stone tile glass tile ceramic tile	cotton shorts silk shorts denim shorts
wicker basket wire basket cloth basket	wool rug straw rug polyester rug	paperback book hardback book spiral-bound book
plastic car mat wool car mat paper car mat	hard plastic glass soft plastic glass throw-away plastic glass	wooden picture frame metal picture frame plastic picture frame
plastic-wrap in picture frame acrylic in picture frame glass in picture frame	leather chair cloth chair vinyl chair	real flowers silk flowers plastic flowers

Recognizing Noise Overload

Directions: Circle each noise source that could be so loud that too much of it could harm your hearing.

Recognizing Proper Posture

Directions: Proper posture should be centered and symmetrical. Explain what makes each person's posture not proper.

Why isn't this posture proper?	Why isn't this posture proper?
Why isn't this posture proper?	Why isn't this posture proper?
Why isn't this posture proper?	Why isn't this posture proper?

Respecting Nature

Directions: Complete the following sentences.

1. Throwing a candy wrapper on the ground is not respecting nature because _____

2. Walking across the grass instead of on the paved paths is not repsecting nature because

3. Dumping car oil in your back yard is not respecting nature because _____

4. Watering your lawn during a drought-induced watering ban is not respecting nature because

5. Recycling paper is an example of respecting nature because _____

6. Not picking wild flowers is an example of respecting nature because ___ _____

Responding to Emergencies

Directions: Decide how you would handle these emergencies.

1. Say you are riding in a car when it is rear ended by the car behind you. Your car twirls around in the road, lands in the ditch, and comes to a stop. You think you are OK, but the driver is not moving. → What would you do?

2. Say you are in the grocery store when a woman with a young child in her car comes down the aisle you are in. The woman leaves her cart to get something. The young child falls out of the cart right beside you. → What would you do?

3. Say you are home alone and are cutting a piece of carpet when you slip and cut your leg quite badly. You feel like throwing up and think you might pass out. → What would you do?

4. You are in a car going down the road when you see an accident about a half mile ahead. You are able to stop, and you see that some people are hurt. → What would you do?

5. You are swimming and diving with a friend in her backyard pool. She dives in, hits her head, and is at the bottom of the pool. → What would you do?

Ridding Hair and Clothes of Static Electricity

Directions: Match the sentence beginnings to the sentence endings.

Answers	Places People Live	Descriptions
	1. Since rubbing your hands or feet on a carpet will build static electricity,	A. when you take it off, electrons can move to your hair and create static electricity.
	2. When electrons move from one item to another, static electricity is formed. So, if you have a hat on,	B. you can lessen the static eletricity by taking clothes out of the dryer when they are still slightly damp.
	3. Static electricity increases when the heat is on in a building because the air is dry,	C. so you could lower the static electricity by touching a water faucet or a metal chair.
	4. Touching a grounded metal object can control static electricity,	D. one way to avoid static electricity is to try not to drag your feet along the carpet.
	5. Since dryness builds static electricity in clothes,	E. so you can use a humidifier to lower the static electricity.
Answers	Places People Live	Descriptions
	6. Static electricity increases when the air inside a building is dry,	F. so you could try opening the window to lower the static electricity.
	7. Fabric softeners can lessen static electricity,	G. so rubbing a fabric softener sheet on the carpet can result in less static eletricity.
	8. You can buy anti-static sprays	H. that you can spray on your clothes or carpet to control static electricity.
	9. Since metal can equalize static electricity,	I. you can rub your wet hands on your clothes or skin to control static electricity in clothes.
	10. Since a little dampness can control static electricity,	J. you can take the static electricty out of clothes by rubbing them with a metal hanger.

Searching for a Reason a Flashlight Will Not Work

Directions: Complete the following sentences to explain reasons that flashlights might not work.

1. If a flashlight will not work and you can hear the batteries rattling around inside the flashlight, _____

2. If a large flashlight will not work and it seems to be very lightweight, _____

3. If you put new batteries in a flashlight and it doesn't work, you should go back and check to make sure _____

4. If your flashlight is not working when you flip the largest of the two switches, you should _____

5. Say you have a flashlight that needs batteries. You find some batteries in the back of a cupboard drawer and put them in, but the flashlight still won't work. One thing to check is _____

6. If you have carefully checked that the batteries are placed correctly and the flashlight still doesn't work, one thing that could be missing is the _____

Setting and Following a Routine

Directions: It is usually easier to stay organized if you have a regular routine. Describe a regular weekday routine and a regular weekend routine that would work for you.

Weekday Routine	Weekend Routine

Starting to Eat After Having Been Sick

Directions: Use the numbers 1–12 to rank the foods below in order from best to worst to eat after having had the flu.

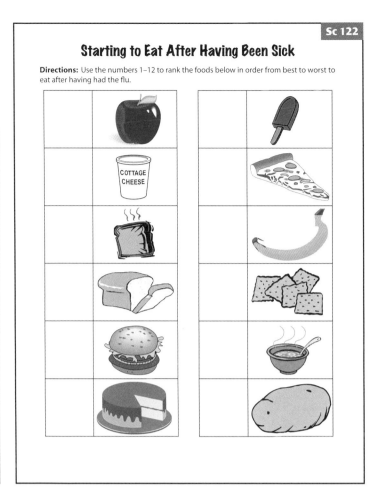

Storing Food

Directions: Use the cupboard, refrigerator, and freezer to put the groceries away.

Groceries

apples	bag of ice	bananas	bread
box of cereal	cake mix	canned peaches	canned peas
canned soup	cheddar cheese	cinnamon	frozen bread dough
fresh broccoli	frozen green beans	frozen pizza	hamburger
ice cream	milk	mixed nuts	orange juice
peanut butter	popsicles	sherbet bars	Swiss cheese

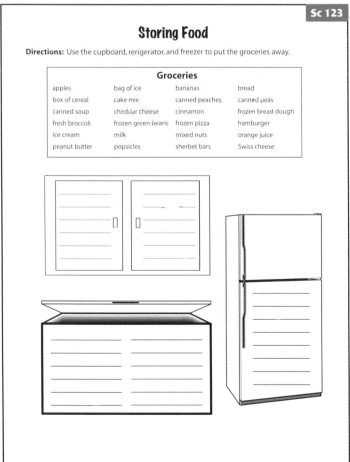

Taking a Child for Proper Medical Care

Directions: Complete each sentence.

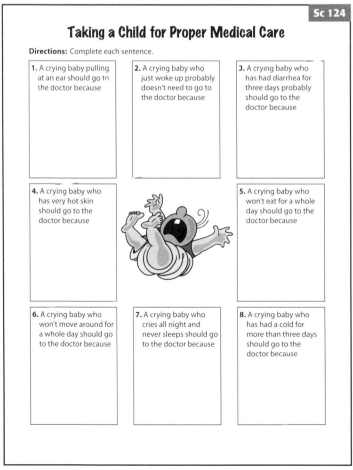

1. A crying baby pulling at an ear should go to the doctor because

2. A crying baby who just woke up probably doesn't need to go to the doctor because

3. A crying baby who has had diarrhea for three days probably should go to the doctor because

4. A crying baby who has very hot skin should go to the doctor because

5. A crying baby who won't eat for a whole day should go to the doctor because

6. A crying baby who won't move around for a whole day should go to the doctor because

7. A crying baby who cries all night and never sleeps should go to the doctor because

8. A crying baby who has had a cold for more than three days should go to the doctor because

Taking Action in Response to TV and Radio Weather Warnings

Directions: Answer the questions.

1. You are planning to run five miles in the park when you see in the paper that it is going to be a cloudy day. Should you go for your run? Explain. _____

_____

2. You are planning to have a picnic with your cousins and your grandmother when you hear on the radio that the area is expecting severe thunderstorms. Should you go ahead with your plans? Explain. _____

_____

3. You are planning to go tubing in a local river with some friends when you hear on the TV that your area is going to have a high of 70°. Should you go tubing? Explain. _____

_____

4. You are planning to drive 30 miles to watch a ball game when you hear on the radio that a snow blizzard is going to hit in about an hour. Should you go to the game? Explain. _____

_____

5. You are planning to plant tomatoes when you hear on the TV that a hailstorm is headed your way. Should you plant the tomatoes? Explain. _____

_____

Taking Care of Indoor Plants

Directions: Choose the correct answers.

1. One good way to protect a plant's roots from getting too much water at once is to
   _____ **a.** only water after the leaves start to fall.
   _____ **b.** put rocks in the bottom of the pot before adding the soil.
   _____ **c.** pull the dirt away from the roots.

2. Since it is easy to forget to water plants, a good plan is to
   _____ **a.** water them every day.
   _____ **b.** always soak all plants thoroughly so they can last a long time.
   _____ **c.** water on a regular schedule.

3. It is important to make sure plants are in pots that are big enough so the roots do not become
   _____ **a.** bigger than the leaves.
   _____ **b.** root bound.
   _____ **c.** too large.

4. When you buy a new plant at a discount store, there is a good chance that
   _____ **a.** you will have to add some good soil.
   _____ **b.** you will pay more than it is worth.
   _____ **c.** it will be a tiny plant.

5. You can tell it is time to water a plant if you stick your thumb an inch into the dirt and
   _____ **a.** the dirt is dry.
   _____ **b.** the dirt is wet.
   _____ **c.** the dirt sticks to your thumb.

Taking Medication on Time

Directions: List three ways you can remember to take medication at each of the times shown below.

Ways to remember to take medication in the morning.

Ways to remember to take medication with meals.

Ways to remember to take medication at bedtime.

Taking Medication Safely

Directions: Use the information from the two medicine labels to answer the questions.

When using this product
- you may get drowsy
- avoid alcoholic drinks
- avoid use of tranquilizers, sedatives, and alcohol since they may cause additional drowsiness
- you may have impaired vision

1. Is it safe to drive while taking this medication? Explain. _____

_____

2. If you take the medication before you go to bed when being drowsy does not matter, is it OK to drink alcohol with it? Explain. _____

_____

WARNINGS: Unless directed by a doctor, do not take this medication if you have a breathing problem, such as asthma or chronic bronchitis, have glaucoma, or have an enlarged prostate that causes difficulty in urination. May cause severe drowsiness. Do not take this medication with alcohol. Unless directed by a doctor, do not take this medication when taking other medication. Not for frequent or prolonged use. Do not exceed recommended dosages. Do not give to children under 10 unless directed by a doctor. Not for children under two years of age.

3. Is it OK for a person with glaucoma to take this medication? Explain. _____

_____

4. Explain all the problems with a parent deciding to give a 10-year-old asthmatic child this medication along with some pills for a headache. _____

_____

_____

_____

Thawing Frozen Foods Safely

Directions: It is safest to thaw foods slowly at a cool temperature or quite quickly at a hot temperature. Circle each picture that shows a safe way to thaw food.

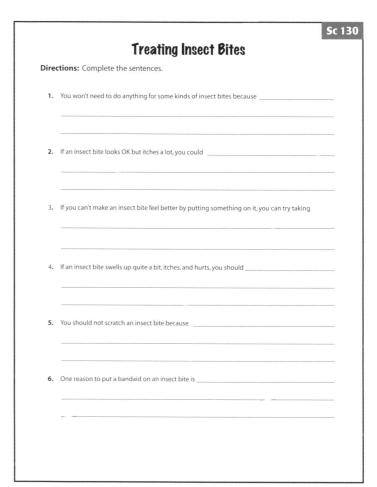

Treating Insect Bites

Directions: Complete the sentences.

1. You won't need to do anything for some kinds of insect bites because _____

_____

_____

2. If an insect bite looks OK but itches a lot, you could _____

_____

_____

3. If you can't make an insect bite feel better by putting something on it, you can try taking

_____

_____

4. If an insect bite swells up quite a bit, itches, and hurts, you should _____

_____

_____

5. You should not scratch an insect bite because _____

_____

_____

6. One reason to put a bandaid on an insect bite is _____

_____

Trying Not to Spread an Illness

Directions: Explain how each of the pictures relates to spreading an illness.

Turning Car Off at Gas Pump or Inside Garage

Directions: Study the pictures to answer the questions.

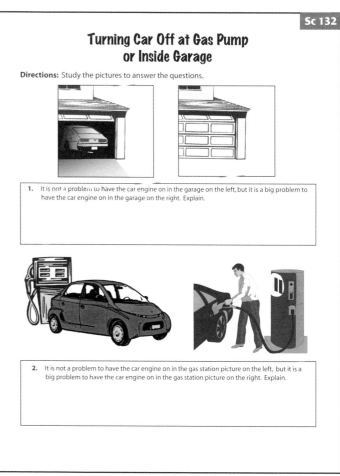

1. It is not a problem to have the car engine on in the garage on the left, but it is a big problem to have the car engine on in the garage on the right. Explain.

2. It is not a problem to have the car engine on in the gas station picture on the left, but it is a big problem to have the car engine on in the gas station picture on the right. Explain.

Science/Health 125

Understanding Causes of Stress

Directions: List things in your life that cause you to feel stress.

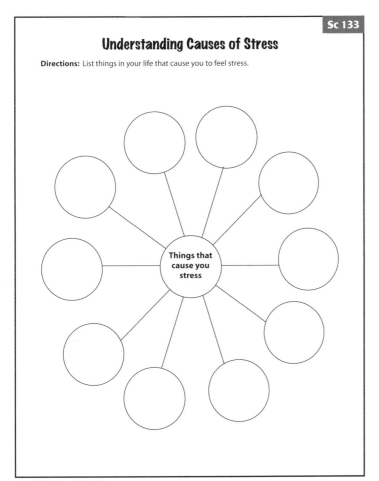

Things that cause you stress

Understanding Common Illnesses and Diseases

Directions: Match the definitions to the illnesses and diseases.

Answers	Definitions	Illnesses/Diseases
	1. Swelling of the bronchial tubes caused by infection or irritation	A. flu
	2. A disease of the immune system that enters the body through the blood system	B. common cold
	3. A respiratory disorder that includes sneezing, coughing, a runny nose, and/or a sore throat.	C. bronchitis
	4. An infection of the throat that includes fever and swollen tonsils	D. AIDS
	5. A contagious viral infection that often includes common cold symtoms as well as vomiting.	E. strep throat
Answers	**Definitions**	**Illnesses/Diseases**
	6. Inflammation and congestion of the lungs	F. cancer
	7. A respiratory problem often caused by allergies and including difficult breathing, congestion, and coughing	G. pneumonia
	8. Growths or tumors that invade surrounding tissues and cause serious physical problems	H. diabetes
	9. A metabolic disorder where the body has a problem with insulin and sugar balance	I. hardening of the arteries
	10. A build up of plaque in artery walls resulting in clogged arteries and blood flow problems	J. asthma

Understanding Heredity

Directions: Complete this chart. If needed, ask your family members for help. Look for traits you inherited and from where you inherited them.

	Eye Color	Hair Color	Complexion	height
You				
Mother				
Sibling				
Sibling				
Sibling				
Father				
Pateranl Grandmother				
Paternal Grandfather				
Maternal Grandmother				
Maternal Grandfather				
Paternal Aunt				
Paternal Uncle				
Maternal Aunt				
Maternal Uncle				

Understanding Hospital Conditions

Directions: Match the patient descriptions to the hospital conditions.

Answers	Patient Descriptions	Hospital Conditions
	1. The patient has a clear problem, but will not require an overnight stay	A. good
	2. The patient ill need to remain in the hospital for a few days to get the problem under control	B. fair
	3. The patient has no apparent serious problem and is likely to be released immediately	C. stable
	4. The patient's body seems to be dealing with the problem and all vitals are normal; Likely to be relieased tomorrow	D. serious
Answers	**Patient Descriptions**	**Hospital Conditions**
	5. The patient is not conscious.	E. guarded
	6. The patient will need round-the-clock hospital care for some time, but the long-term prognosis is good.	F. critical
	7. Within the next few hours, patient is likely to take a turn for the better, but is somewhat unstable right now.	G. life threatening
	8. The patient has serious complications and has a 50-50 chance of survival.	H. non-responsive

Understanding How to Practice Safe Sex

Directions: Complete the sentences.

1. Before you have sex with a new partner, you should both get tested. What does this mean and
    why should you do it? _____
    _____
    _____

2. By limiting your sexual activity to one person, you _____
    _____
    _____

3. If you ever have sex with someone you do not know has tested safely, you should make sure
    to use _____
    _____
    _____

4. Many birth control methods, such as the pill, the patch, and a diaphragm, will protect you from
    getting pregnant, but not from _____
    _____
    _____

Understanding Light Bulbs

Directions: For many years, standard household light bulbs were incandescent bulbs. Now, compact flourescent bulbs have become popular because they are much more eficient and long lasting. For each bulb below, tell if you have seen one like it before. And, if so, where? (Tip: 14 watt flourescent = light output of a 65-watt incandescent)

Light Bulbs	Seen Before?	If so, where?
Fluroescent tube light	Yes / No	
14-watt compact fluorescent light bulb (equals light output of a 65-watt incandescent bub	Yes / No	
60-watt incandescent light bulb	Yes / No	
90-watt incandescent floodlight	Yes / No	

Understanding Optical Illusions

Directions: Optical illusions are images that are tricky or misleading to the human eye. Study the following images and answer the questions.

How many legs does the elephant have?

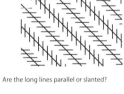

Are the long lines parallel or slanted?

How many black dots do you see?

Describe the dark images.

Describe the light image.

Is the person young or old?

What does the word say?

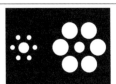

Which center circle is bigger?

Understanding Puberty and Aging

Directions: Sort the body changes into the chart. Chart key: m = male; f = female

Body Changes		
facial hair grows (m)	voice lowers (m)	often get a little shorter
start to perspire	pubic hair grows	bones break more easily
breasts develop (f)	muscles decrease	head/body proportion changes
reach adult height	hearing decreases	advanced muscles develop
vision decreases	periods start (f)	weight increases about 10 times
basic muscles develop	most teeth grow	head hair grows thicker

From Birth to Age 12	From Age 12 to Age 25	From Age 25 and Up

Understanding Talking and Traveling

Directions: When you travel on a bus or airplane, you often end up sitting next to and talking to strangers. Make a list of topics that it would be OK to talk to strangers about and topics that you should not share with strangers.

OK to Talk About	Should Not Share

Understanding the Diet Implications of Eating at Home Versus at Restaurants

Directions: For each food issue, circle "more" or "less" in both the *Eating at Home* and *Eating at Restaurants* categories. In each case, if one is more, the other will be less. By circling the answer in both categories, you end up with an overview of each category.

Food Issues	Eating at Home		Eating at Restaurants	
Calories	more	less	more	less
Portion sizes	more	less	more	less
Number of different food items	more	less	more	less
Healthiness	more	less	more	less
Cost	more	less	more	less

Understanding the Four Seasons

Directions: Think about how the seasons are different from each other where you live. Fill in the chart by checking each season for which each statement is true. If the answer is "none" in your area, do not make any checks.

	Spring (mid-Mar. through mid-June)	Summer (mid-June through mid-Sep.)	Fall (mid-Sep. through mid-Dec.)	Winter (mid-Dec. through mid-Mar.)
I could go swimming in a lake or river.				
I could build a snowman.				
I could rake leaves.				
I could enjoy tulips or wild flowers.				
I would wear a light coat if I went outside.				
I would wear a heavy coat if I went outside.				
I could be comfortable outside in shorts.				
I would take an umbrella with me if I were going out for a couple hours.				

Understanding the Importance of Washing Your Hands

Directions: Clean hands can help a person be healthier. Read the story about Ralph. Put a star at each point where it would be a good idea for Ralph to wash his hands.

Ralph's Big Game

Ralph woke up dreaming that he had just hit a homerun. He jumped out of bed as if he were running the last leg to home plate. He quickly got dresses, put on his game shoes, and tied a double knot. He brushed his teeth, made and ate two pieces of toast, and grabbed his backpack. He got on his bike and rode the two blocks to the park. The coach wasn't there yet, so Ralph quickly went to the restroom and got a drink. When the coach arrived, the team practiced hitting and catching for about an hour. Then, the coach brought out two big boxes of donuts for everyone to share. Coach reminded the players that they had to be at the field by 5:00 tonight for one last warm-up before the game. Then, Ralph got on his bike and rode home.

When Ralph got home, he changed his clothes and his mom asked him to help cut up fruit for lunch. He finished cutting the fruit and had enough time to feed his rabbit before lunchtime. He was so hungry at lunch that he ate two sandwiches and a big bowl of fruit. After lunch, Ralph took a nap so he would have as much energy as possible for the game.

When he woke up, he put on his game uniform and his ball shoes. Then, he joined his parents for a quick spaghetti dinner. As they walked to the ball diamond, Ralph picked up leaves and sticks and practicing swinging at them. He was sure ready for this game!

The game finally started, and Ralph was the fourth batter. Bases were loaded when he stepped up to the plate. With a solid whack of the ball, Ralph's dream came true! He really was running towards home plate! After the game, the team celebrated by going out for pizza. Ralph was hungry and happy.....he ate four pieces!

Understanding the Nature of Illnesses

Directions: For each illness, list two symptoms and tell whether or not the illness requires ongoing doctor care.

Illness	Symptom 1	Symptom 2	Requires ongoing doctor care?
flu			
common cold			
measles			
diarrhea			
obesity			
bipolar disorder			
cancer			
pneumonia			
sinus infection			

Understanding the Pregnancy Process and Related Issues

Directions: Match the pregnancy definitions to the pregnancy terms.

Answers	Pregnancy Definitions	Pregnancy Terms
	1. The final process a pregnant woman's body goes through to get the baby ready for birth	A. delivery
	2. When a baby is first created	B. conception
	3. When a baby is born	C. labor
	4. When the sack that holds the baby inside the mother signals it is time for the baby to be born	D. water breaks

Answers	Definitions	Pregnancy Terms
	5. What a pregnant woman needs to do at home from the day she finds out she is pregnant	E. breast feeding
	6. Garments that include stretch panels and extra width	F. regular check-ups
	7. What a pregnant woman should start having as soon as she finds out she is pregnant	G. eat well and get enough rest
	8. A way to gtive a baby food instead of using baby bottles	H. maternity clothes

Understanding Types of Doctors

Directions: Match the descriptions to the types of doctors.

Answers	Definitions	Types of Doctors
	1. doctor who deals with patients who have cancer	A. obstetrician
	2. doctor who delivers babies	B. pediatrician
	3. doctor who works with children	C. dermatologist
	4. doctor who deals with skin issues	D. oncologist

Answers	Definitions	Types of Doctors
	5. doctor who deals with heart issues	E. gynecologist
	6. doctor who works as a family doctor	F. surgeon
	7. doctor who handles female problems	G. general practitioner
	8. doctor who operates on patients	H. cardiologist

Using a Lawn Mower

Directions: Sort the lawn mowing issues into the correct part of the mowing process.

Lawn Mowing Issues

Make sure the grass is long enough to mow.　　Get gas.

Put the lawn furniture back in place.　　Stay alert.

Keep an eye out for things you might hit.　　Pick up the sticks.

Move the lawn furniture.　　Trim where the mower missed.

Each pass, mow right next to the last pass.　　Put the mower away.

Remember you cannot hear, so watch for moving things.

Prepare to Mow	
During Mowing	
After Mowing	

Using a Seat Belt

Directions: Complete the sentences.

1. In my state, the law about seat belts says adults must _____
   _____

2. In my state, the law about seat belts says that babies must _____
   _____

3. In my state, the law about seat belts says that five-year-olds must _____
   _____

4. Even if there were not laws about wearing seat belts, people should use seatbelts because
   _____
   _____

5. When police see people who are not following seat belt laws, _____
   _____

6. It is not safe for a driver to put his or her seat belt on after starting to move the vehicle because
   _____
   _____

7. Before a car even moves, everyone in the car should have a seat belt on because
   _____
   _____

Using a Vacuum Cleaner

Directions: Complete the activities and answer the questions.

1. LIst four things that are small enough to be sucked into a vacuum cleaner and are sometimes on the floor at your house.

2. How do you know that the vacuum cleaner bag or compartment needs to be changed or cleaned out? _____
   _____

3. Which, if any, rooms in your house have carpet?

4. Why is it important to use a vacuum cleaner in rooms with carpet? _____
   _____
   _____

Using an Iron

Directions: Use the images to answer the questions.

1. What setting should you use to iron a t-shirt? _____

2. What setting should you use to iron a wool sweater? _____

3. What setting should you use to iron blue jeans? _____

4. What setting should you use to iron linen table napkins? _____

5. What setting should you use to iron a nylon jacket? _____

6. What is coming out of the bottom of the iron on the left and why is it coming out? _____
   _____

7. What would happen if the man who is ironing got distracted and left the iron where it is for 10 minutes? _____
   _____

Using Appropriate Cleaning Solutions

Directions: Match the cleaning Jobs to the cleaning solutions.

Answers	Cleaning Jobs	Cleaning Solutions
	1. Clean a toilet	**A.** a little hand dishwashing liquid in water
	2. Clean shower tiles	**B.** bowl cleaner
	3. Wash a tile floor that is not supposed to have any soap or chemicals	**C.** lime remover
	4. Wash the kitchen counters	**D.** water

Answers	Cleaning Jobs	Cleaning Solutions
	5. Get a spot out of a table cloth	**E.** window cleaner
	6. Get a spot out of an area rug	**F.** liquid hand soap
	7. Clean a mirror	**G.** laundry stain remover
	8. When at a restaurant, try to get a spot off of a shirt	**H.** carpet spot remover

Using Basic Appliances and Tools

Directions: Explain one purpose for which you could use each of the appliances and tools.

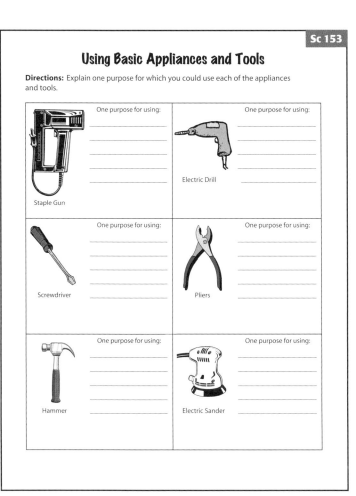

Staple Gun — One purpose for using:

Electric Drill — One purpose for using:

Screwdriver — One purpose for using:

Pliers — One purpose for using:

Hammer — One purpose for using:

Electric Sander — One purpose for using:

Using Bleach Safely

Directions: Answer the questions.

1. Why is it important to dissolve bleach in water before adding clothing instead of pouring the bleach over the clothes like you might do with soap? _____

2. Why is it important to make sure a bleach bottle is not dripping before you carry it from room to room? _____

3. Why does bleach work best with white items? _____

4. Why is it important to read the instructions on a bleach bottle each time you use bleach? _____

5. Why should you make sure not to get bleach on your hands? _____

6. What should you do if you get bleach in your eye? _____

Using Coasters to Protect Furniture

Directions: Circle each piece of furniture that could benefit from the use of coasters. For those where coasters would not be useful, explain why not.

Cloth Armchair — If not, why not?

Wooden Cabinet — If not, why not?

Wooden Desk — If not, why not?

Metal Table — If not, why not?

Plastic Table — If not, why not?

Wooden Table — If not, why not?

Using Dew Levels to Predict Rain

Directions: Heavy dew is a sign of a day that will not have rain. Use the numbers to sort the items in the Experiences Box into "Might Rain" or "Probably Will Not Rain."

Experiences Box
(Assume it hasn't rained shortly before any of the experiences.)

1 – Shoes get wet when walking to the bus in the early morning.
2 – Shoes are completely dry when walking to the bus in the early morning.
3 – Cannot see any water on the grass.
4 – Can see a drop of water on each blade of grass.
5 – The windows have water droplets on them.
6 – The windows are completely clear and dry.
7 – The newspaper is totally dry in the driveway.
8 – The newspaper is very damp in the driveway.

Might rain

Probably will not rain

Using Good Posture

Directions: Work with a partner. Take turns making sure each other is putting the good posture steps below into practice. Check each step off as you check your partner.

Partner's Name: _____

Standing/Walking Posture

_____ Stand on both feet.

_____ Put weight equally on both feet so that body is centered.

_____ Hold chin horizontal, not up or down.

_____ Hold back straight.

_____ Look straight ahead.

_____ Hold shoulders back, not rounded or slumped.

_____ Hold stomach in.

_____ When walking, swing arms with opposite legs.

Sitting Posture

_____ Sit on two hips evenly.

_____ Place feet flat on the floor. (Do not cross legs or feet.)

_____ Hold shoulders back, not rounded or slumped.

_____ Hold back straight.

_____ Place hands in lap or on desk.

Using Kitchen Appliances

Directions: Describe how you could use each appliance to make a food or drink item.

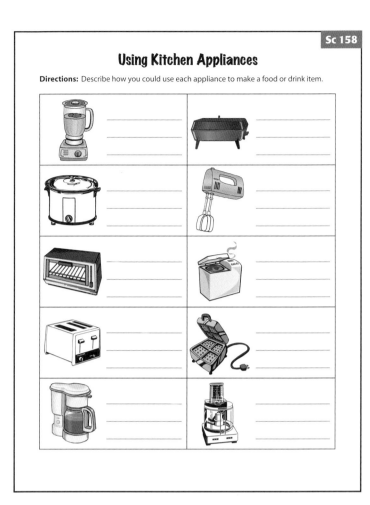

Using Taste Words

Directions: Use the words below in descriptions of foods you have tasted, such as sour lemons.

1. (sour) _____

2. (sweet) _____

3. (bitter) _____

4. (salty) _____

5. (drab) _____

6. (spicy) _____

7. (tangy) _____

8. (sharp) _____

Using the Freezer to Keep
Non-Freezer Foods Fresh

Directions: Some foods do not have to be kept frozen, but will last longer if they are frozen. Write one such food in each circle.

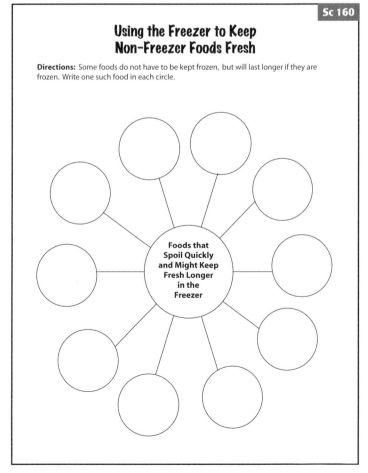

Foods that Spoil Quickly and Might Keep Fresh Longer in the Freezer

Using Vending Machines

Directions: Answer the questions.

1. How much money do you need to get a drink from a typical vending machine? _____

2. How much money do you need to get a something to eat from a typical vending machine?

3. Where might you go and find that drinks or food from vending machines cost more than you are used to?

4. What are three things you could buy from a vending machine that would be OK for treats, but not for meals?

5. What are three things you could buy in vending machines that could be parts of fairly healthy meals?

6. What should you do if you put money into a vending machine and do not get your food or drink?

Using Your Teeth Properly

Directions: Circle the BEST term to complete each sentence.

1. Trying to (**unscrew a bottle top** / **chew on your hair**) with your teeth could break a tooth off.

2. Even though it is (**plastic** / **metal**), pulling the sealer ring off of a milk carton with your teeth could chip or break a tooth.

3. Popcorn kernels prove that (**you can chew any kind of food with your teeth** / **some foods are too dangerous to chew with your teeth**).

4. Sealed plastic packaging (**is too flexible to hurt teeth in any way** / **could slit your gums and harm your teeth**).

5. Even though steak is hard to chew, (**human teeth are intended to chew such food** / **you should not chew such food for fear of breaking your teeth**).

6. A good way to make difficult-to-chew foods, such as hard apples, easier on your teeth is to (**cut the food into small pieces or slices** / **suck the food until it dissolved.**)

7. After eating something sticky, (**a banana** / **an apple**) is a good thing to eat to clean your teeth.

8. When you are eating (**broth** / **solid food**), you should make certain to chew the food completely.

9. Extreme (**temperature** / **laughter**) can cause your teeth to hurt, so you should protect your teeth from it.

Visiting a Hospital Patient

Directions: Read each hospital visitor's guideline. Then, give an example of a possible problem if a person did not follow the guideline.

Hospital Visitor Guidelines	Possible problem if a person did not follow the guideline
Be very careful not to get in the way of the medical staff	
If the patient you are visiting has a roommate, be thoughtful of the roommate.	
Even if the patient is not in his or her bed, do not sit or rest on the bed.	
Do not interfere with the patient's need to rest.	
Even if the patient doesn't seem hungry, do not eat his or her food	

Washing Dishes

Directions: Write out the steps to washing dishes by hand and the steps to washing dishes in a dish washer. Begin with picking dirty dishes up from the table and end with putting clean dishes away.

Steps to Washing Dishes by Hand	Steps to Washing Dishes in a Dish Washer

Washing Fresh Produce

Directions: Write six ways that germs could get on an apple you buy in the grocery store.

How Germs Get on Apples

Washing Hands Before Eating

Directions: Complete the sentences

1. If I am in the school cafeteria, I can wash my hands before eating by _____

2. If I am eating in a fast-food restaurant, I can wash my hands before eating by _____

3. If I am at a picnic, I can wash my hands before eating by _____

4. If I am at a fund raiser in a large parking lot with only portable bathrooms, I can wash my hands before eating by _____

5. If I am eating in a classroom and am not allowed to leave, I can wash my hands before eating by _____

6. If I am a football player eating on the sideline during the game, I can wash my hands before eating by _____

7. If I am backpacking in the mountains, I can wash my hands before eating by _____

Watching Car Oil and Temperature Gauges

Directions: Use the car gauges and lights to answer the questions.

Car gauges and lights	Questions	Answers
	1. Is this RPM gauge reading in the safe zone? Explain.	
	2. Based on this water temperature gauge, why should the driver stop driving immediately?	
Check Engine	3. This "Check Engine" light only shows up when there is a problem. What should a driver do when this light comes on?	
WATER	4. Based on this water temperature gauge, does the driver had a problem? Explain.	
HOT WATER	5. Based on this water temperature gauge, does the driver had a problem? Explain.	
Low OIL	6. Based on this oil light, why should the driver stop driving immediately?	

Watching for Drug Side Effects

Directions: Use the drug side effects statements to answer the questions.

Side Effects
Stomach upset, headache, dizziness, trouble sleeping, or weight gain may occur. If any of these effects persist or worsen, notify your doctor or pharmacist immediately. Remember that your doctor has prescribed this medication assuming that the benefits will outweigh the side effects. Many people using this medication have no serious side effects. Tell your doctor immediately if you have any of the following unlikely but serious side effects: black stools, bone fracture, dark and grainy vomit, easy bruising/bleeding, heartburn, increased thirst and urination, irregular/fast-pounding heart, muscle weakness/pain, ongoing weight gain, puffy face, seizures, swelling of the feet/ankles, trouble breathing, unusual hair growth, or vision changes.

1. Should you call your doctor if you take this medication for two weeks and gain five pounds? Explain. _____

2. Should you call your doctor if you take this medication and you find that you cannot get your shoes on? Explain. _____

SIDE EFFECTS: Stomach upset, nausea, diarrhea, unusual taste, or drowsiness may occur as your body adjusts to this medication. If any of these effects persist or worsen, notify your doctor or pharmacist immediately. Remember that your doctor has prescribed this medication assuming that the benefits will outweigh the side effects. Many people using this medication have no serious side effects. Tell your doctor immediately if you have any of the following unlikely but serious side effects: easy bleeding/bruising, signs of infection (e.g.: fever, persistent sore throat), change in amount of urine, yellowing eyes or skin, severe stomach/abdominal pain, persistent nausea/vomiting/lack of appetite, dark urine, unusual tiredness, or unusual weight loss. Serious side effects are rare. Stop taking the medication and seek immediate medical attention if any of these allergic reaction symptoms appear: skin rash, hives, itching, swelling (especially lips or mouth), dizziness, pain when urinating, blood in the urine, unusual eye redness/pain, fever, and chills, muscle/joint pain, or trouble breathing.

3. What should you do if you take this medication and are nauseous most of the time? _____

4. What should you do if you take this medication and have started having blood in your urine? _____

134   Science/Health

Watching for Use-By Dates
When Grocery Shopping

Directions: Take this activity sheet to a grocery store. Find the food items below and write a use-by date that you see on each. Then, for each food item, complete the chart by placing a check in one of the last three columns.

Food Items	Use-By Dates	Good for less than a week	Good for from a week to a month	Good for more than a month

Language Arts

Expressive Literacy

Receptive Literacy

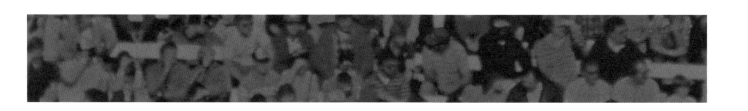

Language Arts: Expressive Literacy

Addressing a Problem with a Purchase

Directions: Decide how you would address the problems with the purchases below.

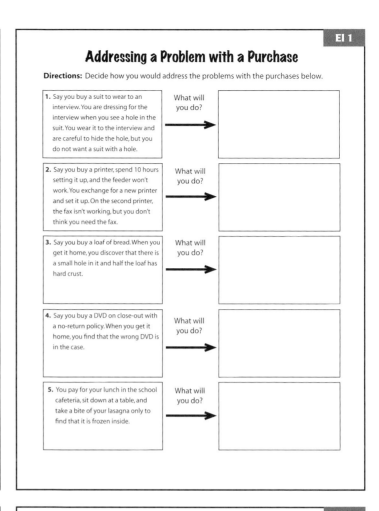

1. Say you buy a suit to wear to an interview. You are dressing for the interview when you see a hole in the suit. You wear it to the interview and are careful to hide the hole, but you do not want a suit with a hole.

What will you do?

2. Say you buy a printer, spend 10 hours setting it up, and the feeder won't work. You exchange for a new printer and set it up. On the second printer, the fax isn't working, but you don't think you need the fax.

What will you do?

3. Say you buy a loaf of bread. When you get it home, you discover that there is a small hole in it and half the loaf has hard crust.

What will you do?

4. Say you buy a DVD on close-out with a no-return policy. When you get it home, you find that the wrong DVD is in the case.

What will you do?

5. You pay for your lunch in the school cafeteria, sit down at a table, and take a bite of your lasagna only to find that it is frozen inside.

What will you do?

Addressing an Envelope

Directions: Address these two "envelopes" to two different friends. Use your name and address as the return addresses. Draw the stamps. Include current postage.

Anticipating Consequences

Directions: List one positive consequence and one negative consequence for each choice. Then, decide if you think the choice was a good one.

Choices	Positive Consequences	Negative Consequences	Was choice a good one?
Tony chose to skip math class on Friday because he wanted to spend an extra hour practicing for the music contest.			
Alyssa ate six jelly donuts for breakfast even though she says she wants to lose weight.			
Marissa is having a party. Marissa is not friends with Jade, but Jade is friends with two of Marissa's friends, so Marissa invited Jade to the party.			
Dana is shopping for a new pair of jeans. She found one pair she really likes for $131 and one pair she likes almost as well for $38. She chose to buy the $38 pair.			
David lost his science book and doesn't want to pay the $60. He sees one of the books in the science room and slips it into his backpack to turn in later.			

Apologizing Gracefully

Directions: Read each pair of apologies and put a check next to the one that sounds most sincere.

1.
_____ I'm sorry I ate your leftover pizza. I know it wasn't mine and I should have left it alone.

_____ I'm sorry I ate your left over pizza. You should have put your name on it if you didn't want anyone to eat it.

4.
_____ I'm sorry we forgot to pick you up. We were in such a hurry that we weren't thinking right. I'm glad you got another ride.

_____ I'm sorry we forgot to pick you up. I guess you just aren't very memorable.

2.
_____ I'm sorry I called you _lazy_, but you just made me so mad that I wasn't thinking.

_____ I'm sorry I called you _lazy_. I know you are a hard worker. I was just jealous.

5.
_____ I'm sorry I stained your shirt. That's what happens when you let people borrow your things.

_____ I'm sorry I stained your shirt. I will get you a new one.

3.
_____ I'm sorry I am late. I fell asleep and just woke up 20 minutes ago.

_____ I'm sorry I am late. You should have called me. You knew I was tired.

6.
_____ I'm sorry I bumped you. Are you OK?

_____ I'm sorry I bumped you. You should stay out of the main walk way.

Applying for Registrations and Licenses

Directions: Put a check next to each job, experience, or item that requires a registration or license. Circle each check that represents a registration or license that you could probably find online. Find one form online, print it, and fill it in.

to go fishing	to own a lawnmower
to own and use a boat	to be a firefighter
to cut hair	to build a shed
to work as a lawyer	to own a gun
to be a teacher	to exercise at a gym
to buy gasoline	to be a realtor
to clean houses	to own and use a cell phone
to drive a car	to be an electrician
to be a waitress	to be a welder
to have a garage sale	to be an architect
to be a doctor	to be a parent
to own a swimming pool	to be a nurse
to run a charity	to be a plumber
to own and use a car	to be an EMT
to be a parent	to get married
to go scuba diving	to sell a car
to own a television	to drive a motorcycle
to run a day care center	to work as a school cook
to build a new house	to own/use a chainsaw
to buy furniture	to own/use a snowmobile

Arranging Babysitters

Directions: Answer the questions to explain how you could find babysitters.

1. if you have a high school student who is your regular babysitter, but he or she can't babysit on a day you need a sitter, how could this student help you find a sitter? _____

_____

2. How could the people with whom you work help you find a babysitter? _____

_____

3. How can you find a babysitter through your neighbors? _____

_____

4. Why is it a good idea to find babysitters through other people you know? _____

_____

5. As a rule, how far ahead of time should you try to get a babysitter? _____

_____

6. Why would it be hard to get a babysitter on the night that you need one? _____

_____

Asking a Phramacist for Advice

Directions: Circle either "doctor" or "pharmacist" to tell the best person to ask for advice in each situation. If your question is directly about how the medication will react, the pharmacist is probably the best person to ask. If your question is about your health, the doctor is the best person to ask.

Situations	Who is the best person to ask?	
1. You want to know if you need to eat each time before you take your mediation.	doctor	pharmacist
2. You want to know if you need medication because your nose bleeds once or twice a day.	doctor	pharmacist
3. You want to know if there is an over-the-counter medication to help with very dry skin.	doctor	pharmacist
4. You want to know if it is a problem to take a double dose of an over-the-counter medicine.	doctor	pharmacist
5. You want to know if it is a problem to take two certain over-the-counter medicines together.	doctor	pharmacist
6. You want to know if it will help to keep taking your prescription medication for a whole year.	doctor	pharmacist
7. You want to know if there is a generic version of your medication.	doctor	pharmacist

Asking for Help When Needed

Directions: Circle one of the two choices to show for which activities you should ask for help.

Situations	Do on Own or Ask for Help?	
1. You are in a social studies class and cannot read the textbook.	do on own	ask for help
2. You have a lot of homework to do, but you only have about 20 minutes before your favorite show comes on.	do on own	ask for help
3. You usually walk the ten blocks to work, but you have a cast on your foot right now and walking gives you blisters.	do on own	ask for help
4. You need to get something from the top shelp and you cannot reach it. You have a stepstool, but your balance is not very good.	do on own	ask for help
5. Someone very close to you has just died, and you feel so depressed that you don't feel like eating, going to work, or doing anything else.	do on own	ask for help
6. You have had seizures before, and you sense that you are about to have another one.	do on own	ask for help
7. At your job, you have to carry glass jars from one lab to another. The jars are really heavy for you, and you are afraid you might drop them.	do on own	ask for help

Asking for Help with Activities

Directions: How you ask for help often determines whether or not people are happy to help you. Read each poor method of asking for help. Then, write three better ways to ask the same thing.

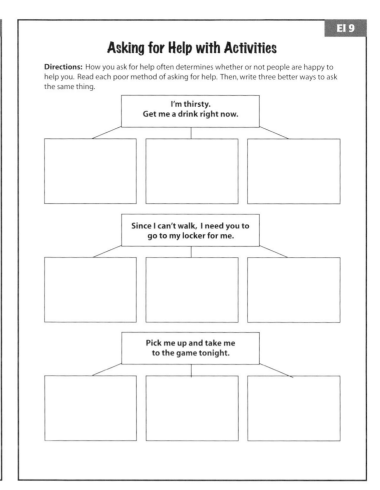

Asking Questions for Clarification

Directions: List questions you could ask in order to clarify each situation. In each case, the speaker is in the picture and is talking to you.

Do you want to go with me?

Just leave me alone.

Do you have something you want to say?

Is this yours?

Are you coming with us?

Would you like some cake?

Being Persistent with Important Issues

Directions: Say you have a child. Explain why each situation below is or is not a situation about which you should be persistent.

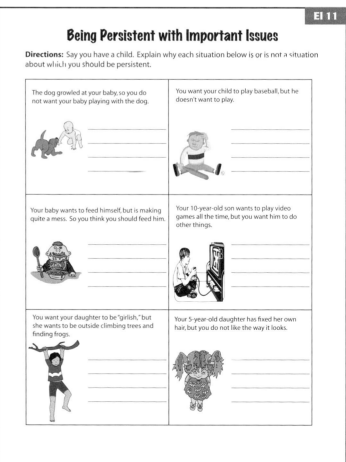

The dog growled at your baby, so you do not want your baby playing with the dog.

You want your child to play baseball, but he doesn't want to play.

Your baby wants to feed himself, but is making quite a mess. So you think you should feed him.

Your 10-year-old son wants to play video games all the time, but you want him to do other things.

You want your daughter to be "girlish," but she wants to be outside climbing trees and finding frogs.

Your 5-year-old daughter has fixed her own hair, but you do not like the way it looks.

Being Positive

Directions: Restate each statement twice: once in a positive way and once in a negative way.

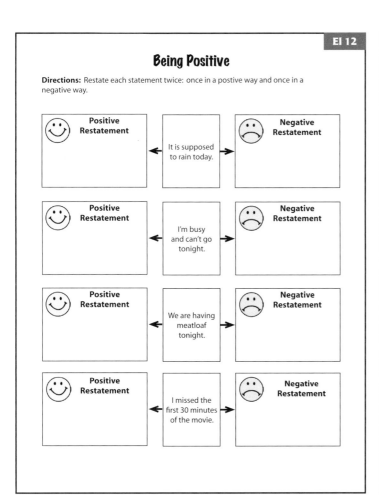

Positive Restatement / It is supposed to rain today. / Negative Restatement

Positive Restatement / I'm busy and can't go tonight. / Negative Restatement

Positive Restatement / We are having meatloaf tonight. / Negative Restatement

Positive Restatement / I missed the first 30 minutes of the movie. / Negative Restatement

Being Tactful

Directions: Respond to each situation twice: once in a tactful way and once in a tactless way.

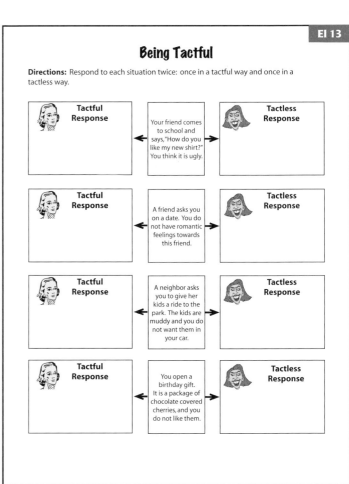

Tactful Response / Your friend comes to school and says, "How do you like my new shirt?" You think it is ugly. / Tactless Response

Tactful Response / A friend asks you on a date. You do not have romantic feelings towards this friend. / Tactless Response

Tactful Response / A neighbor asks you to give her kids a ride to the park. The kids are muddy and you do not want them in your car. / Tactless Response

Tactful Response / You open a birthday gift. It is a package of chocolate covered cherries, and you do not like them. / Tactless Response

Brainstorming with a Group

Directions: Work with a group of four other students to brainstorm the topics below. Take turns being the "writer" for a brainstormed list. Use the lines below when it is your turn to be the "writer." Remember to accept and record all suggestions.

Topics to Brainstorm	
Meaningful TV shows	Games you liked when you were little
Slang words teens use	Crayon colors
Interesting ways to exercise	

Topic:

Calling About a Job Opening

Directions: Work with a partner. Choose one of the ads below and role play that you are calling about the job and your partner answers the phone at the company. Before you make the call, use the lines below to make some notes so you remember what you want to say.

SleepEase Hotels – Now hiring exceptional service staff for Front Desk, Housekeeping, Lobby Attendant, Maint., and Breakfast Attendant. Call 653-555-4323 for more information.

Asistant Manager
Mama's Kitchen needs an assistant manager for new store. 5 day work week. Excellent salary. Background check and drug test given. Promotion from within. Call 555-2222

Receptionist
Full-time, some wknds. Rqmts: multi-tasking, basic computer knowledge, excellent customer service, organization skills, and attention to detail. Enjoy team work in fast-paced customer-driven environment. Ability to comunicate effectively. 555-8932

Job:

Calling Directory Assistance

Directions: Copy each correct step from the first column into the second column.

Possible steps for calling directory assistance	Actual steps for calling directory assistance
• Find the first and last name of the person for whom you want a phone number. • Dial directory assistance (1411 or (area code)-555-1212)	
• Ask the operator to find the city and state where the person lives. • Find the city and state of the person for whom you want a phone number.	
• Plan to remember the phone number when you hear it. • Get pencil and paper ready.	
• Dial directory assistance (1411 or 555-1212). • Wait for the operator to call you.	
• In response to the question "What city please," say (for example), "Dallas, TX." • In response to the question "What city please," say (for example), "Texas."	
• If the operator doesn't find the number the first time, ask him or her to look again. • In response to the question "What listing?" say (for example), "Kyle Gonzalez."	
• Put the digits in the phone number in order so you can remember the number. • Write the number on your paper.	
• Say "Goodbye" and hang up. • Say "Thanks" to the operator and hang up. If you are listening to a recording, just hang up.	
• Write the name (Kyle Gonzalez) next to the number so you remember what the number is for when you see it later. • Leave the number by the phone.	
• Be glad that directory assistance is free. • Plan to pay a directory assistance fee with your next phone bill.	

Choosing Appropriate Discussion Topics

Directions: Use check marks (✔) to show which conversation topics are appropriate with whom and where. Assume that all conversations are in person if it is logical that the people involved would be at the given locations. Otherwise, assume the conversations are by cell phone.

You are talking to...	Topic of Conversation	During Class	At Home	During Work	At a Party
Friends	1. How your sibling got in trouble last night				
	2. Your favorite song				
	3. Your science project				
Siblings	4. Why you are in trouble with your mother				
	5. Whose job it is to wash the dishes tonight				
	6. Why you do not want to share your new sweater				
Parents	7. Why you shouldn't have to help clean house tomorrow				
	8. When parent night is going to be held at school				
	9. If you can get a ride in about 30 minutes				
Grandparents	10. What school was like when they were little				
	11. What you would like to do for your birthday				
	12. Ask them to check on your mother since your mother has been ill and is not answering the phone				
Teachers	13. What you do not understand about today's lesson				
	14. Tomorrow's assignment				
	15. A reference letter for a job				
Boss	16. What time you need to be at work today				
	17. How to handle a certain order				
	18. Where your boss worked for his or her first job				

Choosing Internet Search Words

Directions: Make a list of Internet search words for each topic.

Internet search words for this topic: **Animals that make unusual, but good pets**	Internet search words for this topic: **Fruit trees that grow well where you live**
Internet search words for this topic: **Ways that math is useful in the real world**	Internet search words for this topic: **Games that are popular with teenagers**

Communicating with Fellow Employees

Directions: For the top three situations, tell what you could say without causing a problem between you and a fellow employee. For the bottom three situations, tell what you could say to offer a friendly connection between you and a fellow employee.

Situation where a fellow employee made you angry	What you could say without causing a problem between you and the employee
Jillian works next to you. She made a mistake and when the boss asked about the problem, Jillian blamed it on you.	
Your supervisor asks if anyone would be willing to work overtime on Saturday. Mark offers that you would probably be willing to. You already have plans.	
You bring your lunch each day. You put it in the refrigerator with your name on it. Someone has been taking some of your food. You think it is either Chris or Mel.	

Situation where you have a chance to offer a friendly connection to a fellow employee	What you could say to offer a friendly connection between you and the employee
Tricia works in your department, and she won the employee of the month for the whole company.	
Yesterday, Kayla told you that she was excited to hear how her daughter's speech went at school. Today, you see Kayla as you are walking into work.	
You walk into the lunchroom, and Mandy is sitting there alone and crying.	

Completing a College/Trade School Application

Directions: One common part of a college or trade school application is to write an essay on a given topic. Type a one-page, double-spaced essay about a difficult challenge you faced and were able to turn into a positive. Use this page to plan.

_____
_____
_____
_____
_____
_____
_____
_____
_____
_____
_____
_____
_____
_____
_____
_____
_____
_____
_____
_____
_____

Completing a Job Application

Directions: Fill in this job application.

Date:

Name: (First)	(M)	(Last)

Address:

Home Phone: ( )	Cell: ( )

WORK HISTORY

Job Titles	Companies	Dates	Supervisors	Duties	Why Left?

EDUCATION

Schools	Dates	Areas of Study	Degrees or Certificates

Your Strengths:

Your Weaknesses:

Compromising

Directions: Read each person's wishes. Then, for each pair, suggest a compromise. Remember that a compromise should require each person to give a little.

Wishes of Person #1:   Suggested Compromise:

I think we should have spaghetti and salad for dinner.

Wishes of Person #2:

I think we should have pizza and breadsticks for dinner.

Wishes of Person #3:   Suggested Compromise:

Let's walk to the game and sit in the top row.

Wishes of Person #4:

Let's drive to the game and stand in the end zone.

Wishes of Person #5:   Suggested Compromise:

Let's study for four hours and then go to a movie.

Wishes of Person #6:

Let's go to a movie and then study for four hours.

Controlling Emotional Reactions

Directions: Think of a time when you became angry and said and/or did things that you wish you would not have said or done. Use the situation to fill in the chart.

Describe a time when you became angry and said or did things that you wish you would not have said or done	
What did you say or do that you wish you would not have said or done?	
If you could do this situation over, what would you say or do differently?	

Conversing on Topics Chosen by Others

Directions: Note three points you could add to each conversation.

Summary of Conversation #1:
Two of your friends are talking and laughing about the first time they tried to play tennis, including where they played, who gave them the idea to play, how many times they were able to volley the ball, and how often they had to chase a runaway ball.
They ask you if you play tennis.

| Point #1.1: |
| Point #1.2: |
| Point #1.3: |

Summary of Conversation #2:
Some friends are talking about your favorite current movie. They are discussing whether the actors were good choices, whether or not it is a good movie, if it has a chance to win awards, and how it compares to other current movies. You hear the discussion and want to join in.

| Point #2.1: |
| Point #2.2: |
| Point #2.3: |

Summary of Conversation #3:
You and three friends are discussing funny things that have happened in classes. Share some experiences you have had.

| Point #3.1: |
| Point #3.2: |
| Point #3.3: |

Creating a Computer Password You Can Remember

Directions: Use the chart to create computer passwords you can remember and that match the given requirements. Then, answer the typical password reminder questions.

Create a password with six or more characters. (Always use all lower-case letters.)	Explain why the password will be easy for you to remember.
Sample: checkers	It is my favorite game.

Create a password with six or more characters; include letters and numbers. (Always use all lower-case letters.)	Explain why the password will be easy for you to remember.
Sample: collies2	Collies are my favorite dogs, and I have two of them.

Password Reminder Questions (These are questions that you might be asked when you are signing up for an online site and have to make up a password. If you forget your password and can answer the question(s) correctly, you will receive your password by e-mail.)	Your Answers
What is your mother's maiden name?	
What was the name of your favorite teacher?	
What is your favorite movie?	
What was your childhood pet's name?	

Describing a Problem to a Lawyer

Directions: When you have a problem and need a lawyer, you should tell your lawyer all the details. Even if some of the facts make you look bad, you should tell your lawyer so he or she can best figure out how to help you. A lawyer must keep everything you say confidential. In each situation below, choose the best facts to tell a lawyer.

Situation	Facts to Tell a Lawyer
1. Andy saw Pete and Shelia arguing. Then, Pete hit Shelia and knocked her down. Andy got into a fight with Pete and broke Pete's jaw. Pete is suing Andy for assault and battery.	___ Andy should tell the lawyer that he was just protecting Shelia. ___ Andy should tell the lawyer that he was protecting Shelia and that he has gotten into fights with Pete several times before.
2. Chandra got a ticket for driving 30 miles over the speed limit. The sign was down because of construction at the edge of town. She had driven past the construction and thought she was out of town, so she sped up.	___ Chandra should tell her lawyer that she wasn't going that fast and that the police must have clocked her wrong. ___ Chandra should tell her lawyer that she was going 55 mph because she there was no sign, and she thought she was out of town.
3. At the grocery store, Jon put a package of hotdogs and a package of cheese in his pocket and left the store. Outside, he was stopped by store security who then called police.	___ Jon should tell his lawyer that he shouldn't have taken the food, is out of work and was starving. He should also point out that he has never been in trouble before and will gladly work for the store to pay for the food. ___ Jon should tell his lawyer that he did not take the food and that the store security person must have planted the food in his pocket.
4. Marcy took Julie's homework and put it in her puse. Then, Julie took Marcy's purse and hid it in her car. Marcy then used a hanger to break into Julie's car and take the purse back. Julie is suing Marcy for theft and breaking and entering.	___ Marcy should tell her lawyer that she took the purse because it is hers and Julie had taken it from her earlier. She should also point out that she had taken Julie's homework and it was in the purse. ___ Since it isn't really such a bid deal, Marcy should tell her lawyer that she took the purse and will give it back. She should also say that Julie thought the car was locked, but that it really wasn't.

Describing Symptoms to a Doctor

Directions: Explain why it is or is not important to include each of the "extra details" below when describing your symptoms to a doctor.

Health Problems	Extra details that might or might not be related	Why it is or is not important to include the extra details
1. You have a fever and a bad cough.	You are having pain when you go to the bathroom.	
2. You have a headache and would like some prescription medication for it.	You are already taking over-the-counter pain medication for your arm that you hurt playing ball.	
3. You fell and you think your arm is broken.	You also have a pain in your chest, but you doubt it is anything important.	
4. You have a nosebleed that will not stop.	You got new glasses last week, and they have made the top of your nose sore.	
5. You eyes are burning and you are having trouble seeing.	You had a hamburger for lunch.	
6. You have a an earache.	You went swimming yesterday.	

Language Arts: Expressive Literacy   145

Enunciating Clearly

Directions: Use the words in the Word Box to complete the sentences.

Word Box

clues	customer service	exactly
misunderstand	quickly	quietly
runs	telephone	what

1. To enunciate clearly means to speak very _____ .

2. One common enunciation problem happens when a person speaks too

   _____ .

3. Another common enunciation problem happens when a person _____

   each word into the next word.

4. A third common enunciation problem is caused by a person talking too _____ ..

5. If you do not enunciate clearly, people are likely to _____ what you say.

6. Clear enunciation is especially important over the _____ .

7. When you can't see a person talking, you cannot get _____ about

   what the person is saying by looking at his or her mouth and expressions.

8. Clear enunciation is especially important on the job if a person works in

   _____ .

9. If people often say "_____?" when you talk, you might try

   enunciating more clearly.

Exploring Situation-Appropriate Speech/Actions

Directions: Check things that it is OK to say or do at home, but not at other places.

Things it is OK to SAY at home, but not at other places	Things it is OK to DO at home, but not at other places
1. That picture does not look very good on that wall.	12. Chew with your mouth open.
2. Let's watch a movie at 6:00.	13. Go barefoot.
3. Shut up! (when someone is talking during a TV show)	14. Leave your shoes in the middle of the room.
4. Swear words when others make you angry	15. Throw a baseball around inside the house.
5. Does your oak tree have oak wilt?	16. Drink directly from the gallon milk jug.
6. I don't like fish, so I'm going to eat something else.	17. Eat while you are doing your homework.
7. You should return this chair. It is really uncomfortable.	18. Ignore people you do not want to talk to.
8. I'm going to take a nap now. I'll help clean up later.	19. Listen to music you like no matter what others like.
9. Does that fireplace burn gas or wood?	20. Walk around in your underwear.
10. I think our family should try harder to get along.	21. Sleep in front of the TV.
11. I'm allergic to cilantro. Is there any in this salad?	22. Eat with your fingers.

Expressing Self with Feeling Words

Directions: Use the words in the word box to share some of your thoughts.

Word Box

curious	dejected	delighted
embarraassed	fantastic	gloomy
leery	mysterious	petty

1. _____
   _____

2. _____
   _____

3. _____
   _____

4. _____
   _____

5. _____
   _____

6. _____
   _____

7. _____
   _____

Filling or Refilling a Prescription

Directions: Fill in the chart to explain each prescription label.

Prescription Labels	Can this prescription be refilled simply by calling the pharamacy?	What is the refill number the pharmacy will need for this prescription?	Counting this pill bottle, how many pills remain on the prescription?
Green Pharmacy Rx: 1281130 Dr. J. Wilson Jeremy Baker Take three tablets now and then take one table two times daily for seven days. Prednisone 20 mg NO REFILLS			
Green Pharmacy Rx: 3819953 Dr. Dejiacamo Elise S. Mercer Take 1–2 tablets every 4–6 hours as needed for pain. Hydrocodone/Appap Substitued for Vicodin 5/500 tabs 3 REFILLS REMAINING			
Green Pharmacy Rx: 114480 Dr. Beth Lufin Joaquin Paulson Take 1 capsule 4 times a day until all have been taken. AMOXICILLIN 500 MG CAPSULES; Qty: 30 REFILL 9 OF 9; authorization required			

Filling Out Personal Information Forms

Directions: Fill in this personal information form.

Name: (First)	(Middle)	(Last)

Address:

Home Phone: ( )   Cell: ( )

E-mail Address:

Place of Employment:

Schools Attended and Degrees Earned:

Height	Weight	Eye Color	Hair Color

Birth Date: County of Birth:

Father's Name:

Mother's Name:

Mother's Maiden Name:

Siblings' Names:

Next of Kin: Next of Kin Phone #:

Hobbies:

Favorite color: Favorite meal:

Favorite animal: Favorite TV show:

Following Food Preparation Directions

Directions: Use the food-preparation directions to answer the questions.

Food-Preparation Directions	Questions
Quick and Easy Directions Mix soup + 1 can water **Microwave:** Cover and heat in microwavable container on high for about 3 min. Leave in microwave one minute. Stir and serve. **Stove:** Heat on medium. Serve immediately.	**1.** Would you prefer the microwave or stove? Explain. **2.** About how long would it take to prepare the soup?
DIRECTIONS: Empty contents of one package into large plastic or glass pitcher. Add 1 cup of sugar (more or less as desired). Add cold water and ice to fill pitcher to the 2-quart level. Stir to dissolve. Serve immediately or store in refrigerator. Do not store in metal container.	**3.** Describe the container in your house that would work for these directions. **4.** How will this drink be different if you store it in the refrigerator for a while versus if you drink it right away?
Cooking Instructions • Place 6 cups of water in a saucepan and bring to a boil. • Stir in macaroni. • Stirring occasionally, boil 7 to 8 minutes or until macaroni is tender. • Drain water. • Add 4 Tablespoons of butter, 1/4 cup of milk, and cheese mix. Mix well and serve.	**5.** Describe what comes in the product box. **6.** Explain what you are to do before adding the butter, milk, and cheese mix.

Giving "How To" Directions

Directions: Write step-by-step directions for one of these three activities:
- How to play a certain video game
- How to score tennis (or some other sport)
- How to grill hamburgers

Use additional paper if you need to.

Step 1:

Step 2:

Step 3:

Step 4:

Step 5:

Step 6:

Step 7:

Step 8:

Step 9:

Step 10:

Giving an Opinion on a Movie

Directions: Choose a movie you have seen recently and write a review of the movie. Make sure to discuss the plot, actors, and other key parts.

Movie:

_____

Review:

_____
_____
_____
_____
_____
_____
_____
_____
_____
_____
_____
_____
_____
_____

Giving Compliments

Directions: Imagine these people are people you know.
Give them each a compliment based on what he or she is doing.

People You Know	Compliments Based on What the People are Doing
Your friend dancing at a school dance	
Your grandfather showing why he was the Yoyo Champion of the 1970s	
Your neighbor walking her dog	
Your friend on her way to winning an event at the track meet	
Your cousin walking for exercise	

Giving People Enough Physical Space

Directions: Working with a partner, act out the spacing shown in each picture.
Then, decide whether or not each option shows enough physical space between people.

Act out these spacings with a partner	Enough physical space?	Act out these spacings with a partner	Enough physical space?
Teachers in teacher's lounge		Relatives at a family event	
Friends talking in parking lot		A mother and her child	
Friends on bench at park		Class-mates talking about a science project	
Co-workers talking at work		A grand-mother and her grand-child	
Co-workers talking		Co-workers talking	

Giving Verbal Clarification

Directions: Use the letter-clarification words to spell the names. (There is no set standard for letter-clarification words, but those in the box below are commonly used.)

Letter-Clarification Words					
apple	boy	cat	dog	echo	Frank
green	happy	igloo	jiggle	kite	little
monkey	Nancy	orange	Paris	question	Robert
summer	tree	umbrella	Victor	winter	x-ray
yellow	zebra				

Names	Letter-Clarification Spellings
Example: Spencer	summer–Paris–echo–Nancy–cat–echo–Robert
1. Rebecca	
2. Jonah	
3. Odell	
4. Abigail	
5. Kenalee	
6. Kirsten	
7. Mason	
8. Willow	
9. Gabriella	
10. Falyn	

Handling Personal Issues at Work

Directions: Decide if each personal issue should be handled at work or not.

Personal Issues	Should not be handled at work because.......	OK to handle at work because.......
1. Molly's child called and said she had fallen and hurt her arm. She couldn't stop crying and was throwing up.		
2. Your library books is due today, so you want to finish reading it at work.		
3. Your furnace isn't working, so you want to arrange to have it fixed before nighttime.		
4. You are working overtime on Saturday when a friend calls to see if you want to go out that night.		
5. You plan to look at your favorite store's Web site to see what is on sale so you can shop quickly over lunch.		
6. Your car broke down on the way to work. You left it beside the road and called a cab. You want to get your car off the road.		

Handling Unexpected or Difficult Situations

Directions: Check the choices that BEST complete the sentences.

1. One good way to **stay calm** in a difficult situation is to
   _____ take deep breaths when you feel stressed.
   _____ cover your eyes and plug your ears.

2. You should **ask questions** in a difficult situation when
   _____ you feel curious.
   _____ you need clarification to make a good decision.

3. It is important that you **do not judge** in a difficult situaiton because
   _____ you are not the person who should do the judging.
   _____ you need to focus on how to help, not on who to blame.

4. You must try to **think before you speak** in a difficult situation,
   _____ so you do not make the situation worse.
   _____ because no one wants to hear your first thoughts.

5. **Trying to see others' points of view** is important in a dificult situation because
   _____ the best result is most likely to be reached if all ideas are explored.
   _____ some people will pout if they are ignored.

6. You should **be ready to compromise** in a difficult situation because
   _____ you know you don't really have such great ideas.
   _____ groups cannot be productive if people are not willing to give and take.

Having a Conversation

Directions: Think of comments you can add to the conversation below.

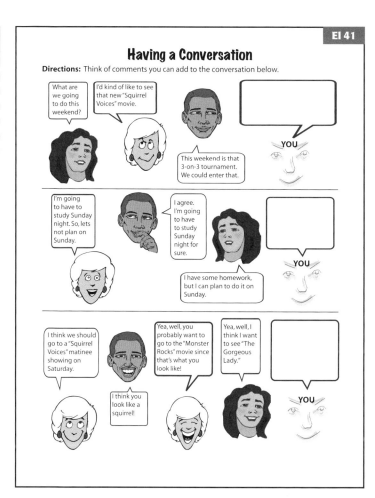

Identifying Interests and Abilities

Directions: Check (✓) each interest that you have and each ability that is a strength for you.

Interests		Abilities	
	dancing		singing
	watching TV		convincing people
	skiing		cooking
	skating		being mechanically inclined
	computer games		drawing
	going to movies		acting
	taking care of animals		organizing
	watching sports		doing math
	playing baseball		thinking critically
	playing tennis		working with computers
	playing basketball		working with kids
	playing board games		working with animals
	playing cards		dancing
	running		thinking creatively
	gardening		persevering
	swimming		writing
	going to museums		working with high energy
	reading novels		working with plants
	cooking		driving large vehicles

Interviewing for a Job

Directions: Answer the interview questions in relation to each job.

Job Ads	Interview Questions	Answers to Interview Questions
Administrative Assistant Seeking a detial-oriented person who can multi-task; must have Excel and Word experience. Job consists of answering phones, daily data entry, filing, etc. Send resumé by Fax (555-348) or e-mail (jobs@tvs.com).	1. What strengths do you bring to this job? 2. Have you any related experience?	
Live-in Caregiver to care for elderly lady. Housekeeping, cooking, and running errands. Car and lic. requd. Sun Evening-Fri PM. $800/mo + room and board. Call 555-4333 after 6:30 pm.	3. What strengths do you bring to this job? 4. Have you any related experience?	
Cable installers needed for cable contracting firm. We will train. Must have a pickup or SUV, and must be albe to pass a background check and drug screening. Med/Dent/Life ins. available. Apply at 43 La Porta St.	5. What strengths do you bring to this job? 6. Have you any related experience?	
CHILDCARE Help, PT/FT. Care for infant after school. NE area. Call M-F. 555-3432.	7. What strengths do you bring to this job? 8. Have you any related experience?	
Like working with people? Prep and clean rental cars. Entry-level career opportunity with advancement opportunities, excellent pay, and benefits. EOE, Drug Screen. E-mail sally.sloan@ edwards.com or call 555-9333.	9. What strengths do you bring to this job? 10. Have you any related experience?	

Introducing Others

Directions: Working with a partner, write introductions for each other.
Use the web below to gather details, and then write the introduction on the lines.
When you are finished, introduce your partner to the class.

How you know the person:	Person's Name:	One interesting fact about the person:

_____

_____

_____

_____

_____

_____

_____

_____

_____

_____

_____

Keeping an Ongoing Grocery List

Directions: As you read the story on the left, keep an ongoing grocery list.

When I had my cereal this morning, I saw that I only had enough for about two bowls left. I eat cereal every day, but I switch off from kind to kind. I like the variety.

After I finished by cereal, I packed a lunch for work. I grabbed my last package of dried fruit since I was out of apples. Thankfully, I had a new loaf of delicious sourdough bread, so I made a turkey and lettuce sandwich. The lettuce was a little wilted since it was the end of the head, but I found enough for a sandwich.

I put my lunch in my backpack and went up to brush my teeth. I used the last stretch of floss as I hurried to finish up and get to work on time.

When I got home from work, I pulled my usual--straight into the kitchen for a snack. I decided to have carrots dipped into ranch dressing, but I really had to shake the dressing bottle to get enough. While I was snacking, I thought about what I wanted for dinner. I decided to have a cheeseburger since I had a whole pack of frozen burgers in the freezer. It smelled so good while I was cooking it, I could hardly wait. I grabbed the second-to-last piece of cheese and watched it melt over the cooked hamburger. I used some of my sourdough bread instead of a bun--and it was great!

While I was eating my cheeseburger, it made me think about lasagna, so I decided to get some for tomorrow night since I have to go grocery shopping anyhow. My grocery store sells a ready-to-heat lasagna that I absolutely love! I'll have to get some garlic bread to go with my lasagna.

After dinner, I talked to some friends online. Then, about 9:00, Chris came over to watch a movie. We were going to make two bags of microwave popcorn, but I only had one bag left, so we just had one. The movie got over at 11:30, my friend left, and I snuggled into bed and dreamed about that great lasagna I'd be having tomorrow night. Only, in my dream, the lasagna was made of apples, horseradish, and tortillas. Funky!

Grocery List

Keeping Private Information Private

Directions: Choose the correct answers.

1. One thing you should never give to a stranger who calls you on the phone is
   _____ **a.** your name.
   _____ **b.** your birthdate.
   _____ **c.** your opinions.

2. One possible problem with giving private information to strangers on the telephone or Internet is that
   _____ **a.** they might not believe you.
   _____ **b.** you might have to buy things you do not really want.
   _____ **c.** they might try to steal your identity.

3. One piece of information you should never give over the Internet is
   _____ **a.** your social security number.
   _____ **b.** your address.
   _____ **c.** the names of your siblings.

4. One piece of information that is usually not private because it is typically publicly avaiable is
   _____ **a.** your middle name.
   _____ **b.** your land phone number.
   _____ **c.** your social security number.

5. One example of family information that you should not tell people outside of the family is
   _____ **a.** where you keep a hidden house key.
   _____ **b.** how your family celebrates holidays.
   _____ **c.** how long you have lived in your home.

Knowing the Front Side of a Piece of Paper

Directions: Circle each paper that shows the front side.

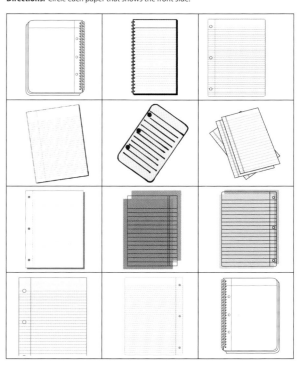

Knowing When to Use and Avoid Slang

Directions: Decide whether or not each statement is appropriate in the given situation and why.

#	Situation	Statement	Why is OK to say	Why is not OK to say
1.	In a research paper for English class	Tree-top tours are wild and crazy experiences.		
2.	When talking to a cousin online	It's EZ to c that Joe is wrong. BTDT. BTW, did you c the new movie? LOL! B4N—Shiny		
3.	When talking to the school principal.	You are such a happenin' guy!		
4.	When giving a presentation at the science fair	This is totally the most hip project and you can totally see that if you totally look.		
5.	When out to eat with some friends	Maura, you can't be my BFF if you spill the beans about me.		
6.	At a job interview	Hey, Dude, like that's not my deal.		

Knowing When to Use Your Signature

Directions: Depending on the directive, write your name in manuscript or cursive.

Directives	Write your name in manuscript or cursive
1. Write your name.	
2. Print your name.	
3. Sign your name.	
4. Write your signature.	
5. Name: First, MI, Last	
6. Name	

Knowing Your Initials

Directions: Use your initials to model the presentation of Tess's initials.

Tess Marie Wilson's Initials	Your Initials
1. TMW	
2. TW	
3. TMW	
4. T.M. Wilson	
5. T. Wilson	
6. TM.Wilson@hardywall.com	

Labeling Files

Directions: Lable these files with the months of the year in order.

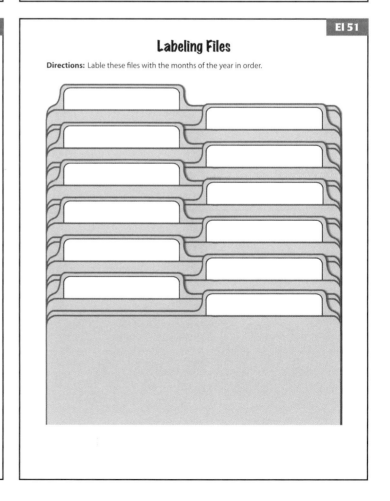

Labeling Moving Boxes

Directions: Look at the items that are to go in each box. Then, label each box with the room it should go to and the key items in the box. Use abbreviations for the rooms

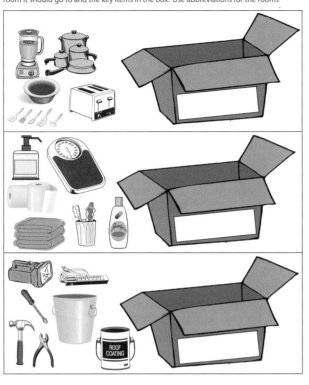

Leaving a Job

Directions: Use the calendar to answer the questions.

OCTOBER						
S	M	T	W	Th	F	S
		1	2	3	4	5
6	7	8	9	10	11	12
13	14	15	16	17	18	19
20	21	22	23	24	25	26
27	28	29	30	31		

1. If you gave two-weeks notice on Oct 9th, what day would be your last day? _____
2. If you gave two-weeks notice on Oct 1st, what day would be your last day? _____
3. If you gave two-weeks notice on Oct 18th, what day would be your last day? _____
4. If you gave two-weeks notice on Oct 7th, what day would be your last day? _____
5. If you want to start your new job on Oct. 28th, what is the last day you can give your two-weeks notice for your current job? _____
6. If you agreed to start a new job on Oct. 21st, would it be fair to your current employer to give notice on Oct. 11th that you are leaving? Explain. _____
7. Why would it be a problem for your current employer if, on Oc. 16th, you said that Oct. 18th would be your last day? _____

Leaving a Message on a Machine

Directions: Say you are leaving a message on an answering machine saying that you will stop by at 10:00 a.m. Write what you might say for each situation below—same general message each time, but different people. For each situation, make sure to identify yourself properly and use words that are appropriate.

Situations	Messages
Your grandmother called and asked you to help her get some boxes down off of a shelf.	
You had an interview yesterday, and the company called and asked if you could come in again this morning for a few minutes.	
You have to pick up some forms from your doctor to send in with an application.	
You loaned a friend some games and are going to pick them up.	

Mailing a Letter

Directions: Read each letter-mailing situation and choose the easiest letter-mailing option that would most likely work. Write the letters in the second column.

Letter-Mailing Options
A. U.S. Post Office
B. Business that has a contract with the U.S. Post Office
C. A private or government office that sends mail out daily
D. A convenience mail box that is maintained by the U.S. Post Office
E. A private or neighborhood mailbox with pickup service

Situations	Letters for Letter-Mailing Options
1. You are at school and have a letter to mail.	
2. You are at home and have a letter to mail.	
3. You are shopping and have a letter to mail.	
4. You are in a strip mall and have a letter to mail. One of the stores in the strip mall is "Mail Spot."	
5. You are at a full-service post office.	
6. You are out for a walk and have a letter to mail. You see a post office box up ahead on the corner.	
7. You use a clothespin to clip a letter to the mailbox by your front door.	
8. You have a letter to mail and you go to a building with the words "U.S. Post Office" over the door.	
9. You are making copies at a copy center and you have a letter to mail, so you drop it in the "outgoing mail" slot.	
10. You are at work and you have a letter to mail.	

Making a General Shopping List

Directions: The images show the supplies you have left at home. For amounts that you think are running low, add those items to the shopping list.

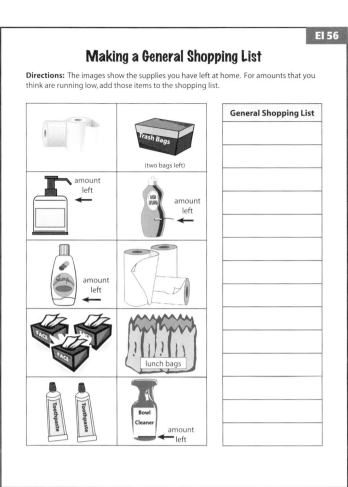

General Shopping List

Making a Grocery List

Directions: Place these food items on the grocery list. Correct spelling is not necessary, but you have to be able to read what you write.

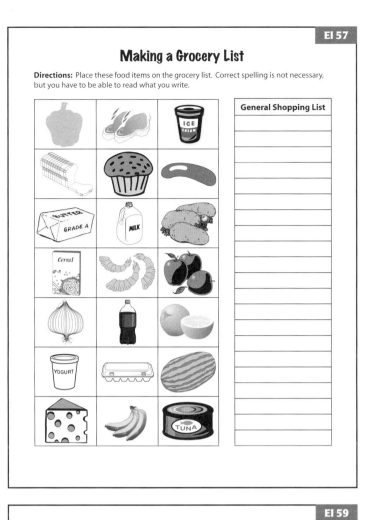

General Shopping List

Making Appointments

Directions: Name six situations where you need to make an appointment before going to see someone.

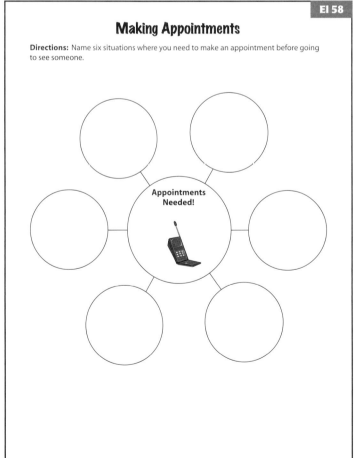

Making Copies

Directions: Match the definitions to the copier-related terms.

Answers	Definitions	Copier-Related Terms
	1. Legal-sized paper	**A.** 8 1/2 x 11
	2. When the copier places copies in sorting bins	**B.** 11 x 17
	3. When the copier takes originals that are printed on one side and copies every two originals back-to-back	**C.** 8 1/2 x 14
	4. Size of a standard piece of paper	**D.** collate
	5. Double-sized piece of paper	**E.** one sided to two sided
Answers	**Definitions**	**Copier-Related Terms**
	6. Holds the different sizes of blank paper to be copied upon	**F.** duplex
	7. A holder on top of the copier from which the copier can pull one original at a time and copy it	**G.** paper trays
	8. To print on both sides	**H.** paper jam
	9. A level glass through which book pages can be copied	**I.** document feeder
	10. When either the original or the copy paper gets caught in the copier and causes the copier to stop	**J.** flatbed

Making Restaurant Reservations

Directions: Choose the correct answers.

1. What are you supposed to say when a restaurant employee asks you for your "party name"?

　_____ **a.** Typically, you would give your favorite holiday for your "party name" since holidays are often party-like events.

　_____ **b.** Give an interesting name or word that is something everyone in your group has in common, such as Big Bowlers.

　_____ **c.** Give the last name of a member of your group so the restaurant knows a name to call out in order to find you when your table is ready.

2. What is one type of restaurant that ALMOST NEVER requires a reservation?

　_____ **a.** fast-food restaurant

　_____ **b.** busy theme restaurant

　_____ **c.** an expensive restaurant

3. What are you supposed to say when you are aked for the "number in your party"?

　_____ **a.** You should try to remember how many people were at your last birthday party.

　_____ **b.** You should tell how many people are in your immediate family.

　_____ **c.** You should tell how many people will be coming to eat in your group.

4. Why does the restaurant need a contact phone number when you make a reservation?

　_____ **a.** so they can make sales calls to you at a later time

　_____ **b.** in case there is a problem with your reservation

　_____ **c.** so they can call you and remind you to come

5. For which meal are reservations most often needed?

　_____ **a.** breakfast

　_____ **b.** lunch

　_____ **c.** dinner

Marking Bills Paid

Directions: Study how the top three bills have been marked paid. Then use today's date and the notes to mark the other bills paid.

Gas Bill — Pd 7-13-08 Online

Water Bill — Pd 7-13-08 Chk #33

Phone Bill — Pd 7-13-08 Debit Card

Gas Bill

Water Bill

Phone Bill

Pay by check　　　　Pay by debit card　　　　Pay online

Naming Cards in a Card Deck

Directions: Below each card, write the card name.

Negotiating a Sale or Purchase

Directions: Match the sentence beginnings to the sentence endings.

Answers	Sentence Beginnings	Sentence Endings
	1. Before you start negotiating to buy something,	A. you probably will not be able to negotiate much of a deal.
	2. Before you start negotiating to sell something,	B. you should wait and see if you can find the item later for less.
	3. If you aren't willing to copromise,	C. you should decide the maximum amount you are willing to pay.
	4. If you think a seller is asking too much for an item,	D. you should decide the minimum amount you are willing to accept.

Answers	Sentence Beginnings	Sentence Endings
	5. If you are negotiating to sell something,	E. you should start with a price that is less than you are willing to pay, but not so little that it insults the seller.
	6. If you are negotiating to buy something,	F. look for something similar in the for-sale ads in the newspaper and check the listed price.
	7. If you have been negotiating to sell something with several different people and have no takers,	G. you should start with a price that is more than you think you will get, but not so much that it scares off the buyer.
	8. One way to get a good idea about how much you can sell something for is to	H. you should consider the possibility that you are asking too much.

Ordering from Catalogs

Directions: Using the search words "online catalog sports equipment," find an online catalog to use to fill in the blanks in the table.

Web Site Address:				
7 different items for sale on the Web site	Product Numbers	Sizes (X if N/A)	Colors (X if N/A)	Prices
			Subtotal	
			Add 10% Shipping	
			Total	

Ordering from Menus

Directions: Use the chalkboard menu to answer the questions.

STARTERS: $5
Cheese Sticks
'Peno Poppers
Tater Skins
Veggies & Dip

SALADS: $7
Walnut & Apple
Grilled Chicken
Cobb
Taco

MAIN DISHES: $8
Spaghetti
Lasagna
Chicken Ravioli
Meatloaf
Beef Stroganoff
Roast Beef
8 oz. Steak
Fried Catfish Fried Shrimp
Grilled Perch
Grilled Salmon

DRINKS: $3
Soft Drinks
Fruit Juice
Ice Cream Shakes
Milk
Coffee or Tea

DESSERTS: $6
Pie á la mode
Cheesecake
Ohio Choc Cake
Banana Pudding

1. How is the pricing on this menu different from most restaurants? _____

2. Choose something to eat and fill in the chart.

Food Choices	Cost
Total Cost:	

Ordering Items Over the Telephone

Directions: Using the search words "board games," find an online catalog to use to fill in the blanks in the table. Then, working with a partner, role play placing your order over the telephone. When it is your turn to be the salesperson, guide the buyer to provide the correct information by offering these directives for each item: "First item, please," "Product number," "Size," "Color," and "Price."

Web Site Address:				
7 different items for sale on the Web site	Product Numbers	Sizes (X if N/A)	Colors (X if N/A)	Prices
			Subtotal	
			Add 10% Shipping	
			Total	

Planning a Surprise

Directions: Answer the questions.

1. Why does telling too many people about a surprise increase the chances of spoiling the surprise? _____

2. Why does a surprise that is planned for one week have a better chance of working out than a surprise that is planned for a month? _____

3. What is the difference between general lying and lying to pull of a surprise? _____

4. Make a list of three people and situations that you could plan a surprise for. _____

5. Choose one of your answers to #4 and explain what the surprise would be like and how you would get the person of honor to the event and still keep it a secret. _____

Reacting to Mistakes

Directions: Choose the correct answers.

1. Who makes mistakes?
   _____ **a.** unlucky people
   _____ **b.** everyone
   _____ **c.** people who do not try hard enough

2. A mistake can be a good thing since it can help you
   _____ **a.** find something that works better.
   _____ **b.** realize that you aren't so smart.
   _____ **c.** have more opportunities to work hard.

3. If you make a mistake,
   _____ **a.** you should try to hide it as long as you can
   _____ **b.** you should explain what happend and why it was not your fault.
   _____ **c.** you should explain what happened and what you plan to do next.

4. To fix a mistake you made,
   _____ **a.** you should ask others for advice since other ideas might be helpful.
   _____ **b.** leave it alone and move onto something else.
   _____ **c.** you should work it out yourself since it was your mistake.

5. If you make a mistake that affects only you, such as an error in your homework that you catch and fix,
   _____ **a.** you should be honest and tell others about it.
   _____ **b.** you should accept that you make a lot of mistakes and aren't very good at most things.
   _____ **c.** you should keep it to yourself as part of your personal learning and development.

Recognizing Slang

Directions: In the chart below, express the ideas in other ways to compare current slang, past slang, and non-slang.

IDEAS	Slang you would use	Slang your parent(s) used	Another way to say it that is not slang
I like the way you do things			
I like your outfit.			
I agree with you.			
This is a friend of mine.			
You are not right.			
I am tired.			

Recording an Answering Machine Message

Directions: Use the lines below to write an answering machine message that you think you an comfortably read within 10 seconds. In your message, make sure to ask the caller to leave a name, phone number, and brief message. Ask a partner to use a clock or watch with a second hand to check your timing while you read your message.

Requesting Adptations/Accommodations

Directions: Write a request for an appropriate adaptation or accommodation in each of the following situations.

1. Say you have only one leg, and you get around fairly well. However, slippery surfaces cause you a problem. At your work, one department has put in new flooring that is rather slippery. → What would you say to ask for an adaptation or accommodation?

2. Say you do not read very well, but have worked at the same job for five years without your reading being a problem. The company has decided that more communication will be done by e-mail, so now you will have to read daily. → What would you say to ask for an adaptation or accommodation?

3. Say you have serious asthma. You manage it rather well, both at home and at work. However, a new person has joined your department at work, and she wears very heavy perfume. The perfume sets your asthma off. → What would you say to ask for an adaptation or accommodation?

4. Say you have a problem functioning in social and group settings. You work in a bookkeeping office where you are responsible for making sure bills are paid on time. Two other people also pay bills. → What would you say to ask for an adaptation or accommodation?

5. You have a back problem that prevents you from standing up for long periods of time. You injured your back at work. You are now back at your job where you watch for problem products on an assembly line. → What would you say to ask for an adaptation or accommodation?

Responding in Your Best Interests When Treated Unfairly by a Coworker

Directions: For each situation, circle the response option that is in your best interest.

Situations	Option A	Option B	Option C
Situation #1: A coworker in your department won't talk to you because you are dating his or her ex-spouse.	Just ignore the coworker.	Always be pleasant and professional towards the coworker.	Try to get moved to a different area of the company so you do not have to work closely with the person.
Situation #2: You are good at your job and often get compliments. A coworker is jealous and has started trying to make your work look bad.	Get specific proof of what is going on and tell your supervisor.	Try to make your coworker's work look even worse so he or she will get fired.	Tell your coworker you are going to have him or her beat up if the problem continues.
Situation #3: A coworker is trying to cover for having stolen a computer. The boss called you in and said the coworker said you stole it. You do not know who stole the computer nor why the	Tell the boss that you did not take it, and then go up to the coworker and say, "What did I ever do to you?"	Tell the boss you did not take it and start asking around to see what others know so you can clear your name.	Tell the boss that the coworker who turned you in was probably the one who took the computer.
Situation #4: You and a coworker are up for the same promotion. For two days, the coworker has been saying nasty things to the supervisor about you.	Get back at the coworker by saying nasty things to the supervisor about him.	Be positive and present yourself well. Your coworker's comments are more likely to hurt himself than you.	Stay close to the coworker so you can hear everything he says and can defend yourself immediately.

Responding to Strengths and Weaknesses

Directions: Identify the strengths and weaknesses in each situation. Then, explain how you could use your strengths to overcome your weaknesses in the real-life situation.

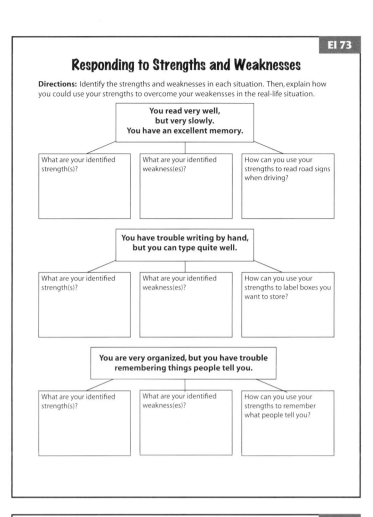

You read very well, but very slowly. You have an excellent memory.

- What are your identified strength(s)?
- What are your identified weakness(es)?
- How can you use your strengths to read road signs when driving?

You have trouble writing by hand, but you can type quite well.

- What are your identified strength(s)?
- What are your identified weakness(es)?
- How can you use your strengths to label boxes you want to store?

You are very organized, but you have trouble remembering things people tell you.

- What are your identified strength(s)?
- What are your identified weakness(es)?
- How can you use your strengths to remember what people tell you?

Returning an Item You Bought

Directions: Read about each purchase and then describe a situation where it would and would not be OK to return it.

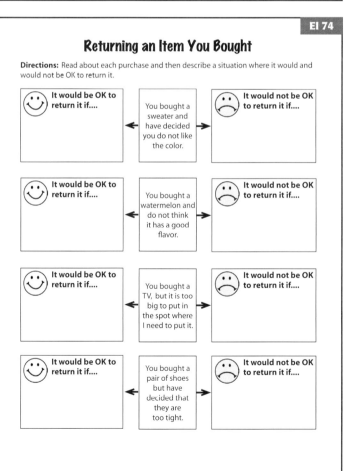

- It would be OK to return it if.... | You bought a sweater and have decided you do not like the color. | It would not be OK to return it if....
- It would be OK to return it if.... | You bought a watermelon and do not think it has a good flavor. | It would not be OK to return it if....
- It would be OK to return it if.... | You bought a TV, but it is too big to put in the spot where I need to put it. | It would not be OK to return it if....
- It would be OK to return it if.... | You bought a pair of shoes but have decided that they are too tight. | It would not be OK to return it if....

Saying Thanks (Orally or in Writing)

Directions: Write a thank you to each of the people below. Then, working with a partner, practice saying thanks orally.

It was your turn to take the garbage out, and your brother did it for you.

Your uncle let you look at the stars with his telescope.

Your neighbor kept your sister for you while you were gone.

Your father grilled brats for you and your friends.

You dropped your books, and your friend picked them up for you.

Your grandmother fixed your torn shirt for you.

Scheduling a Job Interview

Directions: Use your actual schedule to give a professional response to each of these job interview requests.

Job Interview Requests	Your Responses
1. Could you please come for an interview next Tuesday at 10:00?	
2. We'd like to schedule an interview for Friday at 4:00. Will that work for you?	
3. Our interview schedule for the next three days is open between 10:00 a.m. and 3:00 p.m. What would work for you?	
4. Do you have some time next Thursday for an interview?	

Sending an E-mail

Directions: Draw arrows from the explanations to the parts of the e-mail window.

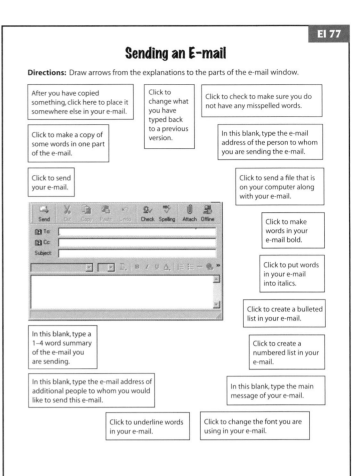

After you have copied something, click here to place it somewhere else in your e-mail.

Click to change what you have typed back to a previous version.

Click to check to make sure you do not have any misspelled words.

Click to make a copy of some words in one part of the e-mail.

In this blank, type the e-mail address of the person to whom you are sending the e-mail.

Click to send your e-mail.

Click to send a file that is on your computer along with your e-mail.

Click to make words in your e-mail bold.

Click to put words in your e-mail into italics.

Click to create a bulleted list in your e-mail.

Click to create a numbered list in your e-mail.

In this blank, type a 1–4 word summary of the e-mail you are sending.

In this blank, type the e-mail address of additional people to whom you would like to send this e-mail.

In this blank, type the main message of your e-mail.

Click to underline words in your e-mail.

Click to change the font you are using in your e-mail.

Sending Greeting Cards

Directions: Identify eight reasons for sending greeting cards. For each reason, identify one person to whom you could send a card, the date you should mail the card, and a comment you could write on the card.

Reason to send a greeting card	Person to whom you might send the card	Date when you should mail the card	Comment you might write on the card
1.			
2.			
3.			
4.			
5.			
6.			
7.			
8.			

Setting Goals

Directions: Write one goal for each area of life that is listed below.

Life Areas	Your Goals
1. School	
2. Family	
3. Friends	
4. Future Plans	
5. Health	
6. Leisure	

Setting Priorities

Directions: Use the numbers from 1–8 to put the issues in each list in order of importance to you.

Rank from 1–8 (1 being most important to you)	List #1 Issues
	Seeing your favorite TV show
	Getting at least 9 hours of sleep
	Seeing all the popular movies
	Going to nice restaurants
	Doing outside activities
	Having stylish clothes
	Dancing with friends
	Listening to music

Rank from 1–8 (1 being most important to you)	List #2 Issues
	Having lots of friends
	Having a job so you have your own money
	Doing fun things with your family
	Doing well in school
	Going to school sporting events
	Having deep conversations
	Being part of family decisions
	Feeling that you are needed

Solving Problems

Directions: Work with a partner to come up with a solution for each problem.

Problems	Solutions
1. You need help to quit biting your fingernails, but you are allergic to the liquids that you can buy to make your fingers taste bad.	
2. You get thirsty in the night, so you keep a bottle of water by your bed. But, the water always dribbles down your chin when you try to drink it in bed.	
3. You have to be really careful of the kitchen chairs or they will scratch the wood floor.	
4. You have ruined three shirts in the past week because they caught on a rough spot on your dresser.	
5. You have ten friends coming over to watch a show on TV. You only have enough space on the couch and the lounge chairs for five people.	

Sorting into Categories

Directions: Cut the images on this page out and sort them into six categories. Compare your categories to your classmates' categories. Then sort them into four categories and compare. Then two categories and compare.

Spelling Names Correctly

Directions: Give each of these people a first name you have heard before. Make sure to use a common spelling of each name.

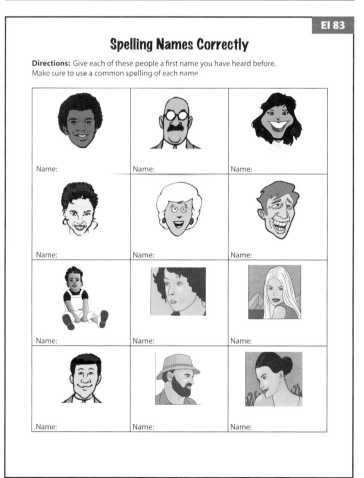

Spelling the Days of the Week Correctly

Directions: Create a word hunt and then trade with a partner and find each other's words. Use each day of the week five times in your word hunt. Make sure to spell the days of the week correctly. Then randomly fill in the rest of the letters.

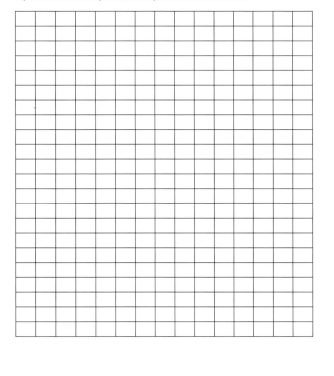

Summarizing Movies and TV Shows

Directions: Think of a movie or TV show you have seen recently. On the lines below, write a summary of the movie or show. Do not use extra paper. Make your summary fit in the space below.

Taking Notes

Directions: Choose a page in a textbook and take notes using the format below. Use as many circles as needed or add circles as needed.

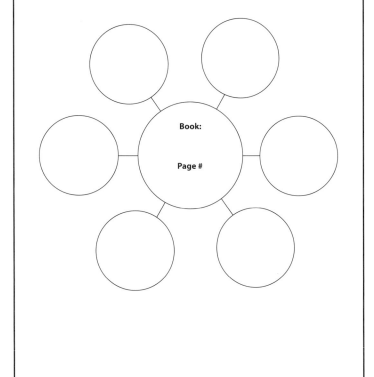

Book:

Page #

Talking in Simple Sentences

Directions: Talking in simple, complete sentences makes it easier for other people to understand what you are saying. Rewrite the original statements in simple, complete sentences. Then, working with a partner, practice saying the simple sentences aloud.

Original Statements	Simple, Complete Sentences
1. Yo! Charlie! Hey big guy! Ready? My car. Steaks! Yo!	
2. Hey, Carrie! Cold? Sweater? Cozy!	
3. Mitch. (Show him a book.) Found in my car. Yours?	
4. I went out for a run in the forest this morning and it started to rain on me and at first I thought the trees were going to protect me, but I got soaking wet and then the wind started blowing and I got so cold.	
5. A skunk got in our garage yesterday and it left the most awful smell and we tried to spray the garage to make it smell better, but it still smells awful and we are going to keep our garage door closed from now on.	

Talking on the Phone with Someone You Do Not Know

Directions: Match the sentence beginnings to the sentence endings.

Answers	Sentence Beginnings	Sentence Endings
	1. If someone you do not know calls and starts talking to you as if you should know him or her,	**A.** you should offer to take a message and make sure to ask for the person's name.
	2. If someone you do not know calls and asks for your mother but your mother is not home	**B.** you should find out who it is so that the conversation will make more sense.
	3. Even if you do not want to talk to a stranger who calls,	**C.** you should hang up without saying anything more.
	4. If a person you do not know calls and says rude things to you,	**D.** you should be polite because there is no reason to be rude to anyone.
Answers	**Sentence Beginnings**	**Sentence Endings**
	5. If you receive a phone call, can tell it is a recording, and are interested in hearing it,	**E.** hang up right away with out listening to the rest of it.
	6. If you receive a phone call, can tell it is a recording, and are not interested in hearing it,	**F.** it isn't rude to hang up since the person isn't letting you be part of the conversation.
	7. If someone starts talking to you as if you should know him or her, but you do not know who it is,	**G.** listen until it ends and then hang up.
	8. If someone you do not know calls and talks nonstop and won't stop to let you say a word,	**H.** you should something like, "I'm sorry, I don't recognize your voice. Who is this?"

Talking to a Supervisor About Personal Problems

Directions: Read each pair of statements and choose the one that would be most appropriate to say to a work supervisor.

Pair #1
_____ The school just called, my daughter is sick, and they want me to pick her up.
_____ My daughter needs me, I have to go. Being a good parent is more important than my job.

Pair #2
_____ My grandmother's beeper just went off, so I have to go see if she is OK. I'll call you when I know what is going on.
_____ I have to leave for personal business. I'll call you and let you know when I'll be able to come back.

Pair #3
_____ I can't work for the next two days, so I'll see you on Friday. I'm sure you can get along without me for a couple days.
_____ I have to go in for some medical tests tomorrow, and I have to spend the night. So I need to take two sick days. I should be fine to be back at work on Friday.

Pair #4
_____ I need to work at home tomorrow. I'm sure that is OK since Andrea did it last week and it worked out OK for her.
_____ My furnace is acting up, so I have a repairman coming out tomorrow morning. If it is OK with you, I'll plan to work at home while I wait for the repairman to show up and get done.

Talking to Authority Figures

Directions: Answer the questions.

1. What does the saying "You'll catch more flies with honey than with vinegar" have to do with talking to authority figures? _____

_____

_____

2. Why should you assume that, in a planning session with your boss, you would have to compromise more than your boss would? _____

_____

_____

3. Make a list of three ideas that it would be best to avoid when talking to one of your teachers.

_____

_____

_____

4. Parents sometimes say you have to do something "because I said so, and I am the parent." What should you say or do if your parent says that? _____

_____

_____

5. Why is it in your best interest to talk differently to authority figures than you do to your friends?

_____

_____

_____

Talking to Children

Directions: When you talk to children, it helps if you use little words, short sentences, few details, and step-by-step explanations. It also helps to talk about ideas with which they are familiar. Rewrite the original statements so they will work better for children.

Original Statements	Statements Rewritten for a 4-yr-old
1. It might rain today, and if it does, we'll have to remain inside in lieu of going to the park, but maybe we could bake cookies or do some other stupendous thing inside.	
2. Why don't you see if you can make yourself a peanut butter sandwich.	
3. Your shirt is a lovely hue that complements you wonderfully.	
4. We are going to go shopping and get lettuce, grapes, oranges, tuna, tortillas, bread, oatmeal, and milk.	
5. Do you want to pretend that you are a business executive and your doll is one of your 200 employees?	

Telling Jokes

Directions: Tell your classmates one of the jokes below or a joke of your own. When you tell the joke, make sure to tell it in a sensible order and include all the key points. Also, keep the punch line for the end and try not to laugh while you tell the joke. Do not read the joke.

Joke #1

Pete and Harold were on the school camping trip. They were sleeping in the same tent when Harold woke up. He called out to Pete, "Pete, look up at the sky and tell me what you see."

Pete woke up and looked at the sky. "I see a clear sky full of stars."

"What does that tell you?" Harold asked?

"It tells me that it isn't going to rain, that we are not in the city, and that stars make a person feel peaceful. What does it tell you?" Pete asked.

"It tells me that someone stole our tent!" Harold said.

Joke #2

When Martin was in first grade, his older brother's friend Luke liked to tease him. One day, Luke said, "Martin, I have five dimes and five nickels, which group would you like?" Martin looked at the two groups of coins carefully and took the nickels. Luke laughed loudly as he went out to find Martin's brother and tell him that his brother thought nickels were worth more than dimes just because nickels were bigger. For the next month, every day Luke stopped to see Martin and offered him either a pile of nickels or a pile of dimes. Every day Martin chose the nickels. Finally, Martin's brother thought the joke had gone on long enough. He said to Martin, "Don't you know that dimes are worth more than nickels?" Martin answerd, "Sure I do. But, if I choose the dimes, he'll quit playing the game with me. I've made $10 this month."

Joke #3

Molly and her mother came home from the grocery store. After they unloaded the groceries, Molly opened the animal crackers and spread them out on the counter.

"What are you doing?" Molly asked.

Molly answered, "The label says 'Do not eat if seal is broken.' I'm looking for the seal and hoping it isn't broken."

Using a Calendar to Keep a Schedule

Directions: Decide whether each activity below takes place often and regularly and does not need to be written down or is harder to remember and needs to be written down. Use the calendar to make a schedule of the things that need to be written down.

April						
S	M	T	W	Th	F	S
				1	2	3
4	5	6	7	8	9	10
11	12	13	14	15	16	17
18	19	20	21	22	23	24
25	26	27	28	29	30	

1. Each day after school, you will have a snack about 4:00.
2. You are getting your hair cut on April 8th.
3. Your science project is due on April 23rd.
4. You won't have school on April 3, 4, 10, 11, 17, 18, 24, or 25.
5. Your favorite TV show is on each Thursday night at 8:00.
6. You have agreed to help your grandmother clean her yard on April 17th.
7. Your cousin Marcy is coming to spend the weekend on April 9–11.
8. You have to take the garbage out every Wedensday morning.

Using a Computer for Basic Needs

Directions: Explain how you would use a computer for each task. (Describe the procedures based on a computer with which you are familiar.)

Tasks	How you would use a computer to complete the tasks
Example: *Make a name tag*	• *Open Word* • *Create a text box the size I want the nametag* • *Click to center the text* • *Use a large and bold font* • *Print and cut out*
1. Write a letter	
2. Send an e-mail	
3. Add a bunch of numbers	
4. Print a photo	

Using a Confident Voice

Directions: Think of a few sentences on a topic you could confidently tell the class about. Write the sentences on the blank lines. Review the "Using a Confident Voice Guidelines" and then use the guidelines to confidently share your ideas with the class.

> **Guidelines for Using a Confident Voice**
>
> • Use good posture with head held high
> • Use eye contact
> • Speak loudly enotugh to be easily heard
> • Know what you want to say

Using a Planner

Directions: Use this weekly planner page to record your school assignments for the week. If you have other things on your schedule, record them also.

Saturday/Sunday
(Dates:)

Monday
(Date:)

Tuesday
(Date:)

Wednesday
(Date:)

Thursday
(Date:)

Friday
(Date:)

Using Abbreviations

Directions: Rewrite each name, address, or sentence using as many common abbreviations as possible.

Names, addresses, or sentences	Rewrite with common abbreviations
Sample: Mister Joe Willis	Mr. Joe Willis
1. Doctor Paulette Meyers	
2. Javus, Incorporated	
3. the third Tuesday in January	
4. 274 South Second Street, Waverly, Iowa, 50677	
5. 55 North Westwood Avenue, Freeport, Illinois 61032	
6. Have you seen my school identification card?	
7. I have an English examination at 10:00 in the morning today.	
8. The meeting lasted two hours and thirty minutes.	
9. Perry attends North Texas University.	
10. The veterinarian we go to is on West Willow Road.	

Using Appropriate Tones and Volume Levels

Directions: Working with a partner, demonstrate voice tones and volume levels that are appropriate for the situations. (Tones vary with emotions and volume refers to loudness or softness.)

Situations	Words to Use for Demonstrations
1. You see 3-year-old Hazel about ready to run out into the street.	Hazel! Stop! Come to me!
2. You are excited for a friend who just learned that she got a job she wanted.	Congratulations, Emma! You deserve it!
3. You are talking to a friend who feels sad today.	Do you want to take a walk? It might make you feel better.
4. You are talking to a teacher about an assignment.	Am I right that we are supposed to answer the questions on p. 34 and write a one-page story?
5. You are talking to some friends about a movie.	I thought it was really funny when Matt walked into work wearing that rooster costume.

Using Change-of-Address Forms

Directions: Fill in the change-of-address form. Use your current address and this "new" address: 482 N. Steckelberg St. Lincoln, NE 68583. Include all members of your household.

Change of address applicant

(First)   (Middle)   (Last)

Home Phone: (   )   Cell: (   )

E-mail Address:

Names of all other parties who receive mail at the current address and will receive mail at the new address

(First)   (Middle)   (Last)

(First)   (Middle)   (Last)

(First)   (Middle)   (Last)

(First)   (Middle)   (Last)

(First)   (Middle)   (Last)

(First)   (Middle)   (Last)

Current address

Last date at this address: (m) _____ (d) _____ (y) _____

Street Address _____ Apt. # _____

City   State   Zip

New address

Street Address _____

City   State   Zip

Using Effective Phone Skills

Directions: Working with a partner, demonstrate each phone skill—both the improper and prover versions. Check them off as you finish them.

Phone Skills	Improper Display of Skills	Proper Display of Skills
Using Appropriate Voice Volume	____ Talk too loudly ____ Talk too softly	____ Talk at a comfortable volume
Identifying Yourself	____ Say something vague, such as "Hi, it's me!"	(To someone you know well) ____ Casually introduce yourself, such as "Hi, it's (first name or nickname) (To someone you don't know real well) ____ Introduce yourself more formally, such as "Hello, this is (first and last name)
Keeping Activity Noise to a Minimum	____ Put the phone on speaker so you can use your hands to do something, such as putting the dishes away	____ If you do something while you are talking, make sure it is quiet, such as moving paper. ____ Just sit or stand still and talk. Do not do anything else.
Paying Attention to the Conversation	____ Pay attention to something else while you are talking (such as the TV) and only participate by vaguely listening and saying "yes" or "no."	____ Be an active part of the conversation. Ask questions and offer meaningful comments.
Ending a Conversation	____ Say what you have to say and then just hang up.	____ Lead in to the end of the call with a comment such as "Talk to you later. "Then say "Good bye."
Handling a Wrong Number	____ If someone calls your number by mistake, hang up	____ If someone calls your number by mistake, say something like "Sorry, you've got the wrong nunber. "Then hang up.

Using Eye Contact

Directions: Sort the words in the word list into the correct columns.

Word List		
confident	mature	bored
dishonest	sincere	disinterested
convincing	proud	like you are not listening
like you do not like the talker	like you care	like you are hiding something

Poor Eye Contact Can Make You Appear.....	Good Eye Contact Can Make You Appear.....

Using Good Judgment When Talking to Strangers

Directions: Decide whether or not it is safe to talk to a stranger in each situation.

Situations		Explain Why? or Why not?
You are walking home when a stranger calls to you from a car and offers you a ride.	Safe / Not Safe	
You are sitting next to a stranger on an airplane and she asks you about the movie.	Safe / Not Safe	
You are at a gas station when a stranger invites you over to his house.	Safe / Not Safe	
You are walking home at night with a friend when you meet a stranger who stops to talk.	Safe / Not Safe	
You are sitting next to a stranger on a bus who asks you for personal information.	Safe / Not Safe	

Using Manners in Conversations

Directions: Respond to each directive below by describing situations where you could use manners in conversations.

Describe two situations when you should smile at the person to whom you are talking even if you feel sad or angry.

Describe two situations when you should apologize both before and after you talk to a person or a group of people.

Describe two situations when it would be OK to walk away from a conversation without saying a word.

Using TO DO Lists

Directions: Make a list of things you have to do this week. Check each item off when you finish it.

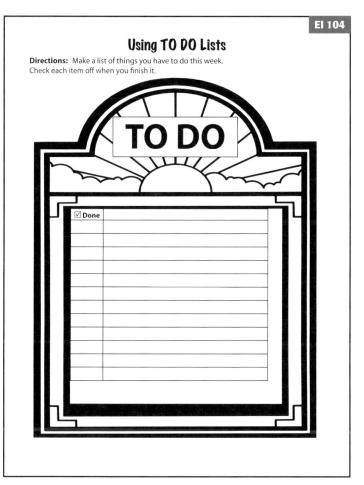

Volunteering to Help a Friend or Neighbor

Directions: In each empty circle, write one thing you could do to help a friend or neighbor.

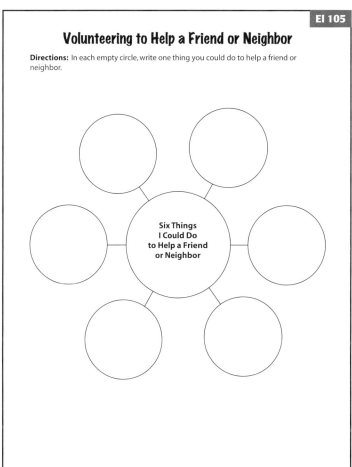

Six Things I Could Do to Help a Friend or Neighbor

Writing a Basic Resumé

Directions: Neatly fill in this form to create a basic resumé. Then, if possible, transfer the information into a computer and format your resumé to look professional.

Name and Contact Information	
Education History	
Work History	
Personal Interests	

Writing a Business Letter

Directions: Circle the BEST option for each part of a business letter. Then, use your answers to create a business letter on a separate piece of paper.

1. Date
a. Feb. 8th
b. 2-8-09
c. February 8, 2009

2. Prior to greeting
a. Ms. Alicia Kirkwood
Bemis Auto
7832 Lorena Street
Paducah, KY 42001
b. Alicia Kirkwood
7832 Lorena Street
Paducah, KY 42001
Bemis Auto
c. Bemis Auto
7832 Lorena Street
Paducah, KY 42001

3. Greeting
a. Dear Alicia,
b. Dear Ms. Kirkwood,
c. Dear Ms. Kirkwood:

4. Opening Sentence
a. Hi There!
b. You probably know what I want.
c. I understand you have an opening for a receptionist.

5. Second Sentence
a. I would like to apply for the job.
b. This job is for me!
c. I'm looking for a job.

6. Third Sentence
a. I have worked as a receptionist assistant for a year and feel I would make a good receptionist.
b. Jabbering on the phone is one of my specialties, so I'm sure I would be good at this job.
c. Even though a receptionist job is low-paying and requires very little thought, I think I would be good at it for a while.

7. Closing Sentence
a. You'll be sorry if you don't hire me.
b. I have attached my resumé and hope to hear from you soon.
c. You won't find a better candidate than me.

8. Salutation
a. Thanks a lot!
b. Nice talking to you,
c. Sincerely,

9. Signature
a. *Joe Bailey*

Joe Bailey
45 W. Lotus
Paducah, KY 42001
b. *Joe Bailey*
45 W. Lotus
Paducah, KY 42001
c. Joe

Writing a Friendly Letter

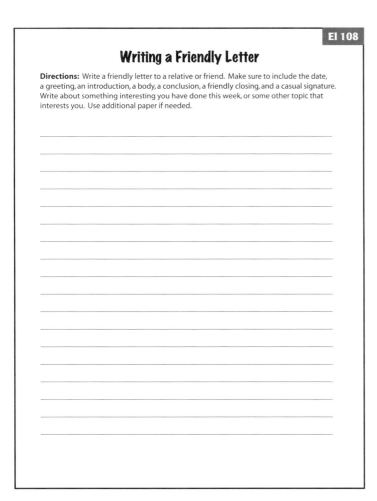

Directions: Write a friendly letter to a relative or friend. Make sure to include the date, a greeting, an introduction, a body, a conclusion, a friendly closing, and a casual signature. Write about something interesting you have done this week, or some other topic that interests you. Use additional paper if needed.

Writing E-Mail Subject Lines

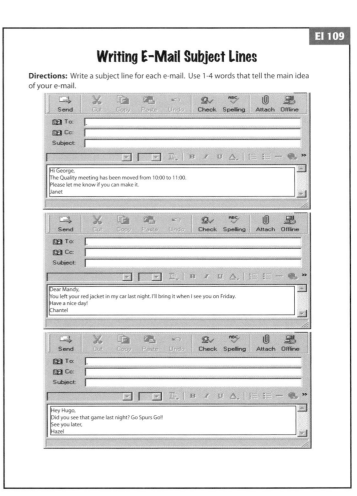

Directions: Write a subject line for each e-mail. Use 1-4 words that tell the main idea of your e-mail.

Writing 'For Sale' Ads

Directions: To save space and money, *For Sale* ads often include many abbreviations and shortened phrases. For example, these ads often include the following abbreviations and phrases:

bdrm (bedroom)	chld rckr (child rocker)	off ch (office chair)
OBO (Or Best Offer)	4' H & 3' W (high and wide)	w/ (with)
Like new	exc cond (excellent condition)	Call after 6:00

Write *For Sale* ads for the two items below. Use as little space as possible, but include all the essential parts. Make up needed details that you do not know. Include a price.

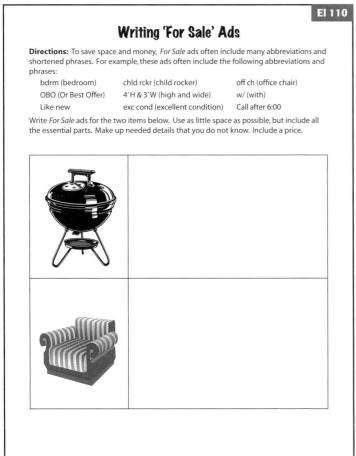

Writing on a Gift Tag

Directions: Address each of the name tags to someone to whom you might give a gift. Make them all from you.

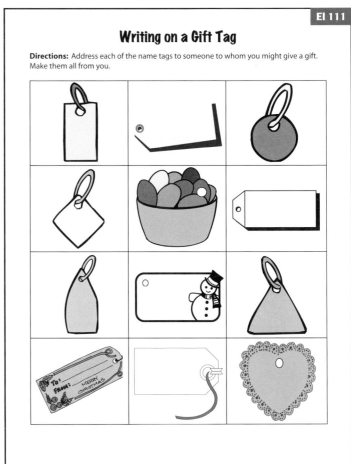

Writing Phone Messages

Directions: Read each phone conversation and take a message. Use today's date and time.

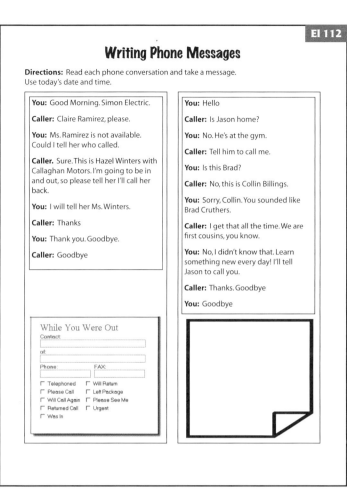

You: Good Morning. Simon Electric.

Caller: Claire Ramirez, please.

You: Ms. Ramirez is not available. Could I tell her who called.

Caller. Sure. This is Hazel Winters with Callaghan Motors. I'm going to be in and out, so please tell her I'll call her back.

You: I will tell her Ms. Winters.

Caller: Thanks

You: Thank you. Goodbye.

Caller: Goodbye

You: Hello

Caller: Is Jason home?

You: No. He's at the gym.

Caller: Tell him to call me.

You: Is this Brad?

Caller: No, this is Collin Billings.

You: Sorry, Collin. You sounded like Brad Cruthers.

Caller: I get that all the time. We are first cousins, you know.

You: No, I didn't know that. Learn something new every day! I'll tell Jason to call you.

Caller: Thanks. Goodbye

You: Goodbye

While You Were Out

Contact:

of:

Phone: ___ FAX: ___

☐ Telephoned ☐ Will Return
☐ Please Call ☐ Left Package
☐ Will Call Again ☐ Please See Me
☐ Returned Call ☐ Urgent
☐ Was In

Writing School Excuses

Directions: Assume you have a child named Henry Lincoln. Write a school excuse for each situation below. Begin each excuse with "Please excuse Henry from school on _____ because _____." Make sure not to include unnecessary details.

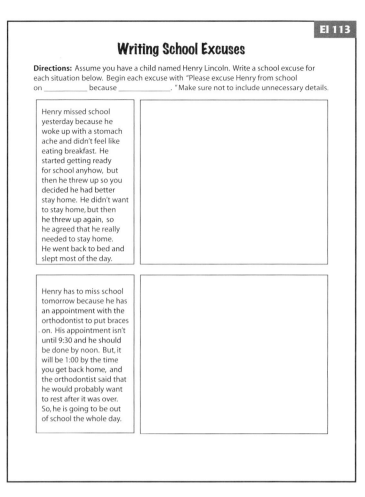

Henry missed school yesterday because he woke up with a stomach ache and didn't feel like eating breakfast. He started getting ready for school anyhow, but then he threw up so you decided he had better stay home. He didn't want to stay home, but then he threw up again, so he agreed that he really needed to stay home. He went back to bed and slept most of the day.

Henry has to miss school tomorrow because he has an appointment with the orthodontist to put braces on. His appointment isn't until 9:30 and he should be done by noon. But, it will be 1:00 by the time you get back home, and the orthodontist said that he would probably want to rest after it was over. So, he is going to be out of school the whole day.

Writing Within Given Space

Directions: When you start filling out a form, you have to look at the amount of space available for requested information and choose your writing size to fit. Write your name and address in each of the spaces below.

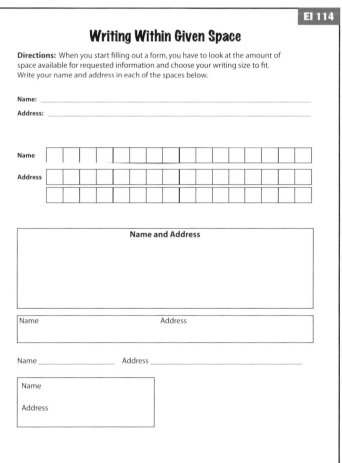

Name: _____

Address: _____

Name

Address

Name and Address

Name ___ Address ___

Name _____ Address _____

Name

Address

Zigzagging Through a Crowd

Directions: It is easier to work your way through a crowd if you politely ask people to let your through and apologize each time you bump someone. Fill in the boxes with comments that could help you make your way through a crowd.

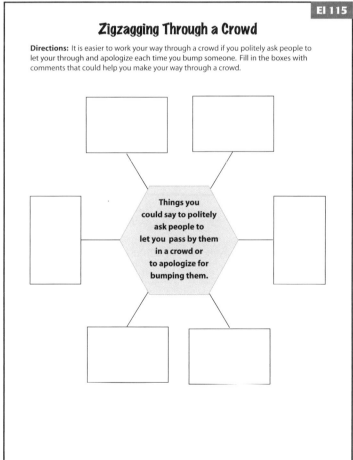

Things you could say to politely ask people to let you pass by them in a crowd or to apologize for bumping them.

Language Arts: Receptive Literacy

Accepting Compliments

Directions: Explain why each response is or is not a good reply to the compliment. For those that are not good, write better ones.

Compliments	Responses	Is the response a good one?	If yes, explain. If no, write a better one.
1. Your hair looks nice today.	It's the same as it always is.		
2. You did a nice job on this test.	Thanks. I thought this unit was interesting.		
3. I hear you brought the avocado dip. It's really good.	I'm glad you like it, but I think I put a little too much salt in this batch.		
4. You sure are good at telling jokes.	Careful! You are encouraging me!		
5. That's a good idea!	I was hoping you would like it.		

Asking for Reading Help If Needed

Directions: For each question, choose the correct answer from the answer box.

Answer Box

A — Ask for help right away.

B — Try to figure out the word(s) before asking for help.

C — Try to figure out the words on own. If can't, should just go on without asking for help.

Answers	Letter-Clarification Spellings
	1. If Carol is reading a story and comes to a word she doesn't know, she should.....
	2. Say Carlos is trying to read a label on a tube in a First Aid kit so he can help a hurt child. If Carlos is not sure what the label says, he should....
	3. If Ollie is reading about a TV show and isn't sure what the words say, he should....
	4. If Malik is reading the words of a song in church and doesn't know all the words, he should.....
	5. If Becca is having trouble reading a menu in a restaurant, she should.....

Asking for Verbal Clarification

Directions: Make a list of last names that include the listed letters. Then, working with a partner, take turns spelling the names aloud so the other person can write them. If you are unsure of a letter you hear, ask for clarification by saying, for example, "Is that *b* as in boy?"

Letters	Your List	Your Partner's List
p *or* b	1.	1.
s *or* f	2.	2.
m *or* n	3.	3.
g *or* t	4.	4.
b *or* d	5.	5.
b *or* v	6.	6.

Blocking Out Distracting Background Noise

Directions: Put a check next to each situation that is likely to cause background noise that a person would want to block out.

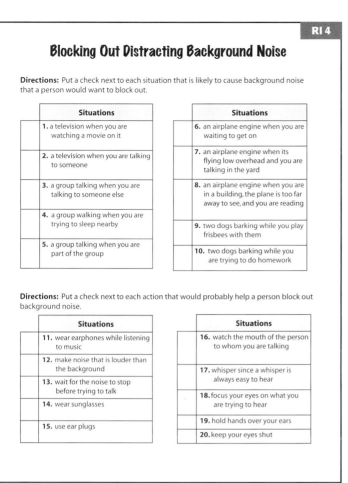

Situations
1. a television when you are watching a movie on it
2. a television when you are talking to someone
3. a group talking when you are talking to someone else
4. a group walking when you are trying to sleep nearby
5. a group talking when you are part of the group

Situations
6. an airplane engine when you are waiting to get on
7. an airplane engine when its flying low overhead and you are talking in the yard
8. an airplane engine when you are in a building, the plane is too far away to see, and you are reading
9. two dogs barking while you play frisbees with them
10. two dogs barking while you are trying to do homework

Directions: Put a check next to each action that would probably help a person block out background noise.

Situations
11. wear earphones while listening to music
12. make noise that is louder than the background
13. wait for the noise to stop before trying to talk
14. wear sunglasses
15. use ear plugs

Situations
16. watch the mouth of the person to whom you are talking
17. whisper since a whisper is always easy to hear
18. focus your eyes on what you are trying to hear
19. hold hands over your ears
20. keep your eyes shut

Buying an Airline Ticket Online

Directions: Choose a date and location for an airplane trip. In the blanks below, write the information that you would enter into the computer windows.

OR: Enter the information into an actual airline Internet site. If you use an actual site, make sure to cancel when the payment window opens if not before.

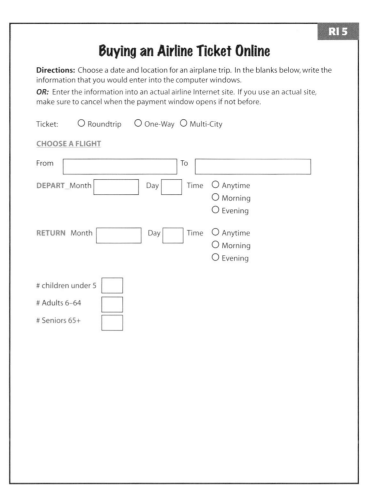

Ticket: ○ Roundtrip   ○ One-Way   ○ Multi-City

CHOOSE A FLIGHT

From [ ]   To [ ]

DEPART _Month [ ]   Day [ ]   Time ○ Anytime
○ Morning
○ Evening

RETURN Month [ ]   Day [ ]   Time ○ Anytime
○ Morning
○ Evening

\# children under 5 [ ]

\# Adults 6–64 [ ]

\# Seniors 65+ [ ]

Choosing E-mail Options

Directions: Draw arrows from the explanations to the parts of the e-mail preferences window.

Go to this window to set-up to have junk mail automatically removed.

Go to this window to set your regular e-mail response font color to red.

Go to this window to set up to have your name and phone number automatically added to the bottom of every e-mail.

Go to this window to change your e-mail address.

Go to this window to say whether or not the original text message will be included in the body of a reply e-mail.

Use this pull-down menu to set your computer to check your e-mail every 10 minutes.

Use this pull-down menu to set your computer to make a bell ringing sound when you receive an e-mail.

Use this pull-down menu to change where files you download are automatically placed.

Click here to get help understanding how to choose e-mail options.

[E-mail preferences window screenshot: General]
Default Email Reader: Mail (2.1.3)
Check for new mail: Every 5 minutes
New mail sound: Hero
☑ Play sounds for other mail actions
Add invitations to iCal: Automatically
Downloads Folder: Mail Downloads
Remove unedited downloads: After Message is Deleted
When searching all mailboxes, include results from:
☑ Trash
☑ Junk
☐ Encrypted Messages
Synchronize with other computers using .Mac:
☐ Rules, Signatures, and Smart Mailboxes
☐ Accounts

Choosing Papers and Things to Keep

Directions: Put a check by each paper, set of papers, or thing that you should keep when you are cleaning out things you do not need.

	Papers and Things
	your report card from last grading period
	an old reading test
	your favorite comic book
	wrapper from your favorite candy
	picture of your grandfather
	directions for using your cell phone
	directions to the drug store
	notes you took in class last year
	35 notes your friends wrote to you during school this month
	an agenda for a meeting you went to last week
	a list of things you packed to take to your grandparents house in the summer

	Papers and Things
	an official copy of your birth certificate
	a grocery list from last month
	your bicycle safety class completion certificate
	your old tennis shoes that you do not wear anymore
	your favorite toy from when you were little
	the paper you used to keep score when you were playing a game last week
	last week's TV guide
	a recipe that you made last week and really liked
	a list of your friends' birthdays
	pencils that you do not use anymore since they are so short
	Your gym membership agreement

Choosing Possible Jobs Through Help-Wanted Ads

Directions: Find six help-wanted ads for jobs that you are qualified to do. Tape the ads in the boxes below. For each ad, explain why you are qualified to do the job.

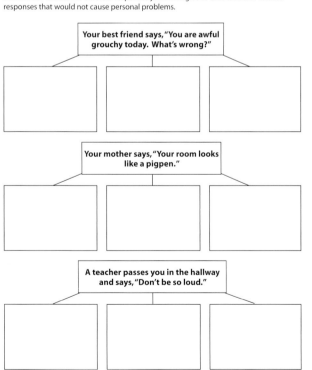

Choosing Recipes for a Meal

Directions: Arrange the foods in the Food Box into three healthy meals.

Food Box		
creamed corn	chicken-rice casserole	grilled steak
French bread	broccoli-cauliflower salad	scalloped potatoes
deviled eggs	tomatoes & pesto sauce	Caesar salad
carrot pie	sweet potato balls	baked salmon

Meal #1	Meal #2	Meal #3

Dealing with Criticism

Directions: Write three different responses you could give to each criticism. Choose responses that would not cause personal problems.

Your best friend says, "You are awful grouchy today. What's wrong?"

Your mother says, "Your room looks like a pigpen."

A teacher passes you in the hallway and says, "Don't be so loud."

Dealing with Speeding Tickets

Directions: Use the part of a speeding ticket below to match the vocabulary words and synonyms based on how the words are used in the speeding ticket.

You are <u>hereby</u> notified to appear in <u>municipal</u> court on the date below to answer the <u>charge(s)</u> above. If you fail to comply herewith within the date/time specified, further charge(s) of <u>violation</u> of promise to appear will be made and a <u>warrant</u> of arrest will be issued.

On the _6th_ day of _January_ _09_ at 4:30 P.M.

A second or <u>subsequent</u> conviction of an offense under the state Motor Vehicle Safety Responsibility Act (No Liability Insurance) will result in the <u>suspension</u> of your driver's license and motor vehicle registration unless you file and <u>maintain</u> evidence of financial responsibility with the Department of Public Safety for two years from date of conviction. The Department may <u>waive</u> the requirement to file proof of financial responsibility if you file satisfactory evidence with the department showing that at the time this <u>citation</u> was issued, the vehicle was covered by a liability insurance policy or that you were otherwise exempt from the requirements to provide evidence of financial responsibility.

Answers	Vocabulary Words	Synonyms
	1. hereby	A. order
	2. municipal	B. city
	3. charges	C. now
	4. violation	D. accusations
	5. warrant	E. breaking

Answers	Vocabulary Words	Synonyms
	6. subsequent	F. forgive or excuse
	7. suspension	G. temporary removal
	8. maintain	H. ticket
	9. waive	I. keep up
	10. citation	J. next or another

Feeding Parking Meters

Directions: Use the parking meter pictures to answer the questions.

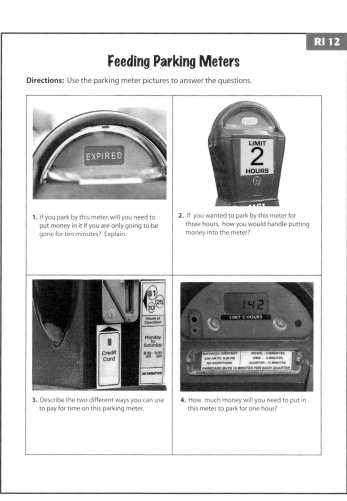

1. If you park by this meter, will you need to put money in it if you are only going to be gone for ten minutes? Explain.

2. If you wanted to park by this meter for three hours, how you would handle putting money into the meter?

3. Describe the two different ways you can use to pay for time on this parking meter.

4. How much money will you need to put in this meter to park for one hour?

Filing Papers and Bills

Directions: "Place" each of the papers in the Papers Box into the correct file.

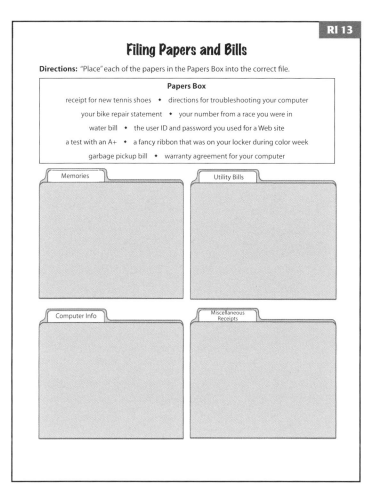

Papers Box

receipt for new tennis shoes ◆ directions for troubleshooting your computer

your bike repair statement ◆ your number from a race you were in

water bill ◆ the user ID and password you used for a Web site

a test with an A+ ◆ a fancy ribbon that was on your locker during color week

garbage pickup bill ◆ warranty agreement for your computer

Memories

Utility Bills

Computer Info

Miscellaneous Receipts

Finding a Book in the Library

Directions: Draw a line from each book number to the bookshelf where you should look for the book.

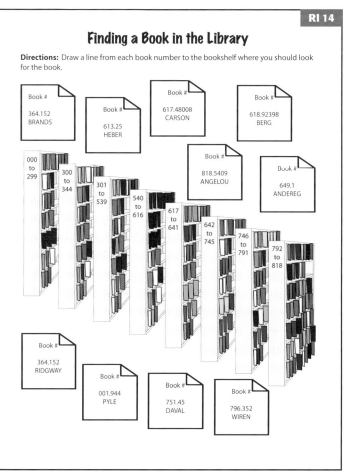

Book #
364.152
BRANDS

Book #
613.25
HEBER

Book #
617.48008
CARSON

Book #
618.92398
BERG

Book #
818.5409
ANGELOU

Book #
649.1
ANDEREG

000 to 299 | 300 to 344 | 301 to 539 | 540 to 616 | 617 to 641 | 642 to 745 | 746 to 791 | 792 to 818

Book #
364.152
RIDGWAY

Book #
001.944
PYLE

Book #
751.45
DAVAL

Book #
796.352
WIREN

Finding a File In a Computer or On a CD

Directions: Say you are at your computer trying to find a picture you uploaded in October of 2007 of your cousin Joelyn in a Halloween costume. Circle each menu item you should select to get to the picture you want.

Applications	Friends	2004	General 2004	All of us
E-mail	Me	2005	Mother's Day 2004	All the candy
Games	Neighbors	2006	Xmas 2004	Getting ready
Internet Connect	Pets	2007	Abby's party 2005	Jerry & Me
My Documents	Relatives	2008	General 2005	Joelyn
Pictures	School Activities		Reunion 2005	Kelly, Jerry, & Allen
Network	Work		General 2006	Me
Web Pages			July 4th 2006	My candy
			Xmas 2006	Pumpkins
			New Year's Eve 2006	Tess
			General 2007	
			Halloween 2007	
			My Birthday 2007	
			Reunion 2007	
			General 2008	
			Father's Day 2008	
			Labor Day 2008	

Directions: Say you are at your computer looking for a job application for a job you applied for at Wilson Shoe Warehouse. Circle each menu item you should select to get to the file you want.

Applications	Budget Stuff	Applications	Deluxe Dept Store
E-mail	Computer Info	Letters	Dick's Drive In
Games	Homework	Responses	Wilson Shoe
Internet Connect	Job Related		
My Documents	Jokes		
Pictures	Recipes		
Network	Volleyball		
Web Pages			

Finding Appliance Repair Numbers and Addresses

Directions: In the second column, list the names of companies that sell the items in the first column. Do not use any company twice. Use the Internet to fill out the third column with phone numbers and/or addresses you could use to talk to the companies about problems with the products.

Situations	Companies	Phone numbers/Addresses
1.		
2.		
3.		
4.		
5.		
6.		
7.		

Finding Emergency Numbers

Directions: Do an Internet search for "(your city/town) emergency numbers." Fill in as many of the blanks in the table as possible. These numbers are for use when you have a problem that does not require calling 911.

Your city/town:

List	Emergency Numbers
1. Closest hospital to you	
2. Your doctor's office	
3. Your health insurance provider	
4. Your home insurance provider	
5. Your car insurance provider	
6. Animal control	
7. Poison control	
8. City Hall	
9. Child Protective Services	
10. The Police Department	

Finding Ways to Remember Facts

Directions: Think of a memory clue to help you remember each fact below.

Facts	Memory Clues
Sample #1: A placebo pill has no real value.	Think of **place**bo **place**holder
Sample #2: Jupiter has 61 moons	J u p i t e r 6 letters + 1 letter = 61 moons
1. President Dwight David Eisenhower was born in Dennison, Texas.	
2. 5 x 25 = 125	
3. The different meanings of their, there, and they're.	
4. Louisa May Alcott is the author of *Little Women*.	
5. The house you are going to is 265 W. Cherry Ave.	
6. The phone number you need to call is 350-2985.	
7. The license plate on the car you saw was 456 K32F.	

Following Multiple Oral Directions

Directions: Make three lists of multiple directions that can be completed in the classroom. Then, working with a partner, see if your partner can follow your directions when they are all given at once and if you can follow his or hers.

Sample:	Set of two directions:
Stand by your desk and count to five. Walk to the door and back. Look under your desk. Roll your eyes to the ceiling.	1. 2.
Set of three directions:	**Set of four directions:**
1. 2. 3.	1. 2. 3. 4.
Set of five directions:	**Set of six directions:**
1. 2. 3. 4. 5.	1. 2. 3. 4. 5. 6.

Following Written Directions

Directions: Follow the directions below.

Directions	Use this space
1. Draw a small circle between each two small circles.	
2. Draw a face on the large circle.	
3. Add ears to the large circle.	
4. Add hair to the large circle.	
5. Add a thought balloon above and to the right of the last small circle.	
6. Below the face, connect the three dots to draw a triangle that is about 2 inches wide at the base.	
7. About one fourth inch in from the base of the triangle, draw a wavy line from side to side.	
8. On the triangle, draw four small circles that are spread out and are not between the wavy line and the base.	
9. Fill in the small circles.	
10. In the thought balloon, write "That pizza sure looks good!"	

Handling an Automated Phone System

Directions: Match the sentence beginnings to the sentence endings.

Answers	Sentence Beginnings	Sentence Endings
	1. If you place a phone call and are greeted by a machine voice,	A. you are almost always given the chance to hear the choices again.
	2. If you miss some choices or do not remember them, it is probably OK since	B. you could end up hearing all the choices again or get sent to a live person.
	3. If you are asked to make a choice and do not make any choices,	C. you might be able to talk to a live person by saying "agent."
	4. If none of the choices are what you need,	D. you should start listening right away so you hear all the choices.

Answers	Sentence Beginnings	Sentence Endings
	5. If you have a choice to go to a company directory, and you know the name of the person you want to talk to,	E. you might be able to get to the department you want or you might have to exit and go back to the main directory.
	6. If you have a choice to go to a company directory, and you do not know the name of the person you want to talk to,	F. you could choose a choice that isn't necessarily what you need in hopes of getting to a live person who can help you.
	7. If none of the choices are what you need,	G. you will have a choice to choose the name or to spell it.
	8. If you keep making choices, but do not end up where you want to be and can't get to a live person by saying "agent" or pushing zero,	H. you might be able to talk to a live person by pushing zero.

Handling Gossip

Directions: Make a list of six problems that can be caused by gossiping (six reasons not to gossip).

Identifying Sources of Occupational Training

Directions: Find the closest location where you can get training for each of the jobs below. Use the yellow pages, look on the Internet, or ask someone who knows.

Jobs	Closest location where you can get training	Where did you find this information?
1. certified babysitter		
2. boat mechanic		
3. beautician		
4. blacktop layer		
5. painter		
6. tractor trailer driver		
7. restaurant cook		
8. commercial printer		
9. welder		
10. upholsterer		

Language Arts: Receptive Literacy 173

Interpreting Idioms

Directions: You can usually figure out the meaning of idioms you hear by looking at the rest of the sentence, listening to the tone of voice, focusing on things going on at the time, or just by using logic. Explain the meaning of each underlined idiom below.

1. <u>Off the cuff</u>, I assume he means that he wants us to wait at the bottom of the hill.

   But, I'm not really sure what he means.

   This idiom means _____

2. The three of them are <u>as thick as thieves</u>, so I doubt they will invite us to join them.

   This idiom means _____

3. Our yard is <u>as flat as a pancake</u>, so it would be a good place to play volleyball.

   This idiom means _____

4. I <u>couldn't see the forest for the trees</u>, so I totally missed that James would be a good candidate

   even though he was only a sophomore.

   This idiom means _____

5. If you <u>give her half a chance</u>, you might be surprised at what a good job she will do.

   This idiom means _____

Interpreting What People Say

Directions: Describe two possible meanings for each statement. Explain how you would know which meaning is correct.

Statements	Possible Meaning #1	Possible Meaning #2	How would you know which meaning is correct?
1. It's really big of you to take the time to help us.			
2. This soup is something else.			
3. You sure look like you are ready to go.			
4. I can't believe Joey is here in our house.			
5. That's quite a car you've got there.			

Keeping Up With the News

Directions: Choose a current news story. Use it to fill in the table.

News story you chose (in a few words):	Related headlines in a newspaper:	Something you heard on the radio about the news story:
Something you heard on TV about the news story:	Web address where you found something about the news story:	Something you heard someone you know say about the news story:

Knowing Basis for Voting Decisions

Directions: Decide whose point of view is present in each political-comment source.

Source of Political Comments	Will Be from a Candidate's Point of View	Will Be from the Point of View of a Candidate's Opponent	Will Probably Include More Than One Point of View	Will Be from the Point of View of One Person Who Is Not a Candidate
1. A political ad you get in the mail				
2. The nightly news on TV				
3. Local newspaper				
4. A flyer left on your doorknob				
5. A friend				
6. A teacher				
7. A speech by a political candidate				

Knowing What Type of Material You Like to Read or Watch

Directions: For each type of show or movie, put a check in one of the three columns to show what you like to watch.

Types of Shows or Movies	Like to Watch	OK to Watch, but Not a Favorite	Do Not Like to Watch
1. adventure movies			
2. mystery movies			
3. horror movies			
4. love story movies			
5. comedy movies			
6. drama movies			
7. talk shows			
8. one-hour mysteries			
9. current half-hour sitcoms			
10. oldie half-hour sitcoms			

Knowing Where to Turn for Advice

Directions: Fill the blanks with names of people in your life from whom you could get advice.

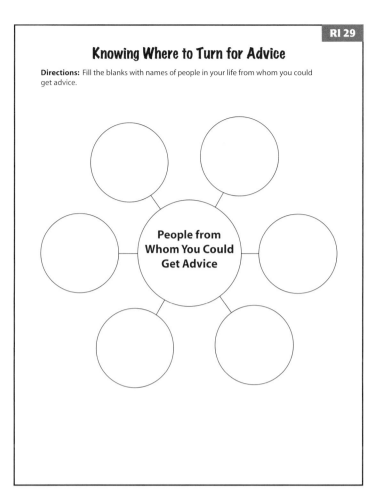

Listening Actively

Directions: Complete these Sentences.

1. One reason to take an interest in the feelings of someone to whom you are talking is

_____

_____

2. An example of a comment that would encourage a person to share his or her thoughts is

_____

_____

3. Think about this question: Are you saying that you planted 15 tomato plants? This question is a good example of active listening because _____

_____

4. Say a friend is talking about how she has redecorated her bedroom. It is good active listening to imagine how the bedroom looks because _____

_____

5. Say a friend says he thinks every country flag should include the color red. It is good active listening to ask "Why do you think that?" instead of saying "That's silly!" because

_____

_____

6. Say a friend says her pet died. It is good active listening to say "I'm sorry" instead of "Oh, well, that happens" because _____

_____

Listening to an Interviewer

Directions: Explain why an interviewer might ask each question and then answer each question.

Interview Questions	Reasons an Interviewer Might Ask the Questions	Your Answers
1. Do you work with pleasant people in your current job?		
2. Are you a late-night person?		
3. Are you more likely to work quickly or carefully?		
4. Do you spend a lot of time on a computer during your free time?		
5. When you were in school, did you tend to procrastinate on getting your homework done?		

Listening to Others' Opinions

Directions: Write your opinions to the questions. Then work with a partner to share and listen to each others' opinions.

Questions	Opinions
1. Should 18 years old be the minimum age for getting a driver's license? Explain.	
2. Should high schools have dress codes? Explain.	
3. Do baby pigs make good pets? Explain.	

Listening When Others Talk

Directions: Work with a partner. Take turns telling each other about a movie or TV show you really liked. When it is your turn to listen, use these guidelines.

Guidelines for Listening When Other Talk

1. Maintain eye contact.
2. Don't Interrupt.
3. Show interest with your facial expressions.
4. Keep your mind from wandering by thinking about what the person is saying.
5. When the person comes to a natural break, ask a question or share a related comment.

Making Choices Based on Advertising

Directions: Explain the sales tactic used in each ad and note whether or not the ad would work for you.

Ads	Sales Tactics Used	Would this ad work for you? Explain.
1.		
2.		
3.		
4.		
5.		

Making Conclusions About What You Hear

Directions: Gather 10 items that can make noise and list them in the first column. Working with a partner, make each noise without your partner seeing the source. Check whether or not your partner can correctly guess the source of the noise.

10 Items That Can Make Noise	Partner Guessed Correctly ✔
1.	
2.	
3.	
4.	
5.	
6.	
7.	
8.	
9.	
10.	

Making Insurance Choices

Directions: Choose the correct answers.

1. If you have a very old car, it might make sense to

     _____ **a.** have no insurance at all.

     _____ **b.** have only liability insurance to cover any one else's car that you damage.

     _____ **c.** have comprehensive insurance that covers both your car and any car you damage.

2. If you have children, you might have them as your life insurance beneficiaries, which means

     _____ **a.** they would have to pay your bills when you die.

     _____ **b.** they would be covered by the life insurance when you die.

     _____ **c.** they would receive money from your life insurance when you die.

3. When you are choosing health insurance options, you would probably want to choose the eye doctor option if

     _____ **a.** you or anyone in your family wears glasses or contacts.

     _____ **b.** you have a family member who is an eye doctor.

     _____ **c.** you want to have good insurance.

4. Two things you want to make sure your renters' insurance covers are

     _____ **a.** your t-shirts and jeans.

     _____ **b.** your TV and washing machine.

     _____ **c.** your childhood souvenirs that you keep at your Mom's house.

5. Before you choose to live in an area that often floods, you should talk to an insurance agent because

     _____ **a.** you might not be able to get insurance to protect your belongings.

     _____ **b.** you might be able to have a group flood-insurance policy with your neighbors.

     _____ **c.** the agent might live near you and can help you learn about the area.

Making Leisure Choices from the Newspaper

Directions: Use a local newspaper to find nine leisure activities that are available in your area. Write the activities in the boxes. Then, circle those you think you would enjoy.

1.	2.	3.
4.	5.	6.
7.	8.	9.

Managing Your Mail

Directions: Complete the Sentences.

1. You should look at each piece of mail on the day it arrives because _____

2. You should have a waste basket nearby when you sort your mail because _____

3. When a bill arrives, you should write the due date on the envelope because _____

4. It is also a good idea to write a bill's due date on a calendar because _____

5. It is a good idea to have a set place to keep invitations because _____

6. When you receive mail that requires a response, it is a good idea to respond right away because _____

Monitoring Your Academic Progress

Directions: Choose one of your classes. Complete the sentences below to tell how you can monitor your grades in that class.

1. On the first day of class, you need to know the big picture, so ask your teacher _____

2. You should make sure you know all the due dates because _____

3. You could use a computer spreadsheet to _____

4. Each time you get an assignment or test back with a grade, you should _____

5. So that you know you can remember where it is, one place you could keep a grade-monitoring chart is _____

6. You should start a new grade-monitoring chart each 9 weeks (or 6 weeks or whatever grading period your school uses) because _____

Paying Attention to Noises and Comments Around You

Directions: Fill the six boxes with background noises and comments that you should respond to even if you are busy.

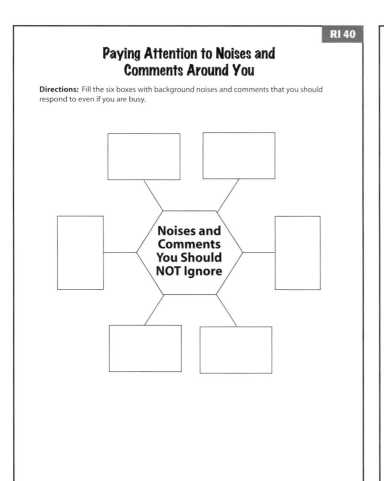

Noises and Comments You Should NOT Ignore

Paying Attention to Notes and Signs

Directions: Explain the meaning of each sign.

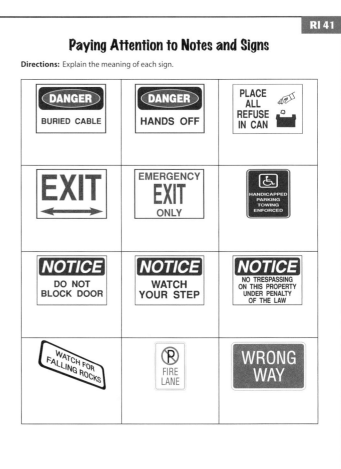

Programming a VCR or DVD Player

Directions: Match the definitions and examples to the programming-related terms.

Answers	Definitions and Examples	Programming-Related Terms
	1. morning	**A.** menu
	2. afternoon	**B.** month
	3. common remote control button that can lead to programming window	**C.** day
	4. May	**D.** P.M.
	5. 27	**E.** A.M.

Answers	Definitions	Copier-Related Terms
	6. select to leave the programming window	**F.** record
	7. enter the time when you want to begin recording	**G.** exit
	8. enter the time when you want to end recording	**H.** start
	9. common remote control button that leads immediately to the programming window	**I.** stop
	10. choice that erases a recording setting	**J.** cancel

Proofreading for Others

Directions: Write a paragraph about hiking in the woods. Working with a partner, proofread each other's paragraphs. Use a colored pen or pencil to mark errors.

Proofreading Your Writing

Directions: Use a pencil to write a paragraph explaining some task for which you use a computer. When you are finished, proofread your work. Erase and fix any errors.

_____
_____
_____
_____
_____
_____
_____
_____
_____
_____
_____
_____
_____
_____
_____

Putting Files in Order

Directions: Place numbers in the first column to show the file folders in ABC order by last name. Put numbers in the second column to show the file folders in date order.

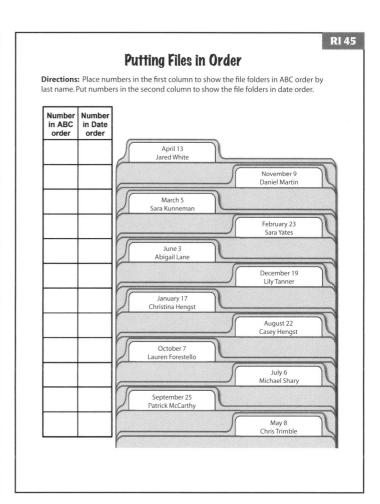

Number in ABC order	Number in Date order

April 13 Jared White
November 9 Daniel Martin
March 5 Sara Kunneman
February 23 Sara Yates
June 3 Abigail Lane
December 19 Lily Tanner
January 17 Christina Hengst
August 22 Casey Hengst
October 7 Lauren Forestello
July 6 Michael Shary
September 25 Patrick McCarthy
May 8 Chris Trimble

Reacting to Others' Moods

Directions: Consider possible moods as you respond to the situations.

Situations	Mood-Based Responses
1. Sometimes your friend, Eva, is easy going and fun. Other times, she is edgy and easily angered. You want to ask Eva if you can borrow a movie.	Explain how your method of asking to borrow a movie will be different based on Eva's moods.
2. Sometimes your neighbor, Phil, is very serious and wants to make sure everything is done just right. Other times, he seems disinterested. You want Phil to help you with a school project.	Explain how Phil's mood will affect how you ask for his help.
3. Sometimes your classmate, Muri, is really quiet. Other times, she will talk and talk. You want to talk to her about a problem you are having with another friend.	Explain how Muri's mood will affect how and when you talk about your problem.

Reading a Movie Schedule

Directions: Use the movie schedule to answer the questions.

May 5th Horizon Movie Theater Schedule

1:00 P.M.
Gowerly Girls
Mission Aware
2:15 P.M.
Run Time
Water Willy
3:00 P.M.
Country Wine and Cows
Mission Aware
4:00 P.M.
Gowerly Girls
5:30 P.M.
Run Time

6:00 P.M.
Water Willy
Country Wine and Cows
Buggy Rides and Cloudy Days
6:15 P.M.
Mission Aware
7:00 P.M.
Gowerly Girls
8:30 P.M.
Water Willy
Run Time
Country Wine and Cows
9:00 P.M.
Mission Aware
Buggy Rides and Cloudy Days

1. How can you tell that _Mission Aware_ is less than two hours long? _____

_____

2. If you are free between 5:45 P.M. and 9:00 P.M., from which movies could you choose?

_____

3. Which movie does not have a "late" showing? _____

4. How long do you think _Run Time_ will last? Explain. _____

5. Which movie does not have a matinee showing? _____

6. What are two movies you know you would be able to watch between 6:00 P.M. and 9:30 P.M.?

_____

Reading Abbreviations

Directions: Write the full spelling for each abbreviation.

Sentences with Abbreviations	Full Spelling for Abbreviations
1. Corrinne lives in Lincoln, <u>NE</u>.	
2. There are <u>approx.</u> 200 students signed up.	
3. Try to drink at least four eight-<u>oz.</u> glasses of water each day.	
4. Chad lives on <u>E.</u> Willow <u>Rd.</u>	
5. Chantilly moved from Doran <u>Ln.</u> to Muffin <u>St.</u>	
6. Nell watched <u>TV</u> for two <u>hrs.</u>	
7. Avery took two tests on <u>Mon.</u> and one on <u>Wed.</u>	
8. David joined at the end of last <u>yr.</u> and has already been elected <u>pres.</u>	

Reading Arrows

Directions: For 1–4, use words to describe the directions the signs say the road turns. For 5–6, draw road signs with arrows as described.

	Road Signs	Road sign descriptions
1.		
2.		
3.		
4.		
5.		The road curves sharply to the left and then sharply to the right.
6.		The road makes a right angle to the left.

Reading Cash Register Receipts

Directions: Use the receipts to answer the questions.

TLC Department Store

```
385463  Socks      0.99
358235  Bandaids   2.07
553264  Ace Sham   4.67
        Subtotal   7.73
        Tax         .58
        Total      8.31
```

1. Look at the numbers on the left side of the receipt (next to each item). What are these numbers for? _____

2. How much did the shampoo cost? _____

The Steak Barn

```
2   12 oz. filet   16.50
                   16.50
1   8 oz. filet    12.95
        Bar        15.00
3   Drinks         12.00
        Total      72.95
```

3. Look at the numbers on the left side of the receipt (next to each item). What are these numbers for? _____

4. How much was the bill before this party sat down at their table? _____

Supreme Gas Station

```
32.5 gal Prem      3.50

        Subtotal   113.75
        Tax          8.53
        Total      122.28
```

5. How much gas was purchased on this receipt? _____

6. How much did the gas cost per gallon? _____

Freddy's Grocery Stores

```
groc   Tel Crackers   3.67
dair   gal Milk       3.90
bake   doz muffins    4.45
groc   Frsh Soup      5.44
       coupon        -3.00
       Total         14.46
```

7. Why is there a "-" in front of the $3.00 amount? _____

8. What does "dair" on the left mean? _____

Reading Clothing Labels

Directions: Draw lines from the explanation boxes to the correct clothing labels.

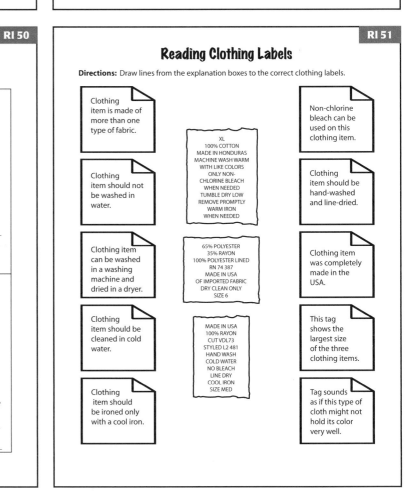

Clothing item is made of more than one type of fabric.

Clothing item should not be washed in water.

Clothing item can be washed in a washing machine and dried in a dryer.

Clothing item should be cleaned in cold water.

Clothing item should be ironed only with a cool iron.

Non-chlorine bleach can be used on this clothing item.

Clothing item should be hand-washed and line-dried.

Clothing item was completely made in the USA.

This tag shows the largest size of the three clothing items.

Tag sounds as if this type of cloth might not hold its color very well.

```
XL
100% COTTON
MADE IN HONDURAS
MACHINE WASH WARM
WITH LIKE COLORS
ONLY NON-
CHLORINE BLEACH
WHEN NEEDED
TUMBLE DRY LOW
REMOVE PROMPTLY
WARM IRON
WHEN NEEDED
```

```
65% POLYESTER
35% RAYON
100% POLYESTER LINED
RN 74 387
MADE IN USA
OF IMPORTED FABRIC
DRY CLEAN ONLY
SIZE 6
```

```
MADE IN USA
100% RAYON
CUT VDL73
STYLED L2 481
HAND WASH
COLD WATER
NO BLEACH
LINE DRY
COOL IRON
SIZE MED
```

Reading Food Nutrition Labels

Directions: Use the Food Nutrition label to answer the questions.

Nutrition Facts Serving Size 1/2 cup (125 g) Servings Per Container about 3.5

Amount Per Serving
Calories 60 **Calories from Fat** 0

% Daily Values*

Total Fat 0g	
Saturated Fat 0g	0%
Cholesterol 0mg	0%
Sodium 370mg	15%
Total Carbohydrates 10g	3%
Dietary Fiber 3g	12%
Sugars 4g	
Protein 4g	
Vitamin A	6%
Vitamin C	10%
Calcium	2%
Iron	8%

INGREDIENTS: PEAS, WATER, SUGAR, SALT

DelFin Manufacturing, Dallas, TX.
DISTRIBUTED BY FREDDY'S
GROCERIES, SAN ANTONIO, TX
78204

Questions	Answers
1. Which of the ingredients have you heard of before?	
2. Are there some ingredients you have not heard of before?	
3. How many calories are in a serving?	
4. How big is a serving?	
5. How many servings are in the container?	
6. What vitamin need will this food satisfy the most?	
7. Why should you reconsider using this product if salt makes you retain water?	
8. Do you think this food item is healthy to eat?	
9. Where was this product prepared and packaged?	
10. For what grocery store is this product a "house brand"?	

Reading Food Preparation Charts

Directions: Use the Vegetable Preparation chart to answer the questions.

Boiling Times for Fresh Vegetables	
artichokes	20–30 min.
asparagus spears	10–15 min.
green beans	20–30 min.
broccoli	10–15 min.
cabbage	10–12 min.
carrots (baby)	15–20 min.
sweet corn ears	6–8 min.
potatoes (chunked)	20–25 min.

1. Why would you need more than 15–20 minutes from the time you think about cooking carrots until they are cooked? _____

2. If you had a pot of boiling water and 11 minutes, which two vegetables could you cook?
   _____   _____

3. If you had a pot of boiling water and 17 minutes, which three vegetables would you NOT have time to cook?
   _____   _____
   _____

4. If you are cooking both fresh artichokes and fresh cabbage, which should you start cooking first?
   _____

5. About how much time do you think you need from the time you think about making mashed potatoes until the potatoes are ready to eat? Explain. _____

Reading Job Ads

Directions: Use the job ads to answer the questions.

A SECURITY OFFICERS
Several full-time positions available with pay rates of $9 to $11 per hour, varying on experience. Dispatcher and mobile patrol positions also available. Applicants must be at least 18 years old and have a high school diploma or GED. Apply at Wilson Protective Services, Inc. 56 Granstand, between Jasper St. and Downs Rd off of IH 235 in the Devine Business Park.

B RECEPTIONIST – Cust Serv & comp exp req. 50 wpm, M-F, Bnfts-Med/Dent/401K/STD. Fax resume 333-4572 or email employment @ Biggerly@mix.com

C Caregiver $10+/hr, FT/PT, Bkgrnd/ref ck. Smkless env. Fax resume 333-8736 or jlewis@mix.com

D Construction
Company taking applications for Laborers for Utility Contractor. Must have own transportation. Excellent Benefits. Apply in person M-F 8:00 a.m.–5 p.m. at 3457 S. Berry located on northeast side of town at I-53 north and 721 east (Exit Tally Blvd and Olmstead. On Deleavan between Tally Blvd and Midtown Exprswy.

Answers AD: A, B, C, &/or D	Questions
	1. Which ad(s) advertise(s) more than one job?
	2. Which ad(s) give(s) a minimum age limit?
	3. Which ad(s) note(s) that smoking is not allowed?
	4. Which ad(s) suggest(s) that the job includes insurance?
	5. Which ad(s) mention(s) an education requirement?
	6. Which ad(s) mention(s) faxing as a way to send a resumé?
	7. Which ad(s) indicate(s) interested people can apply in person?
	8. Which ad(s) list(s) specific required experience?

Reading Medicine Labels

Directions: Use the medicine label to answer the questions.

Uses
°Temporarily relieves minor aches and pains due to:
• headache • muscular aches • backache • arthritis
• the common cold • toothache • menstrual cramps
°Reduces fever
Warnings:
Overdose warning: Taking more than the recommended dose can cause serious health problems, including liver damage. In case of overdose, get medical help or contact a Poison Control Center right away. Quick medical attention is critical for adults as well as for children even if you do not notice any signs or symptoms.
Alcohol warning: If you consume 3 or more alcoholic drinks every day, ask your doctor if you should take this medication as the combination could cause liver damage.
Stop use and ask a doctor if:
• tiredness or swelling is present • new symptoms occur
• fever gets worse or lasts for more than 3 days • pain gets worse or lasts for more than 10 days
If pregnant or breast feeding, ask a health professional before use.
Keep out of the reach of children
Directions
• Do not use more than directed (see overdose warning)
• Adults and children 12 years and over: take 2 caplets every 6 hours as needed
• Do not take more than 8 caplets in 24 hours
• Children under 12 years: do not use this adult strength product in children under 12 years of age. This will provide more than the recommended dose (overdose) and could cause serious health problems.

1. How much should a teenager take at once? _____
2. What symptoms does the medicine treat? _____
   _____
3. Can a person drive while taking this medicine? _____
4. Do the directions say to take the medicine with food or drink? _____
5. How many times a day can you take this medicine? _____
6. Are there any people who should not take this medicine? Explain. _____

Reading Menus

Directions: Match the definitions to the menu-related vocabulary words.

Answers	Definitions	Menu-Related Terms
	1. Additional menu items that go with the main dishes	**A.** marinated
	2. Main item plus fries and a drink	**B.** deep fried
	3. Meat that was soaked in a spicy liquid before being cooked	**C.** basket
	4. Food cooked in hot oil	**D.** broiled
	5. Meat cooked from the top down in an oven	**E.** sides
Answers	Definitions	Menu-Related Terms
	6. A smaller version of a main dish	**F.** salsa
	7. Snacks for eating before the main dishes	**G.** vegetarian
	8. Sauce made with chopped tomatoes, peppers, and spices	**H.** breaded
	9. Meat covered with batter before being cooked	**I.** starters
	10. Menu item that does not include meat	**J.** 1/2 portion

Reading Non-Edible Product Labels

Directions: Use the product labels to answer the questions.

DemToys
BUILDING LOGS
All-Wood Classic Construction
Interlocking Logs
Ages 4+
Warning: Choking hazard—Small parts not for children under 3 years

DemToys, Inc. Updates and improves its products and colors continuously. As a result, actual products may vary slightly from pictures shown on package.
© 2007 DemToys, Inc.
P.O. Box 537
Platteville, WI 53818
www.demtoys.com
Made in China

1. Why shouldn't a 2-yr-old be given this toy?

2. Why shouldn't you return this toy if it has red parts that are blue on the label?

3. Of what is this toy made?

4. If this toy is made in China, why is there a Wisconsin address on the label?

Maurice Products
Insta-Hot
HEAT BUTTON WITH INDICATOR LIGHT
shows when the unit is heating for simple operation.
AUTO SHUT OFF FEATURE conveniently turns the unit off when the heating cycle completes.
WATER RESERVOIR
with 16 oz. capacity
DISPENSE LEVER
allows you to control the preferred amount of water
SPACE-SAVING DESIGN
fits conveniently on countertops, desktops, and more
CORD STORAGE
fits neatly under the base

5. How do you know you can't accidently leave the Insta-Hot on all day?

6. How can you tell if the Insta-Hot is heating?

7. Why is it a good guess that the base is not super-heavy?

8. How many cups of hot water can you get from the Insta-Hot at one time?

Reading Pictures

Directions: Study the pictures. Look beyond the obvious to se what you can learn by studying the background.

	What you have learned by studying the background

Reading Signs

Directions: Tell what each sign means and where it might be needed.

Means: Where Needed:	Means: Where Needed:
Means: Where Needed:	Means: Where Needed:
Means: Where Needed:	Means: Where Needed:

Reading Symbols and Icons

Directions: Explain the meaning of each icon.

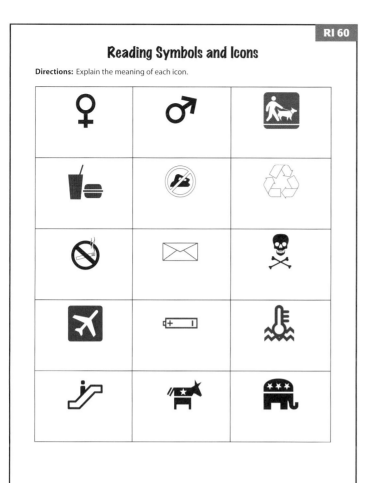

Recognizing and Accepting Authority

Directions: List type of authority figure or personal names of authority figures with which you are familiar in each location. Do not use any names twice.

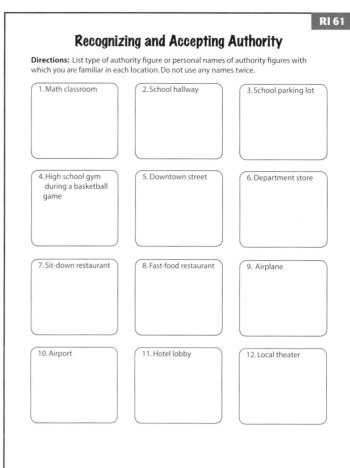

1. Math classroom
2. School hallway
3. School parking lot
4. High school gym during a basketball game
5. Downtown street
6. Department store
7. Sit-down restaurant
8. Fast-food restaurant
9. Airplane
10. Airport
11. Hotel lobby
12. Local theater

Recognizing Important Information

Directions: Identify one piece of important information in each situation.

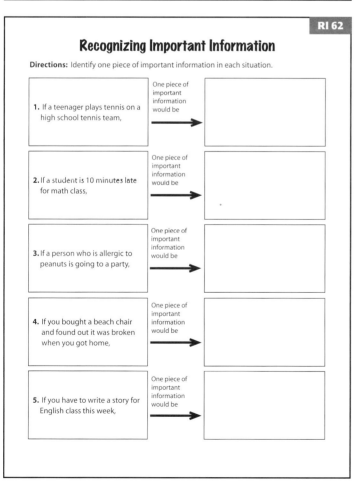

1. If a teenager plays tennis on a high school tennis team,
   One piece of important information would be
2. If a student is 10 minutes late for math class,
   One piece of important information would be
3. If a person who is allergic to peanuts is going to a party,
   One piece of important information would be
4. If you bought a beach chair and found out it was broken when you got home,
   One piece of important information would be
5. If you have to write a story for English class this week,
   One piece of important information would be

Searching for Job Options

Directions: Identify 10 ways you could find out about a possible job.

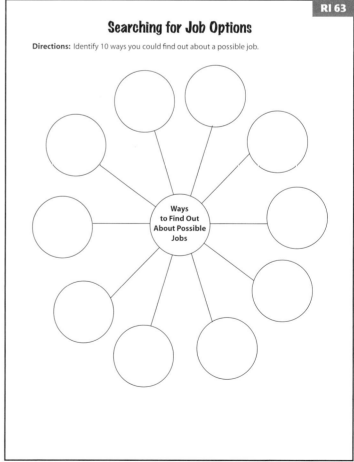

Ways to Find Out About Possible Jobs

Securing Legal Documents

Directions: Complete the sentences.

1. When two people get married, they get a copy of their marriage license. Two reasons they might need another one are _____

2. If you need a birth certificate for identification, you usually cannot make a copy of one you already have and take it because _____

3. The location and phone number you should begin with when you need a birth certificate are ___

4. It is a good idea to keep a copy of your important legal documents in a lock box because _____

5. If you need to provide a birth certificate, you should work on getting it at least a couple days ahead of time because _____

6. You should be careful about where you leave copies of your birth certificate because _____

Seeing Letter and Idea Sequences

Directions: Use numbers to put each list below into a logical order.

Order	List #1: Game files
	Fidget Game Rules
	New Game Ideas
	Game Companies
	Gopher Game Rules
	BigOne Game Pieces

Order	List #2: Decorating Ideas
	March: shamrocks, umbrellas
	February: hearts, Washington, Lincoln
	December: Xmas trees, hollies, poinsettias
	January: streamers, snowmen
	July: flags, watermelon, picnic baskets

Order	List #3: Test Scores
	87%
	98%
	72%
	70%
	100%
	58%
	73%
	69%
	87%
	92%
	95%

Order	List #1: Classroom Deliveries
	Rm 125: two files for Mrs. Miller
	Rm 146: a medical excuse for a student
	Rm 104: a personal note for Mr. Crueger
	Rm 136: an office summons for a student
	Rm 101: a delivery for Miss Terry
	Rm 129: an inter-school packet for Mrs. Nyo
	Rm 152: Homework from a sick student for Mr. Fobli

Separating Fact From Fiction

Directions: Write one fact and one fictional statement about each topic.

Topics	Statements
1. ice cream	Fact:
	Fiction:
2. leather shoes	Fact:
	Fiction:
3. backpacks	Fact:
	Fiction:
4. cafeteria food	Fact:
	Fiction:
5. friends	Fact:
	Fiction:
6. rabbits	Fact:
	Fiction:
7. computers	Fact:
	Fiction:
8. candles	Fact:
	Fiction:

Signing Contracts Knowledgeably

Directions: Fill in the empty boxes to match the headings.

Three problems that could result from not reading a contract before signing it

Three ways you could know what a contract says even if you cannot read it.

Three situations where you might have to sign a contract

Understanding a Lease

Directions: Read the sentences from a lease and rewrite them in your own words.

Sentences from a Lease	Sentences Rewritten in Your Own Words
1. **Term/Beginning Date:** The Term of this tenancy, for Premises is 1 year and the Beginning Date hereto is April 1, 2008.	
2. **Rent/Late Rent Charge:** Tenant shall pay to Landlord the rent due, in advance, for each rental month, in the amount and on the first of each month.	
3. Should Tenant fail to pay an installment of rent or any portion thereof, within three days after due date, Tenant shall pay $75 as a Late Rent Charge to Landlord.	
4. Such Charge may be deeded additional rent for such rental month and Landlord may deduct such charge from Tenant's Security Deposit if such charge is not paid in full within seven days after the due date.	
5. Any claim by Tenant for a refund of the deposit shall be deemed compensated to the extent of any deduction of such Charge.	
6. If rent is paid on time but later on rent check is returned by the bank due to Nonsufficient Funds or any other reason, rent would be considered late and Tenant will be charged a fee of $75 and bank charges.	

Understanding a Warranty

Directions: Read the sentences from a computer-printer warranty and rewrite them in your own words.

Sentences from a Warranty	Sentences Rewritten in Your Own Words
1. **Product Components/Duration of Warranty:** Software Media—90 days; Printer—1 year; Print or Ink Cartridges—Until the ink is depleted or the "end of warranty" date printed on the cartridge has been reached, whichever occurs first. This warranty does not cover ink products that have been refilled, remanufactured, refurbished, misused, or tampered with; Accessories—1 year unless otherwise stated	
2. The Company warrants to the end-user customer that the products specified above will be free from defects in materials and workmanship for the duration specified above, which duration begins on the date of purchase by the customer.	
3. For software products, The Company's limited warranty applies only to a failure to execute programming instructions. The Company does not warrant that the operation of any product will be uninterrupted or error free.	
4. The Company's limited warranty covers only those defects that arise as a result of normal use of the product, and does not cover any other problems, including those that arise as a result of: a. Improper maintenance or modification b. Software, media, parts, or supplies not provided or supported by The Company c. Operation outside the product's specifications d. Unauthorized modification or misuse	

Understanding and Following Your Cell Phone Plan

Directions: Use the cell phone plan to answer the questions.

WorldConnect Cell Phone Plan

This Customer First cell phone plan includes:
- 3000 anytime minutes
- Rollover minutes within each calendar year
- Basic voicemail
- Call waiting
- Caller ID
- Direct bill detail
- Call forwarding
- Message notification
- Three-way calling
- 5¢ Text Messaging
- Unlimited night minutes (7:00 p.m.–7:00 a.m.)
- Unlimited weekend minutes (7:00 p.m. Fri–7:00 a.m. Mon)
- Unlimited calling between WorldConnect customers

1. This cell phone plan provides 3000 minutes. How long do those 3000 minutes have to last before you get 3000 more? _____

2. Say you use 2000 minutes in January, 1500 in February, and 2500 in March. How many minutes are available to you in April? _____

3. What happens if you use 4000 minutes in January? _____

4. How much will you be charged for 20 text messages? _____

5. What are three situations where you can talk without adding to your minutes used? _____

6. What three services are provided to handle phone calls that come in but you cannot or do not answer? _____

Understanding Basic Cell Phone Functions

Directions: Match the cell phone functions to the descriptions.

Answers	Descriptions	Cell Phone Functions
	1. A printout in a cell phone window that tells the name and number of the person calling	A. call waiting
	2. An answering service where a caller can leave a message	B. caller ID
	3. A storage device that holds names and telephone numbers and can be moved from one cell phone to another	C. text message
	4. Visual note typed using phone buttons and then sent to another cell phone	D. SIM card
	5. A phone service that provides a subdued beep to let a person who is talking on the phone know that another caller is calling	E. voicemail

Answers	Descriptions	Cell Phone Functions
	6. A phone function that holds names and phone numbers in ABC order	F. speed dial
	7. A photo or image that can be placed on a cell phone window for viewing when the phone is not in use	G. screen saver
	8. A sound, such as a noise or part of a song, that can be downloaded to a cell phone and will sound to indicate an incoming call	H. address book
	9. A sound that is set to indicate a specific caller is calling	I. ringtone
	10. A phone function that allows a caller to place a call to a frequent callee by pushing one or two set buttons	J. designated ringtone

Understanding Cooking and Baking Words

Directions: Sort the words in the Word Box into the different cooking situations. Words can be used more than once. You do not have to fill all the circles, but try to use all the words at least once.

Word Box						
bake	beat	broil	brown	chop	crush	dice
drain	drop	fry	grate	grease	grill	mash
mix	peel	preheat	sauté	slice	spread	stir

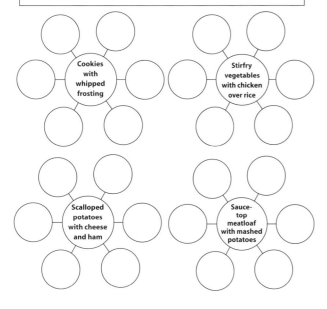

Cookies with whipped frosting

Stirfry vegetables with chicken over rice

Scalloped potatoes with cheese and ham

Sauce-top meatloaf with mashed potatoes

Understanding Insurance

Directions: Match the insurance features to the types of insurance.

Answers	Types of Insurance	Insurance Features
	1. Life insurance	A. covers hospital bills
	2. Health insurance	B. pays for funerals
	3. Vehicle insurance	C. pays for carpet damage if a waterpipe breaks
	4. Household insurance	D. pays for towing if car breaks down

Answers	Sentence Beginnings	Sentence Endings
	5. Life insurance	E. helps pay for repairs if car is in an accident
	6. Health insurance	F. helps pay for prescription medications
	7. Vehicle insurance	G. helps pay for new refrigerator if old one breaks
	8. Household insurance	H. pays beneficiary when you die

Understanding Job Benefits

Directions: Put checks in the different columns to show the types of benefits you might receive with different jobs. For each benefit, check one, two, or all three columns.

Possible Benefits	Job: Wait Staff in a Restaurant ✓	Job: Sales person in a department store ✓	Job: Factory Worker ✓
paychecks			
unpaid vacation			
paid vacation			
health insurance			
company party/picnic			
low cost/free food			
low cost clothing			
retirement fund			
company shirts			
uniforms			
deals on household items			
bonuses			
tips			
discount at exercise/health facility			
discount theater tickets			
free company sports leagues			

Understanding Job Titles

Directions: Match the job duties to the job titles.

Answers	Job Duties	Job Titles
	1. mow grass, pick up sticks, trim bushes	A. health club front desk worker
	2. type information into a computer	B. fabric store worker
	3. check people in and provide information	C. lawn care worker
	4. greet people, direct people, make and answer phone calls, do odd jobs in spare time	D. data entry worker
	5. cut material, help customers find things, stock shelves, and check people out at the cash register	E. receptionist

Answers	Job Duties	Job Titles
	6. give massages	F. mail carrier
	7. hem, repair, and resize clothing as well as make new clothing	G. farm worker
	8. take care of animals, work in fields, clean barns, drive tractors	H. coach
	9. sort, deliver, and pick up mail	I. masseuse or masseur
	10. teach members of a sports team to play the sport and manage the business of the team	J. tailor

Understanding Jokes

Directions: Read each joke and explain why the joke is funny.

Jokes	Why the Jokes Are Funny
1. Knock, knock Who's There? Police Police who? Police let me in, it's cold out here!	
2. A guy hears a knock at his door. When he answers it, there's nobody there, but there's a snail on the welcome mat. Frustrated, the guy picks up the snail and hurls it into the street. Two months later there's another knock at the door. The man answers it, and again there's no one standing there, but there's a snail on the welcome mat. The snail looks up and says, "What the heck was that all about?"	
3. Elsie: Good night! I hope you sleep like a baby. Jenny: Why would you want me to wake up every two hours?	
4. Jake was driving on U.S. Highway 35 when his cell phone rang. He answered and heard his wife's voice, "Jake I just heard on the news that there's a car going the wrong way on Highway 35. Please be careful!" "It's not just one car," said Jake, "It's hundreds of them!!"	

Understanding Nonverbal Communication

Directions: What message is each of these people sending?

Message:

Message:

Message:

Message:

Message:

Message:

Message:

Message:

Message:

Understanding Titles That Go With Names

Directions: Match the tiles to the definitions.

Answers	Definitions	Titles
	1. person is a female	**A.** Ms. Jones
	2. person is a doctor in some field other than medicine	**B.** Sir Alex Jones
	3. person is a religious minister	**C.** Colonel Jones
	4. person has been knighted by the English government	**D.** Rev. Jones
	5. person is a high-ranking military officer	**E.** Alex Jones, Ph.D.

Answers	Definitions	Titles
	6. person has a masters in business administration	**F.** Alex Jones, M.D.
	7. person is a medical doctor	**G.** Alex Jones, Jr.
	8. person is a lawyer	**H.** Alex Jones, MBA
	9. person has the same name as his father	**I.** Sen. Alex Jones
	10. person is a U.S. senator	**J.** Alex Jones, JD

Understanding Utility Bills

Directions: Make a copy of a local gas, water, electric, or garbage bill. Place the copied bill in the box and use it to answer the questions.

1. What type of bill is this one? (gas? water? electric? garbage?) _____

2. When is the bill due? _____

3. Does the bill offer a discount for paying early? Is so, how much? _____

4. Can you tell if this month's bill is more or less than last month's bill? _____

5. How would you contact customer service if you have a question about your bill? _____
   _____

6. Besides the actual fee for the monthly use, what (if any) other fees are included? _____
   _____

7. How or where are you to pay the bill? _____
   _____

Using a Dictionary

Directions: Use a dictionary to complete the table.

Words	Dictionary Page Numbers	Guide Words	Number of definitions	Part(s) of speech	One other fact given in the dictionary entry
party					
elephant					
laugh					
crazy					
lovely					

Using a Newspaper

Directions: Use the newspaper directory to answer the questions.

Directory			
Business	1J	Real Estate	1D
Classified	1E	Local Life	1H
Obituaries	6B	Sports	1C
Metro/State	1B	Travel	1K
Movies	5H	Views	9B
Puzzles	9H		

1. Explain the meaning of the letters and numbers in the right column. _____
_____
_____

Where would you turn to	
2. read the comics?	
3. read about a local person who died?	
4. read about how your neighbor girl did in the high school volleyball match last night?	
5. read the letters to the editor?	
6. read about a change in driver's license procedures?	
7. find some open houses?	
8. check out help wanted ads?	
9. see what movies are on this weekend?	
10. find some vacation ideas?	

Using a Phone Book

Directions: Use your local phone book to answer the questions.

1. List the cities or towns that are included in your phone book. _____
_____
_____

2. List the area codes that are included in your phone book. _____
_____
_____

3. About how many people in your phone book have the last name "Miller"? _____

4. About how many people in your phone book have the last name "Garcia"? _____

5. Find your family in the phone book. If your family is not listed, find where it would be if it were there. What page is it on? _____

   What are the guide names on that page? _____

6. Choose a name from the phone book and write that person's complete mailing address.
_____
_____
_____

7. What phone number should you call if your phone is not working correctly?
_____

Using a Program to Understand an Event

Directions: Use this graduation program to answer the questions.

Duncan High School Graduation Program
Welcome ....School Board President Kenneth Miller
Introduction of Class ....Superintendent Rebecca Gates
Introduction of Speaker ....Student Council President Derrick Buxton
Keynote Speech ....Senator Abigail Spencer
Salutatorian Speech ....Benjamin Fox
Valedictorian Speech ....Rachael Rowe
Presentation of Graduates .... School Board President Kenneth Miller and other board members
Farewell ....Superintendent Rebecca Gates

1. Who is Derrick Buxton introducing? _____

2. Once the valedictorian is finished speaking, is the event about over? Explain. _____
_____

3. Who are some adults that spectators will see on stage but who are not on the program?
_____

4. Rank the steps in the program according to how long you think they will take.

Least time / 1	
2	
3	
4	
5	
6	
7	
Most time / 8	

Using a Table of Contents

Directions: Use this clip art collection Table of Contents to answer the questions.

Table of Contents	
A	Advertising 5
	Agriculture 11
	Anatomy 125
	Animals 128
B	Backgrounds 254
	Beauty 263
	Borders 265
	Business & Office 321
C	Cartoons 357
	Clothing and Accessories 373
	Computers 387
E	Education and Schools 420
	Electrical 437

1. How many pages of animal clip art are included in this collection? _____

2. Why does the lettering on the left go from C to E? _____

3. About how many pages do you think are in this book? Explain. _____

4.

On what page should you start looking for the following pictures?	Subheadings and page numbers
an elephant	
a wall outlet plate	
a blow dryer	
a pair of jeans	
a human hand	
a pale-blue-sky background	
a barn with a silo	

Using a TV Program Guide

Directions: Use a current local TV program guide to answer the questions.

1. If you were going to watch TV today from 10:00 a.m. to noon, what would you watch?	
2. List three movies that are on TV today.	1. 2. 3.
3. Name two shows you might like to watch on TV at 7:00 tonight. Circle the one that you would most want to see.	1. 2.
4. Name two shows that are showing reruns today.	1. 2.
5. If you could watch TV from 8:00 until 8:30 tonight, what would you choose to watch?	
6. Identify the name and time of a talk show that you might enjoy watching.	Name: Time:
7. Name two sporting events that are on TV today.	1. 2.

Using an ATM Machine

Directions: Complete the sentences.

1. It is best not to stop at an ATM machine alone at night because _____

2. You should decide if you want to get $20 or $30 instead of $27 because _____

3. Even if you do not have both a checking and savings account, you will have to say which of the two kinds of accounts you want to withdraw from because _____

4. You should not let other people use your ATM card because _____

5. When your money comes out of the ATM machine, you should check to make sure you have it all since it is easy to _____

Using an Electronic Voting Machine

Directions: Use the named colors to mark this electronic voting window as requested.

State Senator

☐ Millie Dampiere (R)

☐ Joseph J. Fieldton (D)

☐ LaTisha J. Brown (D)

☐ Anthony T. Gonch (I)

Proceed to next screen ☐

1. Use green to circle the position for which these candidates are competing.

2. Use orange to place a vote for the candidate of your choice.

3. Use purple to choose to proceed to the next screen.

4. Use a pink to circle the letter that lets you know that one of the candidates is a Republican.

SUBMIT FINAL BALLOT ☐
Jo Daviess County Clerk

☐ Clyde A. Dorey (I)

☐ Anne Ponce Lopez (D)

☐ Molly Schubert (R)

☐ Gary Martin (R)

REVIEW ALL SELECTIONS ☐

5. Use orange to place a vote for Molly Schubert.

6. Use green to circle the position for which these candidates are competing.

7. Use a blue X to choose to review all your voting choices before submitting your ballot.

8. Use a red X to choose to submit your final ballot as it is.

Using an Index

Directions: Use this index to answer the questions.

Author Index	
Ace, Goodman	**615**
Adams, Henry	**329**, 433
Ade, George	732, 838, **901**, 955
Adler, Mortimer	**347**, 992
Ames, Fisher	**823**
Aristotle	**174**, 232, 834
Austen, Jane	18, **552**
Barrymore, John	**96**, 343
Berlin, Irving	**561**
Bernstein, Henri	**226**
Blake, William	xi, **279**, 320, 331, 346, 422, 522, 581, 828
Burns, Robert	**684**
Capote, Truman	**330**, 649, 774
Chekhov, Anton	201, **225**, 307, 523

1. Which three authors in this section of the index are referenced in this book more than three times? _____

2. Which four authors in this section of the index were referenced before the main page on which they are featured? _____

   _____

3. Which author was referenced in the introductory pages of the book? _____

4. Describe the sequences used to present the names and the page numbers.

   Names: _____

   Page numbers: _____

5. On which page(s) would you look for a reference to John Barrymore? _____

6. On which page(s) would you look for a reference to Aristotle? _____

Using Manners in Meetings

Directions: Match the sentence beginnings to the sentence endings.

Answers	Sentence Beginnings	Sentence Endings
	1. You should sit down soon after you enter a meeting room because,	**A.** you should wait for the person to finish talking and then ask your question.
	2. You should be quiet when others are talking because,	**B.** you should share your comments in a polite way.
	3. Every time you talk in a meeting,	**C.** it is difficult to call a meeting to order when people are walking around.
	4. If you have a question and someone else is talking,	**D.** it is hard to hear what anyone is saying when more than one person is talking.

Answers	Sentence Beginnings	Sentence Endings
	5. If someone is speaking in front of the meeting group,	**E.** you should put it on silent or vibrate.
	6. If you have a cell phone with you,	**F.** you should try to get more involved in the meeting so you can stay awake.
	7. If you disagree with something someone says,	**G.** you should listen without talking to the people you are sitting next to.
	8. If you are having a problem staying awake during a meeting,	**H.** you should state your opinion in a professional way without putting anyone's opinion down.

Using the Internet for Personal Needs

Directions: Explain how you could use the Internet to help solve each problem.

1. You want to get in contact with an old friend, but no longer have his or her phone number.	How could the Internet help? →	
2. You want to find a good deal on a 2-room tent.	How could the Internet help? →	
3. You want to find out who won a professional basketball game that was one last night.	How could the Internet help? →	
4. You have a bright red rash and wonder what might have caused it.	How could the Internet help? →	
5. You have to write a ten-page paper about space exploration.	How could the Internet help? →	

Using the Internet to Find Interview Information

Directions: Go to the Web site of a large local business. Use the information to answer the questions.

1. What is the company's complete full name? _____

   _____

2. According to the Web site, what is the main business of the company? _____

   _____

3. Does the company have more than one location? If so, where are they? _____

   _____

4. Based on information on the Web site, what is one question you could ask about the company during an interview? _____

   _____

5. Based on information on the Web site, what is a second question you could ask about the company during an interview? _____

   _____

6. What is one fact about the company that you did not know before you visited the Web site? _____

   _____

   _____

Watching and Reading Airport Signs and Screens

Directions: Match the airport signs to their meanings.

Answers	Meanings for Airport Signs		Airport Signs
	1. Go this way to leave the airport.	**A.**	Airport Entrance
	2. Go this way to one section of the airport.	**B.**	Airport Exit →
	3. You are on the road that leads to the airport entrance.	**C.**	Terminal A ↗
	4. Go this way to enter the airport.	**D.**	✈
	5. Lets people know whether planes are on time, late, or landed.	**E.**	Arrivals 234 Seattle On time 1536 Chicago Arrived

Answers	Purposes for Airport Signs		Airport Signs
	6. Follow this arrow to find a bus or taxi.	**F.**	Baggage Claim
	7. Go this way to one group of loading locations.	**G.**	Arrivals ↗
	8. Veer this way if you are picking someone up who is flying in.	**H.**	↖ Departures
	9. Go this way to pick up your suitcases.	**I.**	Ground Transportation ←
	10. Veer this way if you are flying out.	**J.**	Gates 17-30 →

Willingly Following Directions

Directions: Choose the correct answers to show examples of willingly following directions.

1. If your mother asks you to peel potatoes, but you want to talk on the phone instead,

   _____ **a.** you could promise to peel the potatoes as soon as you have talked on the phone.

   _____ **b.** you could say that you will peel the potatoes another day.

   _____ **c.** you could agree to peel the potatoes either while or before you talk on the phone.

2. If your teacher asks you to read the next part of the assignment aloud,

   _____ **a.** you could start reading.

   _____ **b.** you could ask if someone else would like to read instead.

   _____ **c.** you could explain that you see no need for the assignment to be read aloud since everyone can read it privately.

3. If you are riding a bus and the driver asks you to sit down,

   _____ **a.** you could pretend you did not hear, but hold on extra tightly.

   _____ **b.** you could squat down so the driver doesn't see you.

   _____ **c.** you could sit down and hold on tightly.

4. If you are in a department store and an announcement says that the store will be closing in 15 minutes so shoppers should select their final purchases,

   _____ **a.** you could decide on the item you are looking at and go to the checkout.

   _____ **b.** you could finish getting everything on your list since you figure the workers will be in the store at least another hour.

   _____ **c.** you could point out that the customer is always right and not worry about the timing.

5. If you are taking part in a race, and the organizers ask you to pin your number on your shirt, but you do not like pinning things to your shirt,

   _____ **a.** you could just not put the number on since everyone knows who you are anyhow.

   _____ **b.** you could tape the number on instead.

   _____ **c.** you could pin it on knowing that it will be just for a short while.

Zooming In On Coupon Dates and Requirements

Directions: On each coupon below, put a box around the expiration date, a line under the purchasing requirements, and a circle around the amount you will save.

expiration date	purchasing requirements	amount you will save

Through Jan 25, 2009

Save $1.00
on any one
Freshy Mouthwash or Freshy Fluoride Rinse

This coupon good only on any 18 oz or 33 oz size Freshy Rinse or Freshy Mouthwash. Any other use constitutes fraud. Customer must pay sales tax. COUPON NOT TRANSFERABLE. LIMIT ONE PER PURCHASE.

75¢ OFF
Any one Large Italia Pizza
Coupon valid for 75¢ off any one Italia Large Pizza. Consumer pays sales tax. Coupons not transferable. Cash redemption value: 1/20 of 1¢. void where taxed, restricted, or prohibited.
Expires 6/25/09.

Sunday 3/30 one day only
extra 10% off
your entire purchase
Coupon must be presented at time of purchase. Cannot be applied to gift cards, previous purchases, or phone orders. Not combinable with other percentage-off coupons.

Present this coupon for
20% off
Any Single Item
Participating stores listed on reverse side. This coupon is valid for one time use on a single item in any of the participating stores. Limit one coupon per customer per store per day. Cannot be combined with any other offer, coupon, or discount card. Must be presented at time of purchase.
Offer expires 4/30/09

We gladly accept competitor's coupons
for the exact same products also available at our competitors.
We will not be undersold, Guaranteed.
If you find a lower-price at any of our competitors, we will meet that price. Exceptions may apply. See stores for details.

Language Arts: Receptive Literacy 191